Dynamic Structures in Biology

Dynamic Structures in Biology

Brian Goodwin
Atuhiro Sibatani
Gerry Webster

Editors

EDINBURGH UNIVERSITY PRESS

© Edinburgh University Press 1989
22 George Square, Edinburgh
Set in CRTronic Plantin
by Polyprint, Edinburgh, and
printed in Great Britain by
Redwood Burn Limited,
Trowbridge, Wilts
British Library Cataloguing
    in Publication Data
Dynamic structures in biology.
1. Organisms
I. Goodwin, Brian
II. Webster, Gerald
III. Sibatani, Atuhiro
574
ISBN 0 85224 599 8

The publishers are grateful for
permission to base the jacket
illustration on a screen from
Muryoji Temple, Wakayama.

Contents

		Preface	vii
		List of Contributors	viii
1.	Structuralism and Darwinism: Concepts for the Study of Form		1
	G. WEBSTER		
2.	How to Structuralise Biology?		16
	A. SIBATANI		
3.	A Structuralism of Process: Towards a Post-Darwinian Rational Morphology		31
	M-W. HO		
4.	A Structuralist Research Programme in Developmental Biology		49
	B. C. GOODWIN		
5.	Keywords and Concepts in Structuralist and Functionalist Biology		62
	D. M. LAMBERT AND A. J. HUGHES		
6.	A View of Species		77
	H. PATERSON		
7.	Structuralism as a Non-vitalistic Alternative to Reductionism		89
	D. ELDER		
8.	A Formalism Linking Structure with Function		96
	R. THOM		
9.	Mathematics, Structuralism and the Formal Cause in Biology		107
	P. T. SAUNDERS		
10.	Dynamical Levels in Developing Systems		121
	L. V. BELOUSSOV		
11.	Structuralism in Evolutionary Biology and Systematics		131
	L. VAN DER HAMMEN		
12.	Sexual Differentiation and Mate Recognition: the Dynamics of Structure		143
	A. J. HUGHES AND D. M. LAMBERT		
13.	DNA Domains — Their Classification and Organisation		156
	A. LIMA-DE-FARIA		
14.	Genetics and the Inheritance of Biological Structures		175
	G. SERMONTI		
15.	Gene-Ecological Aspects of Non-Coding DNA Sequences and Genome Evolution		185
	H. NAORA		
16.	A New Hypothesis on the Mechanism of Macroevolution: a Structuralist Approach		204
	K. IKEDA		
17.	Systematics and Panbiogeography		211
	H. CHIBA		
18.	Molluscan Pigment Pattern Generation by a Dynamic Structure with Intrinsic Time, Illustrating Subjective Autonomy		219
	Y. GUNJI		
19.	'Ethology', 'Ecology' and 'Philosophy'		236
	F. M. SCUDO		
		Authors Index	251
		Subject Index	257

Preface

The papers in this volume are a product of the International Workshop on Structuralism in Biology organised by Atuhiro Sibatani and held in Osaka in December, 1986. The meeting was attended by some twenty participants from various parts of the world together with about thirty others currently resident in Japan.

The participants in the meeting were extremely diverse in terms of their specific disciplines and theoretical positions. What united them was a concern with problems of biological organisation at all levels, a varying degree of dissatisfaction with the current dogmas of 'mainstream' theoretical biology and a feeling that something of importance could be learned from the various forms of 'structuralism' which have flourished since the Second World War. Since a number of the participants were somewhat isolated in their own academic institutions, the workshop served not only as a forum for a valuable exchange of ideas but also as a reassurance that they were not alone in their dissatisfaction with orthodox paradigms and desire to re-think their disciplines.

The meeting was honoured by a visit from Dr Joseph Needham FRS, FBA who along with C.H. Waddington, J.H. Woodger and J.D. Bernal formed the nucleus of the Theoretical Biology Club which met in Cambridge from 1932-8. Since many of the interests and concerns of the Club were close to those of the Osaka Workshop, the presence of Dr Needham reinforced our sense of historical continuity with a significant, if hitherto marginal, tradition in theoretical biology. His visit also had a more personal significance for those participants who trace their own intellectual genealogies, directly or indirectly, back to the members of this group.

For this publication, the papers presented at the workshop have in most cases been extensively rewritten. The editors have not attempted to impose any 'party line' on the contributors and there are probably as many views on the nature and significance of 'biological structuralism' as there are writers. In our view this is as it should be, for a tolerant pluralism is an advantage at this early stage in the double activity of formulating critical evaluations of 'mainstream' theoretical biology and developing positive alternatives. Let a Hundred Flowers Blossom!

The editors would like to thank David Lambert for exceptional help in assembling the final material for the book.

List of Contributors

Prof. Lev V. Beloussov, Department of Embryology, Faculty of Biology,
  Moscow State University, Moscow 119899, USSR.
Hideyuki Chiba, Department of Entomology, University of Hawaii,
  3050 Maile Way, Honolulu.Hl 96822, USA.
David John Elder, 1/42 High Street, Grange, SA 5022, Australia.
Prof. Brian Carey Goodwin, Department of Biology, The Open University,
  Walton Hall, Milton Keynes MK7 6AA, UK.
Dr Yukio Gunji, Department of Earth Science, Faculty of Science, Kobe University,
  Rokko-daimati, Nada-ku, Kobe 657, Japan.
Dr Leendert Van der Hammen, Baronielaan 1, 2242 RA Wassenaar, The Netherlands
Dr Mae-Wan Ho, Department of Biology, The Open University, Walton Hall,
  Milton Keynes MK7 6AA.
Anthony James Hughes, New Zealand AIDS Foundation, PO Box 6663,
  Wellesley Street, Auckland 1, New Zealand.
Dr Kiyohiko Ikeda, Faculty of Education, Yamanashi University,
  4-4-37 Takeda, Kofu, Yamanasi-ken 400, Japan.
Dr David M. Lambert, Evolutionary Genetics Laboratory, Department of Zoology,
  University of Auckland, Private Bag, Auckland, New Zealand.
Prof. Antonio Lima-de-Faria, Institute of Molecular Cytogenetics,
  University of Lund, Tornavagen 13, S-222 63 Lund.
Dr Hiroto Naora, Research School of Biological Sciences, PO Box 475, Canberra City,
  ACT 2601, Australia.
Prof. Hugh E. H. Paterson, Department of Entomology, University of Queensland,
  St Lucia, Brisbane, Queensland 4067, Australia.
Dr Peter Saunders, Department of Mathematics, King's College, London,
  Strand, London WC2R 2LS, UK.
Dr Francesco M. Scudo, CNR Instituto di Bioquimica, Genetica ed Evoluzionistica,
  Via Abbiategrasso 207, 27100 Pavia, Italy.
Prof. Guiseppe Sermonti, Dipartmento di Genetica, Universita di Perugia,
  and Rivista de Biologia/Biology Forum, CP 317, 06199 Perugia Italy.
Prof. A. Sibatani, Biological Laboratory, Kansai Medical University, Hirakata,
  Osaka, Japan/Wissenschaftskolleg zu Berlin, Wallotstrasse 19, D-1000 Berlin 33.
Prof. René Thom, Institut des Hautes Etudes Scietifique, 35 Route de Chartres,
  Bures-sur-Yvette, France.
Dr Gerry C. Webster, School of Biological sciences, The University of Sussex,
  Falmer, Brighton, BN1 9QG, UK.

1. Structuralism and Darwinism: Concepts for the Study of Form

Gerry Webster

Except to violence he yields not one word of advice; entreaties
Have no effect: you must seize him, offer him force and fetters,
On which in the end his wiles will dash themselves to waste.

Virgil *Georgics IV*

I take it that the first task of 'Structuralist Biology' — supposing such to be possible — is to formulate a system of concepts which will play a constitutive role in our organisation of experience and perform a regulative function in the business of 'putting questions to nature'. Since my own interest in structuralism in relation to biology was inspired by Lévi-Strauss' writings on structural anthropology, it would seem that as good a starting point as any is to attempt to extract some of the central concepts from his work (insofar as I understand it) and see to what extent they might have a value in relation to the biological problems in which I have an interest, namely the problem of morphology and the relation of forms. Such an attempt is encouraged by the fact that Lévi-Strauss has himself, from time to time, made comparisons between structural anthropology and certain kinds of biological theory and has described his own work as a kind of comparative anatomy (Lévi-Strauss, 1968a, 1968b, 1971). More significantly, perhaps, his views have been developed, at least in part, in the process of a critical evaluation of, and opposition to, older traditions in anthropology some of which have their counterparts in biology.

A central feature of Lévi-Strauss' 'method' is the treatment of related cultural phenomena (e.g. myths or kinship systems) as formal transformations of each other. Phenomena are thus to be analysed, at an abstract and general level, in terms of the rules governing the transformation. For example, myths are neither to be seen as created *ex nihilo* nor as being immediately or passively received from elsewhere (e.g. inherited from the past, stolen or borrowed from another culture) and accidentally 'distorted' in the process. Rather, they are to be seen as 'active' reproductions of existing and given myths (or something else) which, in being reproduced, are subject to determinate and law-governed modifications such that there is a determinate relation of transformation

1

between the 'originally given' and the reproduced form. Since empirical data on the actual (historical or geographical) origin and genealogy or transmission of any myth is usually lacking, analysis has to be 'ideal'. It is assumed that a given group of existing (and apparently diverse) myths, origin unknown, is not simply an ad hoc collection of nonsensical stories which just happen to co-exist in time or space but is a structured set, i.e., a set of formal transformations. By means of a *Gedankenexperiment* an attempt is made to elucidate the rules of the transformation by studying the formal relations between them and hence to reconstruct the set of possible myths in terms of which any particular and actual myth is to be 'explained' as an instance of the possible. As Sperber (1975) has pointed out, two theoretical hypotheses are involved: firstly that the logic of actual borrowing or transmission is the same as that of mental transformations; secondly that the logic of formation and the logic of transformation are one and the same.

Sperber also observes that in more general terms, Lévi-Strauss' project can be seen as a contribution to the 'rationalism/empiricism' debate as it has manifested itself in anthropology (indeed this is apparent from the above). Social and cultural phenomena are understood as being of a conceptual or symbolic order. However, cultures are assumed to have developed not simply in response to external demands (e.g. of adaptation), as various forms of functionalism propose, but, more fundamentally, in accordance with mind's internal constraints. Behind the diversity of human cultures is the uniformity of human nature, i.e. the human (unconscious) mind — 'the psychological processes which made them possible' (Lévi-Strauss, 1949). It is the assumed existence of such constraints which results in the non-random (i.e. determinate or law-governed) transformation of the 'given' which, of necessity, conforms. Conversely, the discovery of non-randomness (uniformity, coherence or systematic order) in the 'products' is taken to imply constraints in that which 'produces'. In general terms, the discovery that the phenomena comprise a single systematic order, i.e. that there is an invariance of some kind, is taken to imply that they have a single, uniform, systematically constrained (i.e. law-governed) source or origin.

That Lévi-Strauss' work raises formidable problems at all levels from the empirical to the metaphysical should be obvious. That he is on to something important, however vaguely, erratically or obscurely, is, to my mind at least, equally obvious.

From this ridiculously brief summary of Lévi-Strauss' anthropology we can extract a series of conceptual oppositions which are relevant to the problem of biological form:

1. Internal constraints versus external demands.
2. Reproduction versus inheritance.
3. Law-governed transformation versus accidental or random variation.
4. A 'rational' system of transformations (a structure) versus a purely 'empirical' (temporal or spatial) order.

Now, in relation to biology, if the first member of each pair of concepts is structuralist, then the second member is certainly Darwinist in the sense in which that term was used in the late nineteenth century, and to a considerable extent is used today, to refer to the theory of descent plus the theory of natural selection. This opposition of structuralism and Darwinism is not simply a debating device. In the first place, it is of historical significance for a number of earlier writers (Bateson, Driesch, D'Arcy Thompson) who employed structuralist concepts did so in the course of formulating critical evaluations of Darwinism. In the second place, it is of contemporary significance since a number of those present at the Osaka conference seemed to feel that structuralist concepts would either serve to remedy the defects of an otherwise satisfactory Darwinism resulting in a 'new synthesis', or, alternatively, would provide the basis for new and more satisfactory 'theory of evolution'. In more general terms, the opposition might be taken to reflect differences in the idea of what can, or should, constitute biological knowledge. In what follows I attempt some consideration of these issues.

In certain respects, the opposition between internal constraints and external demands could be regarded as spurious since Darwinian theory might be supposed to leave a space for the appropriate structuralist concept. It is clearly important to make a distinction between the stability of an individual form as such arising from internal constraints of some kind and the stability of that same form as a given, functional member of a population of forms. The theory of natural selection, properly understood as a theory of the stability or self-regulation of populations of given forms, requires only that variation in a population of forms should be unconstrained with respect to the external demands of functional adaptation. Even if this aspect of the theory is correct, therefore, a space is left for internal constraints and the possibility that, in principle, morphology can be studied quite apart from any consideration of the functional, adaptative significance of the forms in question. In practice, there might be little or nothing to study, for variation could be unconstrained (or only weakly constrained) and organisms completely (or largely) plastic. This seems to have been a view held by some in the late nineteenth century (see Bateson, 1894; Driesch, 1914) and also seems to be the position of Monod (1972), though to what extent he is representative of contemporary Darwinism is difficult to decide.

On the other hand, it is clear that the theory of descent neither requires nor incorporates any concept of internal constraints (apart from 'inheritance') and that an excessive preoccupation with 'external demands' has characterised Darwinism from its inception, together with the concomitant belief that the only universal law operating within the organismic domain is that which pertains to the necessity of functional adaptation (see Webster & Goodwin, 1988). It would appear that this is largely a consequence of the Natural Theological–Deistic paradigm within which Darwin worked and from which he was unable, in the final analysis, to liberate himself. If organisms are regarded as the artefacts of the Deity they can only be defined, ultimately, like any other artefact in terms of function; the only thing that 'chairs' have in common is that we sit on them. Thus although Darwin follows Owen in rejecting the idea that such invariant features of organisms as now exist should be understood in functional terms, he suggests that these features were of use to the 'common progenitor' and hence that 'every detail of structure . . . may be viewed, either as having been of special use to some ancestral form, or as being now of special use to the descendents of this form' (1859: p.58). While it is fairly clear that many aspects of form can be understood in terms of function, a number of writers, past and contemporary, have discussed the problems of such an all-embracing functionalism (see Cassirer, 1950; Lambert and Hughes, 1984 and this volume). As Bateson (1894) notes, the utility to the organism of many of the characteristic features used in the contruction of taxonomies is problematic or obscure, a fact which raises difficulties for a theory which claims to have identified the cause of specific differences. Perhaps we can settle for a more modest functionalism of the kind advocated by Bateson. He suggests that whereas it is reasonable to suppose that all organisms are 'more or less adapted to their circumstances', this does not require us to believe that 'every part an animal has, and everything which it does, is useful and for its good' (1894: p.12). To be asked to believe this, he maintains, 'is to be asked to abrogate reason' (p.572).

For Bateson, as indeed for Driesch (1914, 1929), two of the most interesting and suggestive of the early writers, the 'space' left by Darwinism is non-empty and everything is not possible. Bateson develops his views in the masterly theoretical sections of the massive *Materials for the Study of Variation*. He questions whether the discontinuity of species is to be understood as a consequence of the natural selection of particular forms from a continuous, i.e. unconstrained, series of variant forms or whether it should rather be understood in terms of the intrinsic nature of the organism which manifests itself as an 'original discontinuity' or variation of form. He presents a large amount of empirical, largely observational, evidence both that variation can be discontinuous in various ways and that its nature is consistent with its being internally constrained. He feels that this evidence provides good reason to reject the view that organisms are 'plastic conglomerates of miscellaneous attributes' (1894: p.80) whose regularities of form are to be understood solely in the functionalist terms of natural selection.

I would draw attention to two classes of observations which have proved particularly fruitful for subsequent studies on the intrinsic contraints on form. Firstly, the apparent correlation between the geometrical organisation of a form and the kinds of variation it displays; e.g. the tendency of duplicated limbs to be mirror images of each other (Bateson's rule). Secondly, the phenomenon of homoeosis, that class of variation, particularly common in flowering plants and arthropods, in which one member of a meristic series assumes the form and characteristics of another, either of the same species or a different one, suggesting, in addition to constraints, some kind of equivalence or correspondence between the different forms. Both these phenomena have been of central significance in classical and recent work in experimental morphology (e.g. Harrison, 1921; Postlethwaite and Schneiderman, 1971; French, Bryant and Bryant, 1976).

At a theoretical level, though, it is arguable that Bateson's most important contribution is the reintroduction and refinement of Galton's concept of 'Positions of Organic Stability' as a means of comprehending some aspects of form. This is the idea that organisms are to be understood in terms of relatively discontinuous and alternative, determinate stable states whose nature is such that weak perturbations allow a particular state to re-establish itself but stronger ones result in transformation to an alternative determinate state. As Bateson puts it: 'the system of an organised being is such that the result of its disturbance may be specific' (1894: p.74). Using this concept he is able to criticise Darwin's (1859) view that the existence of 'an insensible series' of forms (i.e. apparent continuity) 'impresses the mind with the idea of an actual passage' (i.e. a gradual or continuous passage). As Bateson notes, the question is not whether all 'intermediate' forms are possible or indeed exist but whether any of them have been, or could be 'Positions of Organic Stability'. If the answer to this question is 'no', then the gradual 'passage' could not have occurred and we have to accept the existence of an 'original discontinuity' — which requires explanation.

Bateson's position is in certain respects close to that of Driesch (1914, 1929; see Webster and Goodwin, 1982, 1988 for a full discussion). The latter points out that much of the work in experimental morphology carried out in the late nineteenth and early twentieth centuries was done in an attempt to refute the Darwinist view of the organism as an aggregate of independent parts constrained only by external functional requirements — 'outer purposiveness'. Driesch argues that the reproduction of 'typical' forms following experimental perturbation points to the existence of internal constraints on form — 'inner purposiveness' — and suggests that empirical transformations are not 'random' but determinate and law-governed. These ideas are implicit in his conception of the organism as a self-regulating system, i.e. an autonomous causal order.

I have argued elsewhere (Webster and Goodwin, 1988) that the arguments of Goldschmidt (1958) and Waddington (1940,1957) concerning the results of experimental genetics lead to similar conclusions to those of Bateson and Driesch. Thus by three somewhat different routes the same conception of internal constraints has been achieved. It seems well founded.

I turn now to the opposition of 'inheritance' and 'reproduction' which in many respects is far more significant than the previous opposition since the concept of inheritance plays a crucial explanatory role in Darwin's theory of descent: 'the chief part of the organisation of every being is simply due to inheritance'; 'On my theory, unity of type is explained by unity of descent' (1859: p.228, p.232).

It was Bateson (1894), I think, who first pointed out that Darwin's use of the concept of inheritance in a biological context was based on an unexplicated analogy between the biological domain and the human, social domain (as of course is the theory of descent). It is worth attempting an explication to see what is at issue and to pinpoint the ambiguities and confusion which it generates. In ordinary English usage, 'inheritance' refers to the acquisition of anything from a progenitor or a previous generation; in legal usage its meaning is more restricted and refers to property devolved in accordance with law or legal right as opposed to will (Wedgwood, 1929). A system of inheritance in the social domain presupposes (at least) two things: firstly, the existence of private property in durable forms — material goods or immaterial rights/titles; secondly, a distinction between individuals as proprietors — the original possessor and the heir — and some relation between them which determines the transmission of the property in question; filiation is the only relevant relation in the context of this discussion.

Within the social world, the inheritance of private property is (or was) a major cause of the existence and perpetuation of inequality in the ownership of property since it functions to restrict the distribution of property by permitting it to be preserved within a single line of descent over the generations. A corollary of this is that a lineage can maintain its identity (defined in terms of the specific property it owns) over time and, by the same token, its difference from other lineages. If new property is progressively acquired by any lineage and accumulated by inheritance, difference (inequality) will progressively increase over time.

From this account, it should be clear, in general terms at least, both how the concept of inheritance functions in Darwin's theory and why it is of such crucial importance. It serves to transform the theory of descent from a merely factual claim that all the organisms that have ever existed comprise one or a few unilineal descent systems to an explanatory theory of the similarities and differences between organisms that are systematised in an empirical taxonomy. I defer consideration of this aspect of the theory of descent for the moment.

For a critical evaluation of the concept of inheritance as employed by Darwinism I turn first to Bateson (1894) who argues, in effect, that there is no phenomenon in the biological realm which corresponds to that in the social and therefore that the concept should be eliminated from biological discourse. Bateson's argument is effectively concerned with the first presupposition noted above, namely the existence of property in durable forms.

That this is presupposed by Darwin can be seen by a careful consideration of his remarks on homology and Unity of Type (1859: pp.415-19). He conceives homology as a relation of independent, individual elements which happen to be juxtaposed in space in particular patterns. Thus all vertebrate limbs include the 'same bones, in the same relative positions. . . . Hence the same names can be given to the homologous bones in widely different animals' (pp.415-16). The 'sameness' (of the bones) referred to here has to be read as an assertion, admittedly vague and ambiguous, of substantial identity, i.e. these bones are in effect items of durable property. If it is not read in this way, implausible though it may seem, then I can make no sense of Darwin's claims concerning the explanatory role of 'inheritance'. This reading is consistent with his remarks on changes in 'organisation' (p.417) and with his subsequent (1868) views on pangenesis where individual 'parts' are seen as effectively materially continuous, hence substantially identical. It is also the reading of the palaeontologist Osborn (1915; see Webster and Goodwin, 1988) and, of course, Bateson. I presume that de Beer's (1932: p.478) characterisation of the 'Darwinian concept of homology' must be read in a similar way: 'the sole condition which organs must fulfil to be homologous is to be descended from *one and the same representative* in a common ancestor' (my emphasis).

Bateson's criticism of the 'durable property' thesis is straightforward (see p.32 *et seq.*). Firstly he argues that the concept of 'individual homologies' (in the sense understood by Darwin) is in fact employed in an arbitrary, inconsistent and anthropocentric fashion. Secondly he argues that there are situations in which it apparently cannot be used at all; for example, in situations in which the number of petals of a flower or the number of segments in an insect limb changes from one generation to the next — instances of 'original discontinuity'. In a striking analogy, he compares the theory of descent plus inheritance to the human activity of transforming a wax model of the skeleton of one animal into a model of another by making small additions to or subtractions from its different parts. Nature, however, makes the new model new from the beginning: 'just as if the wax model had gone back into the melting-pot before the new model was begun'. In other words, the natural phenomenon is that of reproduction, not inheritance. In each generation we are confronted by the reproduction (sometimes with variation) of a specific pattern and it is in terms of this phenomenon of 'repetition' and not in terms of 'descent' or 'inheritance' that the empirical Unity of Type (insofar as it exists) must be understood. It is also worth noting his argument that a preoccupation with descent and inheritance results in a possibly artificial separation of relations of similarity between individual organisms from relations of similarity within an individual organism (serial homology), particularly clearly exhibited in metamerically segmented forms. In both cases we are confronted by a phenomenon of serial repetition (with variation) and Bateson speculates on the possibility of a general theory which could account for all such cases.

I turn now to the second presupposition involved in all notions of inheritance, namely a distinction between individuals as proprietors. The basic argument here is due to Woodger (1945), though I depart slightly from his formulation of it. As he observes, there has been a persistent tendency in many departments of biology to identify organisms with adults; to neglect or ignore the time-extended nature of organisms; to forget that the conventionally individuated 'stages of development' are arbitrary divisions of 'a life'; that to refer to the beginning and ending of 'a life' also involves conventional cuts. Thus we tend to think of development, say from an egg, as a process whereby the 'offspring comes to resemble its parents', i.e. comes to possess the same properties as its parents. But this is true in only the most superficial sense. The egg is a temporal part of a continuum of which the 'parent' and 'offspring' are also temporal parts, conventionally divided into distinct 'lives'. The 'resemblance', therefore, is always already present; it is not acquired, either gradually or otherwise. In the biological domain there can be no real distinction between individuals as proprietors and therefore no scope for a concept of inheritance. In passing, I wonder whether the concept has ever been seriously employed in situations where the continuity of 'lives' is manifest, e.g. asexual reproduction by budding? We should follow Bateson's proposal (and molecular biology's example) and eliminate the concept from biological discourse.

The alternative concept of reproduction implies an ontological distinction between the 'product' — the manifest form or pattern — and the 'means of production' — the generative structures or causal mechanisms; that is a transcendental realist ontology (see Bhaskar, 1978). If the concept of inheritance is to be entirely discarded, it follows that the generative mechanisms must themselves be reproduced.

A significant, though faltering, step towards a theory of reproduction was taken by Weismann (1883, 1885, 1904) but it is crucial in any consideration of his work to make a clear distinction between the formal and substantive content of his ideas, i.e. between his ontology *per se* and the specific theory in which it was embodied. For Weismann, the phenomenon of heredity is, in effect, only appearance, which must be explained in terms of the real phenomena of growth and development; the task is to 'trace heredity back to growth' (Weismann, 1883). His argument, rationally reconstructed, is that offspring resemble parents because they are both the effects of identical processes of growth and development, and constant effects imply constant causes, a classical empiricist view of causation. The cause is to be found in a specific substance with a specific structure, the 'germ plasm', which 'has remained in perpetual continuity from the first origin of life'. The supposed constant nature of the cause, and hence the effect, that is the phenomenon of hereditary resemblance, is simply a reflection of the historical 'continuity of the substance . . . of the germ plasm'. During the course of time successive changes have occurred in this substance such that there have been successive changes in the manifest patterns of organisms which are its effects. Thus individual pattern elements which are thought to be the 'same' are here considered to possess a specific identity of resemblance; what endures (or not) is the *species* of element.

Weismann's ontological dualism is expressed in terms of these theoretical concepts: 'the germ plasm and the substance of the body, the somatoplasm, have always occupied different spheres'. In a later development and modification of his theoretical views (Weismann, 1885), the 'sphere' of the germ plasm is spatially located in the cell nucleus which thus becomes the seat of the generative mechanisms. Since a similar, or at least compatible, ontology to that of Weismann is present in the theories of the early Mendelians, a fusion of theories could occur in the chromosome theory of the gene giving birth to that powerful paradigm — 'Weismannism–Mendelism–Morganism' (*pace* the old, cold warriors).

This paradigm has, in certain respects, been extremely successful since it has given rise to good theories of both the production of protein macromolecules and the reproduction of the means of production — DNA replication. It has not, however, resulted in the development of any satisfactory theory of the reproduction of forms or morphogenesis; current references to the 'genetic programme', outside the specific domain of molecular biology, appear to be nothing more than rhetorical gestures in a theoretical void. Elsewhere (Webster and Goodwin, 1982; Webster, 1984; Webster and Goodwin, 1988), I have attempted a critical evaluation of the tradition in this context. I have argued that the articulation of the paradigm in classical experimental genetics has actually undermined its basic conception of the causal basis of form and the relations between forms. I have also criticised the spatial formulation of the crucial ontological dualism and argued that there is a failure to make a clear distinction between causal agents and causal mechanisms. In my view, the Weismannist notion of a 'central directing agency' does not provide an appropriate conceptual framework in terms of which a satisfactory theory of the production of forms could be elaborated. Together with Goodwin (*op. cit.*), I have suggested that such a theory would conceive the generative mechanisms in terms of developmental or morphogenetic fields; that is, in terms of the organism as a whole, or in terms of parts of it, insofar as they behave as relatively autonomous wholes. These wholes are the structured, dynamic, self-regulating, causal mechanisms which produce morphological patterns and which respond to perturbation or causal agents in a unified and specific way which is determined by their repertoire of powers and current state.

Although a good deal is known about the behaviour of organisms as fields, there is as yet little sign of the emergence of a satisfactory and general theory of production, let alone a theory of the reproduction of the means of production. It is evident that the formulation of such a theory will be a formidable task since it will need to account for all the significant findings of classical genetics and experimental morphology, including those findings which have tended to be relegated to the margins of orthodox discourse. I am thinking especially of the phenomenon of phenocopying which Goldschmidt (1958) correctly regarded as being of central significance in understanding the causal basis of reproduction.

I consider now the question of transformations. Since I have already discussed the issue of 'randomness' in the context of the possibility of internal constraints on form, little more needs to be said on this point.

As Lévi-Strauss (1949) has observed (*contra* the empiricists): 'it is not comparison that supports generalisation, but the other way around'. It is evident that the project of constructing a taxonomy presupposes both that forms are systematically interrelated as kinds and that criteria for identity (the determination of similarity and difference) are available.

The basic comparativist methodology in the construction of natural groups was formulated by E. Geoffroy St Hilaire at the beginning of the nineteenth century. It should be seen not as a new invention but rather as the explication of principles which had hitherto been used intuitively. According to the 'Principle of Connections', the basic 'elements' of morphological patterns are entities which are to be identified or defined, for the purposes of comparison, in purely relational terms by the 'place' they occupy in a system of relations and not by any intrinsic properties they happen to possess as isolated individuals. Two 'elements' are said to be the same if they occupy the same 'place' in the system, so that the 'Principle of Connections' serves as a method for identifying an 'element' through all variations of shape, size and function and for recognising isomorphisms between sets of 'elements', i.e. homologies or invariant structural plans ('Unity of Type'), and hence constructing taxonomic groups. It is important to be clear that the 'sameness' of 'elements' involved here is a matter of formal rather than substantial identity and that a relation of homology is a relation of relations — an invariance under transformation — not a relation of things. The 'Principle of Connections' is an empirical structuralism in the strict sense of the term (see Descombes, 1980; Webster and Goodwin, 1988), since structuralism is nothing more than a comparativist methodology which seeks formal unity — invariance under transformation — in apparently diverse phenomena. I have suggested elsewhere (Webster, 1984; Webster and Goodwin, 1988) that the confused and unsatisfactory nature of Darwin's discussion of homology and 'Unity of Type' and his attempts at explanation in terms of 'inheritance' are a consequence of his failure (and he was not alone) to recognise the formal and relational nature of the comparative method and its limitations.

At the time of writing the accounts referred to above, I was unaware that Woodger (1945) had already presented a scholarly discussion of transformations in a paper which must be regarded as the first systematic formulation of structuralist ideas in biology. He discusses the logic of the comparative method along lines similar to, but more systematic than, my own accounts, and shows how the existence of different, invariant structural plans ('Bauplans') is used to determine (in the logical sense) different taxonomic groups and the 'overlapping' of these structural plans the inclusion and exclusion relations between these groups. The transformations of classical comparative morphology are thus 'taxonomic transformations' and Woodger demonstrates how the famous transformations of D'Arcy Thompson (1942) are of a similar kind. Whereas classical studies had involved the study of one-to-one morphological correspondences between finite sets of elements, D'Arcy Thompson's involve one-to-one continuous correspondences between infinite sets of points. In this way he is able to reveal the systematic relations between organisms or 'elements' of the same form which differ in shape (a non-relational property); the morphological correspondences are the invariants of the transformations. The demonstration of a formal unity within superficial diversity, the fact that one organism (or element) can be seen as a systematically transformed representation of another, indicates that 'variation' of this kind is constrained.

D'Arcy Thompson's method of transformations is an empirical structuralism which deals with the comparative study of manifest, visible forms. Like classical studies of homology, it is restricted to forms which are 'closely related' in the sense that there is complete morphological correspondence between the constituent elements. In his hands it was further restricted to 'taxonomic transformations', i.e. adult segments of 'lives'. D'Arcy Thompson points out that there appear to be mutually exclusive sets of forms which cannot be compared with each other; a beetle and a cuttlefish, for example, are 'essentially different . . . there is no *invariant* basis for transformation'. This appearance of 'original discontinuity', reminiscent of that noted by Bateson, leads D'Arcy Thompson to conclude that these forms 'are unrelated things' which 'have come into existence independently of one another'. Woodger, however, prefers to see this conclusion as indicative of a limitation of the method rather than of real discontinuities in nature. He argues that the theory of transformations must be developed so that comparative studies can be extended to whole 'lives' via a study of 'embryological transformations'. What is needed, he suggests, is a theory of 'zygote transformations' and of 'genetic transformations'. This is surely correct, but in the light of the above discussion of reproduction I would prefer to speak of 'field transformations' since not all organisms reproduce via zygotes and embryos and the term 'genetic', although literally appropriate, has acquired specialised and restricted connotations in contemporary biology. Virtually all organisms, however, both non-cellular and multi-cellular, display field properties at some stage of their lives (see Webster and Goodwin, 1988). As Woodger observes, actual or possible taxonomic transformations 'will be immediately deducible' from a theory of field transformations. That is, there will be a basis for relating forms in a lawful way and in this sense explaining the structure of empirical taxonomies, though this will not necessarily enable predictions to be made of what transformation will actually occur. Goodwin (1983 and this volume; Goodwin and Trainor, 1980) has made essays in the direction of such a theory.

It is clear, I think, from the above remarks that an analysis of taxonomic transformations in terms of field transformations would, if successful, result in a rational ordering of actual and possible forms (the latter to be revealed by experimental interference) as a hierarchy of structures in the strict sense of the term (see Descombes, 1980). The result would be an ideal taxonomy — a Tree of Knowledge — in terms of which the contingently irregular empirical taxonomy — the Tree of Life — would become intelligible. There is, of course, nothing 'dynamic' about such structures — the title of this book notwithstanding; their role in conferring intelligibility upon diversity depends upon their static nature.

It would seem, moreover, that a given system of field transformations (individuated in a manner to be specified by whatever field theory is devised) would determine a natural kind in the sense that it would group together forms which as a matter of fact share the same means of production, i.e. the same (in a sense to be theoretically defined) causal or generative mechanisms (see Bhaskar, 1978). I take it that this would be an example of identity defined in terms of what Hull (1981) calls 'abstract similarity'.

This yet-to-be-produced science of transformations, if it materialises, will attain the goal which Driesch (1914) believed to be that of classical comparative and systematic morphology: '[it] sought . . . to construct what was typical in the varieties of form into a system which should not be merely historically determined but which should be intelligible from a higher and more rational standpoint'. The reference to an 'historically determined' system (we can pass over the 'merely') is of course a reference to the theory of descent and to Darwin's (1859) prediction that: 'Our classifications will come to be, so far as they can be so made, genealogies; and will then truly give what may be called the plan of creation.' A classification will thus become a verbal or pictorial representation of the temporal order of forms arranged into one or a few unilinear descent groups.

In terms of the theory of descent, the identity of an organism is a function of its origin; it is individuated in terms of its pedigree. As Hull (1984 and bibliography therein) has demonstrated, the forms with which the theory of descent is concerned, i.e. particular species, are conceptualised in the theory not as natural kinds but as individuals; historical entities. Individuals cannot feature in scientific laws so a significant part of evolutionary explanation consists of constructing historical narratives recounting the adventures of these individuals.

Like the theory of inheritance, the theory of descent is based on an unexplicated analogy with the social world. As ideology, it should probably be seen in the context of the attempts of the new industrial capitalists (like the Wedgwoods) to attain 'respectability' and social identity by claiming ancient ancestors and constructing elaborate genealogies. It is no accident that Romer's (1933) classic textbook, for example, is a vast genealogical narrative, comparable in form (and even, to some extent, in content) to the mediaeval *chansons de geste* or the Icelandic sagas.

For my part, I can see no possibility of (or, indeed, necessity for) a 'new synthesis' between the theory of descent and any structuralist theory of the kind outlined above. They are metaphysically incompatible in the sense that they individuate the entities with which they deal in radically different ways — similarity versus origin and descent — and a structuralist theory of transformations refers to natural kinds whereas the theory of descent refers to individuals. It is true that there is little immediate prospect of any theory of field transformations which deals with the forms of particular species (species taxa) *per se*; most of the current attempts at transformational theories deal with much more general aspects of form such as relations of symmetry (e.g. French, Bryant and Bryant, 1976) which might be regarded as instances of 'high level' taxonomic transformations (of course particular species may be exemplars of such forms). Nevertheless, species taxa are taxonomic transformations and it would seem that, in principle, they ought to be incorporated in a general structuralist theory, so the difficulty remains. It may be that only those who still adhere to a positivist belief in the Unity of Science will find this disturbing. After all, few people are worried by the fact that mechanics ignores natural kind distinctions which are crucial to chemistry, even when the 'same' entities (defined ostensively say) are concerned.

As for a 'new' structuralist theory of 'evolution': I am not sure what this could mean. It is true, as Pouillon (1966) has pointed out in relation to the human sciences, that insofar as temporal change takes the form of transformation then 'history' is susceptible to structural analysis; structures can be, and often are, realised in time. Moreover, Woodger (1945) has implied that a theory of transformations would assist phylogenetic speculations. But what would be the point of attempts to reconstruct genealogies? In Darwinism, such reconstruction, in conjunction with the notion of 'inheritance', has an important explanatory role in relation to the structure of empirical taxonomies. But I have already suggested, following Woodger, that the structure of taxonomies should be immediately deducible from a theory of transformations. If such a theory is developed then knowledge of what actually happened in history would be of no great interest and phylogenetic speculation would become a purely antiquarian activity.

Darwin (1859: p.433) made grand claims for his theory: 'On this . . . view of descent with modification, all the great facts in morphology become intelligible.' They do not. This was apparent even before the end of the century in which he wrote (see Russell, 1916; also Bateson, 1886) and is even clearer today. If we are to deal with 'a Proteus more manifold and more intangible than the Proteus of legend' (D'Arcy Thompson, 1942), we do not need a revised Darwinism but a different conceptual framework. There is plenty for the 'young and rising naturalists' to do.

REFERENCES

Bateson, W. (1886) The ancestry of the chordata. *Quart. J. Micros. Sci.* 26, 535-71.
——(1894) *Materials for the Study of Variation.* Macmillan, London.

14   G. WEBSTER

Bhaskar, R. (1978) *A Realist Theory of Science*. Harvester, Brighton.
Cassirer, E. (1950) *The Problem of Knowledge*. Yale University Press, New Haven.
Darwin, C. (1859) *The Origin of Species*. 1st edn, reprinted. Penguin Books,
    Harmondsworth.
——(1868) *Variation of Animals and Plants Under Domestication*. John Murray,
    London.
de Beer, G. (1932) *Vertebrate Zoology*. Oxford University Press, Oxford.
Descombes, V. (1980) *Modern French Philosophy*. Cambridge University Press,
    Cambridge.
Driesch, H. (1914) *The History and Theory of Vitalism*. Macmillan, London.
——(1929) *The Science and Philosophy of the Organism*. 2nd edn. Black, London.
French, V., P. J. Bryant and S. V. Bryant (1976) Pattern regulation in epimorphic
    fields. *Science*. 193,969-81.
Goldschmidt, R. (1958) *Theoretical Genetics*. University of California Press, Berkeley.
Goodwin, B. C. (1984) A relational or field theory of reproduction and its evolutionary
consequences. In *Beyond Neo-Darwinism* (eds. M-W. Ho and P. Saunders.
    Academic Press, London.
——and L. E. H. Trainor (1980) A field description of the cleavage process in
    embryogenesis. *J.theoret. Biol.* 85, 757-70.
Harrison, R. G. (1921) On relations of symmetry in transplanted limbs. *J. exp. Zool.*
    32, 1-118.
Hull, D. L. (1981) Discussion: Kitts and Kitts and Caplan on species. *Philosophy of
    Science.* 48, 141-52.
——(1984) Historical entities and historical narratives. In *Minds, Machines and
    Evolution*. (ed. C. Hookway). Cambridge University Press, Cambridge.
Lambert, D. M. and A. J. Hughes (1984) The misery of functionalism. *Riv. Biol.*
    77, 477-90.
Lévi-Strauss, C. (1949) History and Anthropology. In 1968b, 1-27.
——(1968a) *The Scope of Anthropology*. Jonathan Cape, London.
——(1968b) *Structural Anthropology I*. Allen Lane, London.
——(1971) *L'Homme Nu*. Plon, Paris.
Monod, J. (1971) *Chance and Necessity*. Collins, London.
Osborn, H. F. (1915) On the origin of single characters as observed in fossil and living
    animals and plants. *Amer. Nat.* 49, 193-239.
Postlethwaite, J. H. and H. A. Schneiderman (1971) Pattern formation and
    determination in the antenna of the homoeotic mutant Antennapaedia in
    Drosophila melanogaster. *Dev. Biol.* 25, 606-40.
Pouillon, J. (1966) Présentation. *Problèmes de structuralisme: Les Temps modernes.*
    246, 784.
Romer, A. S. (1933) *Man and the Vertebrates*. Chicago University Press, Chicago.
Russell, E. (1916) *Form and Function*. John Murray, London.
Sperber, D. (1975) *Rethinking Symbolism*. Cambridge University Press, Cambridge.
Thompson, D'Arcy W. (1942) *On Growth and Form*. 2nd edn. Cambridge University
    Press, Cambridge.
Waddington, C. H. (1940) *Organisers and Genes*. Cambridge University Press,
    Cambridge.
——(1957) *The Strategy of the Genes*. Allen & Unwin, London.
Webster, G. (1984) The relations of natural forms. In *Beyond Neo-Darwinism*
    (eds. M-W. Ho and P. Saunders). Academic Press, London.
——and B. C. Goodwin (1982) The origin of species: a structuralist approach.
    J. Sociol. Biol. Struct. 5, 15-47.
——and B. C. Goodwin (1988) *Il Problema della Forma in Biologia*.
    Armando Armando, Rome.

Wedgwood, J. (1929) *The Economics of Inheritance.* Routledge, London.

Weismann, A. (1883) On heredity. Reprinted in T. S. Hall (1972) *A Source Book in Animal Biology.* Hafner, New York.

——(1885) The continuity of the germ plasm as the foundation of a theory of heredity. Reprinted in J. A. Moore (1972) *Readings in Heredity and Development.* Oxford University Press, New York.

——(1904) *The Evolution Theory.* Edward Arnold, London.

Woodger, J. H. (1945) On Biological Transformations. In *Essays on Growth and Form Presented to D'Arcy Wentworth Thompson* (eds. W. E. Le Gros Glark and P. B. Medawar). Oxford University Press, Oxford.

2. How to Structuralise Biology?

Atuhiro Sibatani

THE NATURE OF THE REVOLUTION IN BIOLOGY THAT WAS

The seminal papers by Webster and Goodwin (1982, 1984) advocating the structuralist viewpoint in biology made a significant impact on a number of biologists in different parts of the world. I myself, then working in a biological institution in Australia and interested in the criticism of neo-Darwinism, was stimulated by their papers and turned my attention to structuralism at its sources. I had then just completed a series of essays on the critique of molecular biology (Sibatani, 1981a, b, c) in which I defined the period of 1953-63 as the golden decade that culminated in a revolution in biology. After that crucial period, molecular biology became a Kuhnian normal science and has, more recently, transformed in part into biotechnology. As will be detailed below, I initially believed that the revolution was achieved, as in physics, by a determined and systematic application of logical and theoretical methods to biology. However, I later came to realise that as physical reductionism in biology it was simply a very successful extension of the trend that had been constantly strengthened since the beginning of modern science. Hence, the rise of molecular biology during that golden decade could not have been a revolution if the word meant a discontinuity in the dominant régime. However, we could still view the process as a revolution in biology, and that was in the vein of structuralism which actually achieved a very substantial triumph through molecular biology. The only trouble was that the nature of the revolution was at that time not correctly recognised (since modern structuralism was then in the making). Instead, almost everybody was then enthralled by the idea that it represented the last, definitive triumph of physical reductionism in biology. Quite significantly, Polanyi (1967) was an exception.

SAUSSURE'S LINGUISTIC THEORIES AND THE ELEMENT OF ARBITRARINESS IN 'STRUCTURE'

Webster and Goodwin (1982, 1984) stated that their structuralist view stemmed from the non-functionalist framework of pre-Darwinian rational morphology, and was inspired by the theories developed recently by Lévi-

16

Strauss, Piaget and Chomsky. By contrast, I developed my own version of structuralist biology using several concepts introduced by the Swiss linguist, Ferdinand de Saussure. His theories became subject to reappraisal nearly half a century after his death in 1913, and are now deemed to be the source of all the modern trends of structuralism which blossomed mainly in the European continent. Unfortunately, they still seem to be largely misrepresented and hence neglected or subjected to irrelevant criticisms in the anglophone world (Maruyama, 1981).

I sought to apply structuralism in biology (Sibatani, 1985) by identifying, by analogy, the infinitely variable act of protein synthesis in the cell with the *parole**** of Saussure (1972) ['speaking' in Saussure (1959)]. By so doing I related the creative aspect of synthesising different proteins to the similarly creative aspect of personal discourse, which emerges under the social constraint relevant to any language at any time and place, i.e. the *langue* of Saussure (1972) ['language' in Saussure (1959)]. Then, the biological counterpart of the *langue* should be the genetic code, or more precisely, the genetic code system. If it is correct to characterise the *langue*, as Saussure did, by its arbitrariness, then it may be predicted that the genetic code system should also involve at least a certain element of arbitrariness.******

Indeed, it soon emerged that there is a definite element of arbitrariness in the genetic code system, since a given amino acid or termination of polypeptide chain need not always be coded by the same set of nucleotide triplets, the genetic code thus being not absolutely universal (Osawa *et al.*, 1988; Leinfelder *et al.*, 1988) as it was initially supposed to be (Table 1). From this it can be argued that even if the assignment of individual triplets to the standard amino acids was initially determined by the then prevalent exacting physical/chemical conditions, these did not preclude subsequent modification of assignments under appropriate conditions.

NATURE AND MEANING OF ARBITRARINESS AND STRUCTURES
INVOLVING IT

Now let me consider, in some detail, what arbitrariness in the above context

* For the reason to be described below, I use the French terminology as introduced by Saussure (1972) instead of their English translations (Saussure, 1959), which I also give when individual terms appear for the first time.
** Barbieri (1985), quite independently of me (Sibatani, 1985), compared Saussure's *parole* and *langue* to phenotype and genotype of an organism, respectively, and thence derived the concept of 'natural convention' in association with the social convention of *langue* which is supposed to be arbitrary. Barbieri's objective was to give a semantic aspect to information. He put forward the concept of natural convention as complementary to natural selection, which alone he argued was insufficient to explain evolution. The framework of Barbieri's theory of evolution is marred by the conventional confusion of information with entropy — see Wicken (1987) for this point. Further Barbieri, while referring to Saussure, does not use the concept of structure. Hence he took genotype (which I regard as a configuration of a structure (Ikeda, 1988a), rather than structure itself) as the biological equivalent of *langue*. This would then miss the creative aspect of the biological counterpart of *parole*. Rather the whole genetic mechanism may be taken as *langue* or a deep-seated structure, which will then generate various phenotypes or surface phenomena, with genotypes as metastable configuration of a very stable structure (Ikeda, 1988a).

Table 1. The non-universal genetic code mainly based on Osawa and Jukes (1988).
Unusual code assignments are listed in parentheses.
Scy signifies selenocysteine (Leinfelder *et al.* 1988)

First base of codon	Second base of the codon				Third base of codon
	U	C	A	G	
U	Phe	Ser	Tyr	Cys	U
	Phe	Ser	Tyr	Cys	C
	Leu(Gly)	Ser(Trp)	Stop(Gln)	Stop(Trp,Scy)	A
	Leu	Ser	Stop(Gln)	Trp	G
C	Leu	Pro	His	Arg	U
	Leu	Pro	His	Arg	C
	Leu(Gln)	Pro	Gln	Arg	A
	Leu	Pro	Gln	Arg	G
A	Ile	Thr	Asn	Ser	U
	Ile	Thr	Asn	Ser	C
	Ile(Met)	Thr	Lys	Arg	A
	Met	Thr	Lys	Arg	G
G	Val	Ala	Asp	Gly	U
	Val	Ala	Asp	Gly	C
	Val	Ala	Glu	Gly	A
	Val	Ala	Glu	Gly	G

implies. Rules of chess or cricket are obviously highly arbitrary as indicated by
the existence of related but distinct games such as Japanese chess or baseball.
Modern Western music has been developed along the lines of the tempered
scale and derivations therefrom such as the diatonic and chromatic scales, but
music in other cultural traditions (e.g. Indian, Chinese or Japanese music,
among others) has adopted various alternative scales and rules. Arbitrariness
in fine arts and vogues is more obvious; individual artists may be bound by
contemporary artistic traditions, but what is produced is simply a
materialisation of arbitrariness when viewed in a more general, or universal
perspective. Assignment and arrangement of typewriter keys, their evolution
in a milieu of competitive commercialism, and their conservatism in relation to
the . ongoing improvement and innovation in mechanical and electronic
supporting systems, as depicted recently by Gould (1987), represent another
beautiful example of arbitrariness under the necessity of social constraints.

All these cases may appear quite anthropomorphic, and arbitrariness might
be considered to be a property peculiar to human artefacts. Apparently,
Saussure himself seems to have thought that arbitrariness is not opposed to
necessity but rather to naturalness that pertains only to the non-human world,
either animate or inanimate (Maruyama, 1981).

However, the recent progress in biology, including discoveries concerning
the genetic code and in ethology, has made the distinction rather obsolete. In
my view, here lies the real significance of introducing structuralism into
biology: what is being considered here is not a biological, let alone physical,
reduction of human beings, but rather the other way around, i.e. extension or

'elevation' of biology to what has traditionally been regarded as unique in human science.

Returning to biological phenomena proper, it now becomes clear that possible relationships among components, which are our primary definition of 'structure', need not be uniquely derived from the underlying physical/ chemical principles alone as clearly argued by Elder (1986) — cf. also Polanyi (1967) and Ikeda (1988) in this respect. We can now present the axioms that deep-seated, hardly accessible, arbitrary structures in biology mediate between physical/chemical laws on the one hand and biological surface phenomena readily accessible and familiar to biologists on the other; and that, as such, they cannot be reduced to physical/chemical laws, whereas all the biological phenomena may be reduced to such structures.

Infinite varieties of some surface phenomenon, such as *parole* can be generated (I wish to avoid the use of the term 'cause') from the underlying deep-seated structure, such as the cognate *langue*, which however need not be uniquely conserved in a given system under varying circumstances. What is important is the fact that this nature of structure, such as the genetic code or the *signe* of Saussure (1972) ['sign' in Saussure (1959)], was not discovered as a culmination of extensive investigations into the nature of the substrate in which the structure materialises, e.g. the physical/chemical nature of individual code words and amino acids or the two components of the *signe*: *le signifiant* and *le signifie* ['signifier' and 'the signified' in Saussure (1959)] or *signans* and *signatum* (Sibatani, 1985).

In a previous paper (Sibatani, 1985) as well as the presentation at the Osaka Workshop, I used a tentative distinction between the two classes of structuralism: structuralism I (St I) and structuralism II (St II), the former comprising Saussure and Claude Lévi-Strauss and the latter Jean Piaget and Noam Chomsky. However, I now feel that there is a profound difference between the last two (Piatelli-Palmarini, 1979). Whereas Piaget assumed that learning as a part of ontogeny was a process of integrating, on the part of a developing subject (child), the structure extant externally (hence Piaget's affinity to Lamarckism), Chomsky compared the innate faculty of language possessed by every subject with the more obvious innate ability of the same subject to autonomously develop into its adult form and function during the course of ontogeny, owing to the genetic endowment of the human species (hence Chomsky's position is apparently rather consonant with the one taken by molecular biologists and neo-Darwinists). My current position in this matter is, in accordance with that taken by Ikeda (1988), that Chomsky's language faculty is virtually equivalent to Saussure's *langage* (Saussure, 1972) ['speech' in Saussure (1959)], both being obviously intrinsic in *individual* human brains, and giving rise to quasi-identical structures, i.e. the *langue*, which materialise in common in all these brains. Such structures in individual brains would then mediate formation of the social aspect of the *langue* (or the social convention as it is often referred to in a vulgarised version of Saussure's theory), which is in fact inseparable from its personal aspect in the process of unfolding of the language faculty. Actually, this process would be triggered by appropriate external stimuli or the *parole* of other persons, to which each individual is exposed postnatally. Thus, the positions held by Saussure and Chomsky are in fact not so far apart as generally supposed (and it is Piaget's position that is farther away from both). For this reason, the distinction between St I and St II no longer looks adequate (Ikeda, 1988). Rather, as Ikeda (1988) argued, the positions held by all these 'giants' of structuralism need reappraisal to various extents. For example, establishment of an arbitrary 'social convention' is actually mediated by quasi-isomorphic structures materialising in the brains of individual persons involved in this convention.* Hence, social convention which arises by necessity from an originally arbitrary structure in the brain is tightly bound to the 'natural' structure intrinsic in human brains and thus open to analogy with that found in non-human organisms. Such is the synchronic aspect of a structure (Sibatani, 1985), whereas its diachronic aspect must be conceptualised only as evolution of the whole system in which various structural parts are integrated in networks of mutually associated components (Maruyama, 1988).

Once we envisage the structure in the way outlined above, we would clearly conceptualise deep-seated structures in biology and define each one of them by its specific characteristics. Only after finishing this task could one hope to look into the possible course through which those structures initially arose in the actual world. In what follows I wish to give several examples of such deep-seated structures to be posited in various aspects of biology.

PATTERN FORMATION IN LEPIDOPTERAN WINGS

In recent years several attempts have been made to devise models for pattern formation in lepidopteran wings based on reaction-diffusion systems or other physical/chemical mechanisms (Nijhout, 1980; Bard and French, 1984). However, inspection of the acutal wing patterns shows, in addition to its apparently endless variation, certain regularities pointing to the existence of some underlying structures. Lepidopteran wing patterns, from the very simple to the extremely complex, can be understood in terms of some uniform and universal prototypes (Schwanwitsch, 1956; Nijhout, 1985). It has been demonstrated that actual pieces, or ostensible (i.e. false) units, of the wing pattern may sometimes be composed of separate pattern elements such as the transverse bands, called Externae, Mediae, Basalis, etc. by Schwanwitsch (1956). Such a composite pattern is produced through merging of diverse parts of those band elements, one band being dislocated at appropriate veins to join

---

* The fact that we cannot expect apes to use a typewriter indicates that the arbitrary keyboard of conventional typewriters as discussed by Gould (1987) is not simply the product of social convention, but that it reflects structure which exists in our brain. Likewise, the ability of rats, not shared by humans, to easily cope with an experimental labyrinth (Chomsky, 1987) reflects a structure in the brain of the rat. Thus, the concept of arbitrariness is not only compatible with social necessity, but also merges with naturalness.

other bands at some distance from the origin of the former at the same vein. Various parts of separate band elements are thus integrated into a unified, 'meaningful', continuous pattern 'unit', which can actually be quite heterogeneous in composition despite its integral appearance (Schwanwitsch, 1949/50; Nijhout, 1985) — a process called 'pierellisation' by Schwanwitsch (1929). Moreover, such pattern pieces, as they appear at various positions of individual wings or other parts of the body, such as the abdomen, may further be 'synthesised' to generate a continuous or apparently meaningful 'systematic' pattern when the insect takes its species-specific resting posture, in which different parts of the body suddenly generate a new meaning as parts of a significant holistic pattern (Oudemans, 1901; Portmann, 1960; Sibatani, 1987).

Such a pattern configuration may well have been produced, as neo-Darwinists contend, by gradual accumulation, through natural selection, of minor modifications of the pattern with slight adaptive advantages. However, such a 'selection' must act upon the existing pattern-forming elements (which by itself may form only dispersed pattern fragments in actual wings). Pattern can then be generated and further modified by exploiting parameters available for variation in the actual morphology of those elements. This implies that the pattern can evolve solely through modification of the underlying structure whose properties can only be defined biologically, hence on the basis of arbitrariness of a system actually adopted rather than by directly affecting physical/chemical processes involved in individual pattern units. The structure must be conceived as a more or less universal machinery, to be met with commonly in different taxa. Consequently, we have to assume the existence of a structure available, through the action of necessary or contingent factors, for adjustment of the interrelationship between individual pattern-forming elements.

What is required here is a model for such a structure and not one that assumes entities subject to a direct physical and mathematical manipulation by model builders, which might be assumed to be operative in developing and evolving insects as well. Rather, individual insects must employ that structure to express itself in terms of the visual pattern which may suddenly take a new meaning, upon certain kinds of 'configuration', a term introduced by Ikeda (1988) of the structures involved.

CORRELATION OF DIFFERENT PARTS OF THE BODY DURING ONTOGENY

Take the well-known example of the giraffe's long neck which is typically explained in functionalist terms in both Lamarckian and Darwinian theories. In structuralist terms we argue that a long mammalian neck must be generated by appropriate elongation, rather than an increase in number, of cervical vertebrae during ontogeny, wherein such elongation would not serve any 'purpose' before the neck starts functioning. However, it is obvious that the specific or preferential elongation of cervical vertebrae must be accompanied by corresponding elongations of the neck muscles, of the nerves innervating in thse muscles as well as of the cervical spinal cord, and also of the blood vessels for the cervical and supracervical tissues, in addition to, of course, the skin covering the neck. Besides, such an elongation of the neck must be accompanied by a corresponding elongation of trachea and oesophagus.

It is known that the pattern of muscle formation is modified by a change in skeletal formation in a developing limb (Müller, 1986). Presumably a similar regulative modification would apply to elongating blood vessels and nerve fibres. However, the development of trachea and oseophagus, of the endodermal origin, may be assumed to be more independent than those mesodermal tissues mechanically supporting the body as well as the tissues of ectodermal origin. Moreover, the same developmental relations among these organs and tissues must likewise apply to all the other ordinary amniote animals with extremely short or long necks such as those of the crocodile, brontosaurus, flamingo, owl, whale or pig. Hence, such internal constraints among the parts of the body must be a ubiquitous phenomenon during ontogeny which may be considered to transcend the adaptational as well as developmental modification of the neck length. Here again, primacy should be placed on the mutual relationship and interaction among the body parts rather than to specific changes during the course of development to generate novel features apparently well adapted to the newly adopted lifestyle. Without this structuralist framework, developmental coordination among various parts of the body would have been acquired piecemeal during the course of evolution of individual taxa, thus requiring an extremely *ad hoc* explanation in functionalist terms.

THE NUMBER OF PHALANGES IN THE DIGITS OF TETRAPOD LIMBS

Gould (1986) cited Richard Owen concerning the very remarkable constraints that the number of skeletal segments or phalanges of the first digit in the tetrapod limb is typically less by one than those of the other digits (from the second up to the fifth). Recent analysis by Holder (1983) demonstrated that, although this rule does not hold with some tetrapod limbs, even in such minority cases phalangeal numbers of the first digit very seldom exceed those of the second. Impressively, Owen's rule seems to hold in variants in the phalangeal number as well as in the shape of limbs, which bears the usual conspicuously adaptational connotation. Such a transcendant feature of the body structure seems to provide a strong argument for a structuralist framework, which is probably related to the developmental constraints of the vertebrate limb, thus defying the functionalist explanation of neo-Darwinism.

DISCRIMINATIVE RECOGNITION AND IDENTIFICATION OF TASTES AND ODOURS

Here I will not go into the field of the physiology or molecular biology of the sensory detection of chemical signals. I only wish to make notes on their phenomenological features. Apparently, the taste and olfactory sense of humans (and presumably many other animals) are open-ended systems in the sense that there does not seem to be a limit to their ability to distinguish different chemical entities. This is because many newly synthesised chemicals, or newly encountered natural products of remote origin (foods, medicines, etc.) may be distinguished by humans from all the other known substances, as long as the sense organs can respond to them presumably thanks to a specific set of receptors. Essentially the same seems to hold with animals, because they show preference for certain kinds of novel food and discriminate and identify numbers of other animals according to their own rules, clearly pointing to their ability to differentiate any number of various chemical signals.

It is very difficult, however, even for us to define and classify different chemical signals according to our own sensory perception. For us, and presumably also for other animals, the chemical signals may be defined or identified negatively, as *different* from all the other familiar signals. This *negative* articulation is obviously based on the genetic endowment, as can be deduced from the lack of perception for a certain range of chemicals which are in many instances demonstrated to be specific to a species or a genotype. Such a negative definition of chemical signals on the part of animals as well as human beings seems to be rather similar to the negative definition of the *signe* in an articulate language, as pointed out by Saussure (1972) (see also Maruyama, 1981). This is one of the focuses which would lead us to a reappraisal of the often expressed belief (Maruyama, 1981; Chomsky, 1987) that the *langage* is a unique structure in human beings. Albeit chemical perceptivity in humans and animals is due to a specific genetic endowment, occurrence of each viable genotype should be taken as arbitrary in a sense similar to the *langue.*

FACIAL EXPRESSIONS AND RELATED BEHAVIOURS

Here again I will restrict my argument to the phenomenology without referring to physiology of muscles and nerves and cerebral integration of the sensory inputs which may be treated in an adaptationist framework.

Young babies may learn to decipher facial expressions worn by the mother or any other persons approaching them by virtue of the ensuing experience. But they soon learn to wear similar expressions themselves. Even if they imitated it with a subconscious intention, would they do it by learning through trial and error, i.e. would they learn how to regulate movements of their facial muscles with feedback from the response made by others, to whom the baby has tried to convey its feelings through wearing the specifically chosen expression? Would that performance be moulded and modulated in accordance with their perceptions of other persons' expressions as in the case of a young bird's learning songs from the repertoire of the local conspecific population (Konishi, 1985)? Of course, a smile on the part of the baby may be reciprocated by the mother, and they may mutually reinforce their reflex circuits. The question is whether the first smile worn by a child is a poor example of a smile to be improved by learning, or whether it 'structurally' attains quasi-perfection at the very outset. Does it convey the message 'intended' (albeit unconsciously) without practice? At least, the latter seems to be the case with the expression of anger, which is usually uncontrollable but nevertheless, sometimes even against our own intention to contain it, achieves its communicative 'purpose'.

With some of these expressions at least, the situation seems to be similar to the Chomskian language faculty in the sense that we can communicate with each other through this channel *correctly* without learning how to do it (Chomsky, 1986, 1987). This faculty would also apply both for our abilities to wear pertinent expressions and to understand similar expressions in other persons. According to Ikeda's new and highly original theory of structuralist biology (Ikeda, 1988), communication and understanding between individuals are realised through construction and materialisation of quasi-identical structures in their inner worlds or minds. Add to this the Chomskian thesis (Chomsky, 1986, 1987) that children being exposed to a given language correctly follow subtle twists in the grammar even without first learning it. According to Ikeda (1988), this means that the structure corresponding to the *langue* uttered by other persons would trigger materialisation of the presumptive *langue* of that language in a child, through 'self-organisation', say. Then, by analogy, we can assume that postnatal acquisition of the ability to communicate through facial expressions is accomplished *via* materialisation of a preexisting structure for this faculty in individual persons and by dint of the quasi-identity of such structures (like the *langue*) materialising in them all. This would indicate that, contrary to the suggestion by Chomksy (1987), the structure represented by the language faculty is not absolutely unique but has a certain parallel in the human brain.

Now communication through facial (and vocal) expressions can successfully take place between higher animals and humans, too. We can recognise, among pets and captive primates, happiness, uneasiness, complaints, anger, sorrow or amusement. I have witnessed a surprised cow and irate cockatoo. Obviously, the more remote the taxonomic relation is between them and us, the less easy the communication becomes. Thus, we can hardly perceive the feeling of a goldfish. We can, nevertheless, recognise a threatening message of a seagull to its fellows or that of a bull-ant directed to us.

These experiences strongly suggest that certain structures closely similar to the language faculty exist among higher animals as something like an open-ended set. This again indicates that certain structures in the human brain may have their counterparts in some higher animals. This prompts us to suspect that the arbitrariness characterising the structure is not the antithesis either of necessity or of naturalness (Maruyama, 1981). Structuralists may thus be led to declare that nature *is* arbitrary at its very foundations.

RECOGNITION OF CONGENERS

This was originally conceived as recognition of conspecifics, which was thought to be wider and more general, and hence more basic, than the concept of specific mate recognition or fertilisation system originally advanced by Hugh Paterson (1985). Restriction of recognition to conspecifics in my previous paper (Sibatani, 1983) was later criticised by Kortmulder (1986) who advanced the concept of the congener, rather than the conspecific, recognition. I think that this is an excellent idea, which can embrace all the extant, biologically irrelevant noises (Paterson, 1985), such as interspecific hybridisation and all the other 'false' recognition of the conspecific.

Here I wish to concentrate on the fact that recognition of the like is rather characteristic of, and quasi-universal in, eukaryotes, whereas it is unusual among, if not totally absent from, prokaryotes: it occurs in myxobacteria which form aggregations of cells/individuals (Alberts *et al.*, 1983). Most eukaryote cells can aggregate and sort out, and the recognition of the like by those cells seems to underlie the evolution of multicellular organisms with faculties of cell differentiation, development and morphogenesis. Via intermediates as embodied by slime molds, we can shift our scope from facets of the cellular life to the gregarious behaviour of animals and plants as well as mate recognition between the opposite sexes, a principle which underlies the emergence of species and speciation (Paterson, 1985). Mutual recognition among conspecifics or congeners is not limited to sexual partners, but covers the interaction between individuals of the same sex as well (Thurillazzi, 1983; Sibatani, 1989). In this context, I am not yet certain how to treat the recognition of the like by chromosomes or DNA strands for conjugation and recombination.

In all these instances, recognition of the like through physical/chemical signals deriving from the like organisms, as in biological recognition in general, are coupled with response, usually in the form of movements or some other activities, by the organism that perceives and recognises the signal. Probably the recognition act should be understood always as a part of the recognition/response circuit, which in the case of slime molds is shared by cell aggregation and food intake (Devreotes, 1982). Predation and cellular interactions are considered theoretically under the same framework by René Thom (1987). Vladimir Lefebvre advocated the principle that 'various manifestations of the same structure that he believes to be so widespread must all derive from a transcendent source' (Wheeler, 1987).

In relation to this last-mentioned point, associational flights (such as the co-rotational and catenate flights) of conspecific male butterflies (Sibatani, 1989), an indicator of congener recognition, have been observed in widely scattered taxa of butterflies. With a given species, they may often be only intermittently observed and may well not occur at all in a given population at a given time. Hence it would seem that congener recognition among butterflies as expressed by the characteristic associational flights is a structure with which most butterflies are endowed but whose manifestations may be much more limited in their actual life. This would then draw our attention to structures which involve genes and genotypes.

GENOMIC ORGANISATION

Recent progress in developmental genetics of *Drosophila melanogaster* clearly demonstrates that there is a highly organised structure or constraints among genes involved in pattern formation during early embryogenesis (Akam, 1987). Since all the insects or even some other arthropods have similar segmented body plans, all the developmental processes in these animals must be a manifestation of similar interplays among various genes related or unrelated to *Drosophila* genes, ultimately bringing about accurate construction of segmented bodies. Therefore, individual genes are always parts of a self-consistent structure regardless of this or that modification which is imposed on individual developmental genes. This should mean that a supra- and intergenic organisation must be maintained at some length throughout evolutionary alterations of individual genes and their mutual interactions. Hence such a genic organisation, or structure, would have to be inherited and maintained more or less invariant throughout whatever genomic modifications may occur in the course of evolution of individual taxa. Thus a structure that relates DNA parts is self-replicated like DNA itself.

It is thus clear that, with respect to inheritance, DNA now represents a surface phenomenon and hence, as *parole*, need not be maintained invariant in a given species as long as the structure integrating the developmental (and many other) genes (as *langue*) remain invariant and hence hereditary in the more fundamental aspect than individual genes. A failure on the part of the structure to do so will lead either to a lethal path or to macroevolution of higher taxa. These aspects of the genome have recently been discussed and exemplified in more concrete terms by Ikeda (1988, 1989).

Furthermore, there is evidence for the existence of cryptic genes, which apparently are only very weakly functional as illustrated by globin genes presumably in all plants (Bogusz *et al.*, 1988), or ostensibly not functional at all, as exemplified by the genes for the synthesis of tooth enamel proteins in birds (Kollar and Fisher, 1980), yet have still been maintained intact. Occurrence of the functional haemoglobin gene in both higher plants and animals indicates that this gene has existed throughout the main lineages of plants and animals, being co-opted in scattered groups for certain intensified requirements such as nitrogen fixation in the nodule of legume plants or systemic respiration in vertebrates and annelids. At the same times, we are struck by the fact that organisms can show, intermittently or reproducibly, features not normally displayed by individuals belonging to the same species, such as certain aberrations of butterflies, some of which may be reproduced as phenocopies (by temperature shock, for example) (Kühn, 1926), or a mutant of the snapdragon bearing an ordinary radially symmetric flower morphology

(Lima-de-Faria, 1983: p.1028). Again, certain kinds of cacti can be grown under appropriate humid conditions into an ordinary morphology equipped with slender and branching stems and flat leaves. These examples clearly indicate that regular absence of a trait from a given species does not necessarily mean the absence of 'genetic information' for it in the genome (or the integral organism) of that species. This in turn would mean that speciation does not necessarily modify the existence of a gene but affects the conditions under which its particular expressions is permitted. What varies from one species to another may be the pattern of expression of individual genes without changing the structure involving a given set of genes. Hence speciation may involve combinatorics of varying expressions of genes whose existence and maintenance are largely determined by the structure underlying genomic organisation and serving as an internal constraint to the organism.

STRUCTURE FOR EVOLUTION

Here I wish to point out that when the genetic code system emerged, all the possible variations of the amino acid sequence in the prospective protein molecules have been logically defined and hence presumptively generated if not materially realised. What matters, then, is their actual, but entirely contingent, manifestation or embodiment during the course of organic evolution, over which the structure (i.e. the genetic code system) itself would not exert any control.

Indeed, most of the possible sequences of amino acids, hence polypeptides, have not been and will never be materialised in the Universe, because the possible permutations are immense in number. Neither will most of the possible *paroles* for a given *langue* (otherwise there would not be a chance of creative aspect of the *parole* including literary arts). By the same logic, when the main structure pertaining to a major taxon of organisms has been established during the course of evolution, most if not all the prospective lower taxa belonging to that major taxon will have been logically defined and will be awaiting their contingent materialisation during the course of history (hence history does not create a taxon but only triggers its materialisation).

If this be admitted, it could be stated that there is a structure for macroevolution, if not megaevolution corresponding to emergence of major higher taxa which may have different structures. By the same token, when the language faculty has evolved or emerged, probably concurrently with the emergence of the human being (Ikeda, 1988), structures for all the possible grammatical varieties of human languages (*langues*) have been installed once and for all in the human brain, at the very outset, simply waiting for their contingent manifestation in descendent populations or individuals in the future.

These considerations bring to the fore the idea of parallel evolution of morphology and behaviour as encountered repeatedly by different taxonomic workers. I have given examples above with wing patterns and behaviour of butterflies and recognition of the likes at large. Among others, I should mention Croizat (1964), Gould (1982, 1985) and Wake and Larson (1987). In this context, the perfect imitation, once performed by a swallow's chick hatching in a magpie's nest into which it had been artificially introduced during the egg period, of the behaviour of the well-known parasitic cuckoo, is quite suggestive (Alvarez, de Renya and Segura, 1976): the young swallow repeatedly threw away a magpie's egg in the same nest exactly in the way a cuckoo's chick would have done. This observation is significant, even in the face of the newly established fact that swallow mothers may introduce fresh or partially incubated eggs into nests of other conspecific mothers (Davies, 1988). The immediately successful execution of such a complex behaviour as displayed by the newly hatched swallow chick should have been generated at one stroke from an innate structure rather than being acquired piecemeal through mutation and natural selection. In this context, the stereotyped assumption that the repeated, independent evolution of eusocial behaviour among insects, especially among Hymenoptera, is due to the neo-Darwinian/ Hamiltonian concept of inclusive fitness, may lose its persuasive strength.

ACKNOWLEDGEMENTS

I express my hearty thanks to David Elder for his continuous criticisms and assistance in various ways to my writing this article including linguistic improvements and suggesting many relevant references. I am also indebted to Kiyoshi Aoki, Noboru Hokkyo, Fusato Ogawa and Ryuichi Ogushi for valuable information.

REFERENCES

Akam, M. (1987) The molecular basis for metameric pattern in the *Drosophila* embryo. *Development* 101, 1-22.
Alberts, B., Bray, D., Lewis, J. Raff, J., Roberts, J. and Watson, J. D. (1983) *Molecular Biology of the Cell.* Garland, New York.
Alvarez, F., de Reyna, A. and Segura, H. (1976) Experimental brood parasitism of the magpie. *Anim. Behav.* 24. 907-16.
Barbieri, M. (1985) *The Semantic Theory of Evolution.* Harwood Academic Publishers, Chur.
Bard, J. B. and French, V. (1984) Butterfly wing patterns: how good a determining mechanism is the simple diffusion of a single morphogen? *J. Embryol. exp. Morph.* 84. 255-74.
Bogusz, D., Appleby, C. A., Landsmann, J., Dennis, E. S., Trinnick, M. J. and Peacock, W. J. (1988) Functioning haemoglobin genes in non-nodulating plants. *Nature.* 331. 178-80.
Chomsky, N. (1986) *Knowledge of Language: Its Nature, Origin and Use.* Praeger, New York.
——(1987) Language in a psychological setting. *Sophia Linguistica.* 22. 1-73.
Croizat, L. (1964) *Space, Time, Form: The Biological Synthesis.* Publication by the author, Caracas.

Davies, N. B. (1982) Chemotaxis. In Loomis, W. F. (ed.) *The Development of Dictyostelium discoideum.* Academic Press, New York. pp.117-68.

Devreotes, P. N. (1988) Dumping eggs on conspecifics. *Nature.* 331. 19.

Elder, D. (1986) Structuralism and reductionism. *Riv. Biol.* Perugia. 79. 75-81.

Gould, S. J. (1982) Morphological channelling by structural constraint: convergence in styles of dwarfing and gigantism in *Cerion*, with a description of two new fossil species and a report on the discovery of the largest *Cerion. Paleobiology.* 10. 172-94.

——(1986) Archetype and adaptation. *Natural History.* 10/86. 17-27.

——(1987) The panda's thumb of technology. *Natural History.* 187. 14-23.

Holder, N. (1983) Developmental constraints and the evolution of vertebrate digit patterns. *J. theor. Biol.* 104. 451-71.

Ikeda, K. (1988) *Koozoosyugi Seibutugaku no Kiso (Foundation of structuralist biology).* Kaimeisya, Tokyo. In Japanese.

——(1989) A new hypothesis on the mechanism of macroevolution: a structuralist evolution. This volume, 205-210.

Kollar, E. J. and Fisher, C. (1980) Tooth induction in chick epithelium: expression of quiescent genes for enamel synthesis. *Science.* 207. 993-5.

Konishi, M. (1955) Birdsong: from behaviour to neuron. *Ann. Rev. Neurosci.* 8. 125-70.

Kortmulder, K. (1986) The congener: a neglected area in the study of behaviour. *Acta Biotheoretica.* 35. 39-67.

Kühn, A. (1926) Üeber die Äenderung des Zeichnungsmusters von Schmetterlingen durch Temperaturreize und das Grundschema der Nymphalidenzeichnung. *Nachr. Ges. Wiss. Göttingen Math.-Phys. Kl.* [1926] 2. 120-41.

Leinfelder, W., Zehelein, E., M,andrand-Berthelot, M.-A. and Boeck, A. (1988) A gene for a novel tRNA species that accepts L-serine and cotranslationally inserts selenocysteine. *Nature.* 331. 723-5.

Lima-de-Faria, A. (1983) *Molecular Evolution and Organisation of the Chromosome.* Elsevier, Amsterdam.

Maruyama, K. (1981) *Sosyuuru no Sisoo (The thought of Saussure).* Iwanami Syoten, Tokyo. In Japanese.

Müller, G. (1986) Effects of skeletal changes on muscle pattern formation. *Biblthca anat.* 29. 91-208.

Nijhout, H. F. (1980) Pattern formation in lepidopteran wings: determination of an eyespot. *Devl Biol.* 80. 267-74.

——(1985) The developmental physiology of colour pattersn in Lepidoptera. *Advances in Insect Physiology.* 18. 181-247.

Osawa, S. and Jukes, T. H. (1988) Evolution of the genetic code as affected by anti-coden content. *Trends in Genetics.* 4.

Oudemans, J. T. (1903) Études sur la position de repos chez les Lepidopteres. *Verh. k. Akad. Wet.* 10(2). 1-90.

Patterson, H. E. H. (1985). The recognition concept of species. In E. S. Vrba, (ed.) *Species and Speciation.* Transvaal Museum Monograph No. 4, Transvaal Museum, Pretoria. pp.21-9.

Piattelli-Lamnarini, M. (ed.)(1979) Centre Royaumont pour une science de l'homme: *Theories du langage Theories de l'apprentissage: Le debat entre Jean Piaget et Noam Chomsky* (Noizet, Y. transl.), Seuil, Paris.

Polanyi, M. (1967) Life transcending physics and chemistry. *Chemistry and Engineering* Aug. 21. 54-66.

Portmann, A. (1960) *Die Tiergestalt.* Friedrich Reinhardt, Basel (1960).

Saussure, F. de (1959) *Course in General Linguistics* (Bally, C. and Sechehaye, A., eds.) [1916]; Baskin, W., transl.; (1966). McGraw-Hill Book Company, New York (reprinted).

——(1972) *Cours de linguistique générale*. Édition critique (de Mauro, Y., ed.). Payot, Paris.

Schwanwitsch, B. N. (1929) Pierellisation of stripes in the wing-pattern of the genus *Rhaphicera* Btl. (Lepidoptera Satyridae). *Z. Morph. Oekol.* Tiere 11. 1-12.

——(1949/50) Evolution of the wing-pattern in the lycaenid Lepidoptera. *Proc. Zool. Soc. Lond.* V119. 189-263.

——(1956) Color-pattern in Lepidoptera. *Revue Entomol.* URSS 35. 530-46.

Sibatani, A. (1981a) You carry out eukaryote experiments on shellfish selfish DNA: an essay on the vulgarisation of molecular biology. In *Science and Scientists: Essays by Biochemists, Biologists and Chemists*. (Kageyama, M., Nakamura, K., Oshima, T. and Uchida, T., eds.). D. Reidel Publishing Co., Doldrecht. pp.409-71.

——(1981b) Molecular biology: a paradox, illusion and myth. *Trends Biochem. Sci.* 6(6). VI-IX.

——(1981c) Two faces of molecular biology: revolution and normal science. *Riv. Biol.* Perugia. 74. 276-96.

——(1983) Kinji Imanishi and species identity. *Riv. Biol.* Perugia. 76. 25-42.

——(1985) Molecular biology: a structuralist revolution. *Riv. Biol.* Perugia. 78. 373-97.

——(1987) Oudeman's principle and its extension in pattern formation on the wings of Lepidoptera (Insecta). *J. Liberal Arts Dept. Kansai Med. Univ.* 11. 1-10.

——(1989) Conspecific recognition in male butteflies: co-rotating and catenate flights. Biology Forum (in press).

Thom, R. (1987) A formalism linking structure with function. *Biology Forum.* 80. 355-76.

Thurillazzi, S. (1983) Extranidal behaviour of *Parischnogaster nigricans serrei* (Du Buysson) (Hymenoptera, Stenogastrinae). *Z. Tierpsychol.* 63. 27-36.

Wake, D. B. and Larson, A. (1987). Multidimensional analysis of an evolving lineage. *Science.* 238. 42-8.

Webster, G. and Goodwin, B. C. (1982) The origin of species: a structuralist approach. *J. social biol. Struct.* 5. 15-47.

——(1984) A structuralist approach to morphology. *Riv. Biol.* Perugia. 77. 503-31.

Wheeler, H. (1987) A constructional biology of hermeneutics. *J. social biol. Struct.* 10. 103-23.

Wicken, J. S. (1987) *Evolution, Thermodynamics, and Information*. Oxford University Press, New York.

3. A Structuralism of Process:
Towards a Post-Darwinian Rational Morphology

Mae-Wan Ho

STRUCTURALISM AND PROCESS

Herman Hesse (1959) projected his deeply divided self into the two main characters of his novel, *Narziss and Goldmund*. Narziss was the brilliant scholar who chose the cloisters in his spiritual quest for eternal truth and rationality. Goldmund was the artistic genius who opted instead for a life of picaresque adventures in order to experience by direct intuition, the elusive beauty of kaleidoscopic nature.

This archetypal division between the platonic idealist and the romantic existentialist also separates the natural scientist from the natural historian with regard to the understanding of biological form. While the one dwells on unity and sameness, the other delights in diversity and change. The problem of form itself consists precisely in how those fundamental polarities can become resolved. My suggestion is that this can be accomplished through a 'structuralism of process'.

In the broadest sense, 'structuralism' attempts to explain entities — biological or social — in terms of relationships or organising principles, rather than as a sum of parts. Piaget (1968) defined a *structure* as a system of transformation. From an evolutionary perspective, however, it is *structuring* rather than structures that should concern us. This takes us right into the heart of Whitehead's (1920) nature as *process*. The aim of the present essay is to carry forward the interweaving of these strands of thought that might at first glance appear mutually incompatible. In the time-honoured tradition of the resolution of opposites, a 'structuralism of process' offers a synthesis of the eternal and the existential. And it does so via the participation of the organism in the *con-structuring* of reality (see Ho, 1986, 1987, 1988). Time and creativity are thus of the essence. In those respects, a structuralism of process transcends the mechanical worldview of forces and objects where time is irrelevant, and nothing new can ever happen.

REPRODUCTION AND HEREDITY

Piaget (1968) identified three main properties of structures: *wholeness, transformation* and *self-regulation*. I introduce a fourth, which is characteristic of organismic structures: heredity, or memory.

31

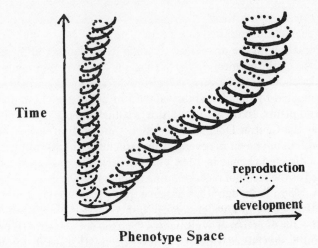

Time

reproduction

development

Phenotype Space

Figure 1. The re-enactment of life-histories. An original lineage has
split into two which diverge phenotypically.

Biological heredity is expressed in the process of reproduction: the re-
enactment of life histories wherein the organism is reconstructed anew in each
successive generation. The term 'life-cycle', so often used in this context, is
misleading because there is no closed cycle. A more realistic representation is
given in Figure 1. Here, each 'cycle' or generation is an open ring stacked one
on top of another to form an open-ended helix which constitutes a lineage (see
also Ho, 1984a). Each lineage can split into two or more descendent lineages.
The generations are distinct, yet each re-enacts a sequence of developmental
transformations more or less parallel to the previous. This is accomplished by
way of a continuity of process to which we give the name *heredity*.

Heredity is that which accounts for the stable and repeatable nature of
reproduction. Until quite recently, this feature was widely attributed to the
constancy of the genetic material, or DNA, which is transmitted from one
generation to the next. Since the advent of recombinant DNA research,
molecular geneticists have discovered that the genome is essentially fluid. In
other words, genomic DNA is functionally and structurally as flexible and
changeable as the rest of the organism.

The fluidity of DNA is best understood in the context of the regulating
system as a whole, which maintains itself by the ability of all of its parts to
respond and adjust as appropriate to their existing *milieu*. Heredity does not
reside exclusively in the DNA transmitted but in the entire system of
interrelationships between organism and environment at all levels (Ho, 1986).
Thus, the repeatability of development depends as much on the organism's
active maintenance and choice of the environment for reproduction as on the
biological heritage such as the genes, cytoplasm and physiological status of the

mother. Furthermore, these 'internal' and 'external' factors are inextricably interwoven and interramified.

Concomitant with the discoveries relating to the fluidity of the genome are observations on the permeability of Weismann's barrier. Weismann's doctrine of the independence of the germ cells from direct somatic influences has long been invalidated by detailed embryological investigations in many groups of animals and plants. In the Watson-Crick era, however, Weismannism became restated as the Central Dogma: that genetic information flows from DNA to RNA to protein but never in reverse. Consequently, somatic influences cannot result in a directed change in DNA. This revised Weismannism too has been invalidated as the result of recent finding from molecular genetics (see Pollard, 1984; Ho, 1986). Although it may seem a trivial point to those of us who have consistently argued for a wider concept of heredity (Ho and Saunders, 1979; Ho, 1984b), the violation of Weismann's doctrine does serve to focus attention on some important issues which have never been satisfactorily resolved.

One of these is the connection between development and evolution through the process of heredity. Previously, it has been said (Maynard Smith and Holliday, 1979) that the gift of Weismannism to evolution is that development can be effectively ignored. The breakdown of Weismannism should finally convince us otherwise. One central role of development is that by the very process of con-structing the present generation, the next generation is enstructured. Enstructuring takes place both physiologically in the reproducing organism as well as in the environment of reproduction. The environment, too, is highly structured, from the physiochemical to the biological and sociocultural domains. It is this simultaneous con-structuring and enstructuring which gives repeatability of reproduction (heredity) in the short term and a complexification of life histories (evolution) in the long term.

THE ENSTRUCTURING OF ORGANISM AND ENVIRONMENT IN EVOLUTION

An overall picture of the enstructuring of organism and environment in evolution may be envisaged as follows (a preliminary version was contained in a previous paper (Ho, 1984a).

Organisms as dynamical systems for transformation, or structures (S) are functions of enstructuring principles (P) and certain boundary conditions which may be regarded as internalised contingencies (iC) due to the experiences of past generations. In addition, novelties (nC) may arise within the system. These include fluctuations, inventions, discoveries, mutations, will, impulse, and so on. Thus,

$$S (P, iC, nC)$$

Structures undergo particular transformations (F) or life-histories in conjunction with the existing environment (E). The environment contributes to structuring via enstructuring principles (P), historical contingencies (hC),

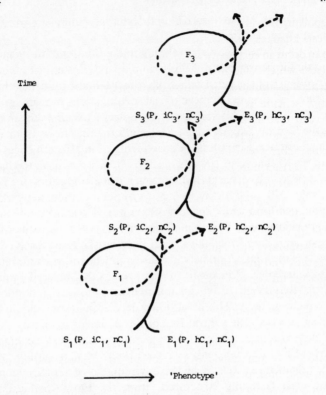

Figure 2. The enstructuring of organisms in evolution.

such as codified laws and conventions, language, culture and so on; and novelties (nC). Thus,

$$E \, (P, \, hC, \, nC)$$

The partitioning of enstructuring principles between the organism and the environment is for convenience of representation and to emphasise that enstructuring occurs in the environment as it does in the organism. It is not intended to suggest that necessarily different principles are involved.

A life-history is thus presented as a sequence of forms connected by transformation from a particular structure in the context of the co-existing contingencies. Enstructuring occurs during the enactment of individual life-histories. In the environment, novel contingencies can become codified into conventions. For example, when individuals of a population invade a new habitat, or adopt a new habit, their descendants will acquire these as heritage. In our species, the invention of the computer within our generation has resulted in our children being born into an environment where home microcomputers are as commonplace as television sets used to be thirty years ago.

In the organism, the novel environments or habits adopted may result in physiological changes which predispose the development of the next generation to occur in certain ways. This is the essence of the internalisation of contingencies, which Waddington (1957) expressed as the canalisation and eventual genetic assimilation of a novel developmental response (see below).

The entire scheme is diagrammatically represented in Figure 2. It can readily be seen that necessity (in the form of enstructuring principles) and contingency are not opposed. Rather, they co-operate in the process of enstructuring, corresponding to the synchronic and diachronic aspects respectively. Furthermore, enstructuring *necessarily* involves an interweaving of both factors 'internal' to the system and 'external' to it in the environment.

STRUCTURE AND FORM — THE POSSIBILITIES FOR A RATIONAL TAXONOMY

The aim of taxonomy, ever since Linnaeus, was to establish natural kinds in biological forms; and in so doing, discover some aspects of the eternal order that pervades the universe. This aim was uppermost in the minds of all rational morphologists, such as Goethe, Geoffroy St Hilaire, Cuvier and Richard Owen — none of them evolutionists in the modern sense. As evolution became accepted, taxonomy gave way to phylogenetic systematics, whose aim it was to discover the true *genealogy* of groups. This is a very important distinction. A lot of confusion is generated by the erroneous implicit assumption that genealogical relationship necessarily corresponds to that based on rational morphology. I will show that although a rational morphology is possible (cf. Webster and Goodwin, 1982), organisms themselves do not evolve rationally.

To be sure, there is a natural order in the evolution of forms, but it is not the all-pervading order from which every form can be arrived at by pure deduction. Instead, it is akin to the Goethean ideal of a dynamic archetype, that resides in what I call 'enstructuring principles' in order to emphasise their necessary though not sufficient role in creating biological structures.

The enstructuring principles are both timeless and universal. 'Timeless' implies an independence from history and 'universal' implies an independence from substrate. In those respects, they come close to René Thom's (1975) catastrophe theory, which gives a universal taxonomy of pure forms or 'elementary catastrophes'. The latter are independent of substrate or of detailed mechanisms. As Thom himself admits, catastrophe theory by itself is insufficient to account for biological forms, which, he says, requires a consideration of catastrophes on spaces of many more dimensions. I have suggested (Ho, 1984a) that biological forms are elaborated by the internalisation of contingent transformations via the system's memory of heredity, and that those internalised contingencies may well be the extra dimensions required to sufficiently enrich the dynamics of epigenetic systems for generating the complexity and diversity of biological forms.

Do 'pure' forms exist in nature? The best evidence comes from certain archetypal forms that may be found within both the physicochemical and the biological realms (Ho, 1984a, 1988). One class of these includes the shapes of falling drops which are similar to those of various jellyfish (see D'Arcy Thompson, 1917). Another class consists of segmented patterns such as those generated by calcium salts in solutions of colloids, which are also found in many algae (see Bateson, 1913). Dynamic spirals or concentric circles are typical of aggregating slime-mould amoebae as well as the Belouzov-Zhabotinskii reaction (Winfree and Strogatz, 1983). Complex stripes and spots may be generated as standing-wave patterns on thin vibrating plates or as coat colour patterns (see Murray, 1988). The physicochemical forms and their biological counterparts in each case bear a relationship of *similitude* (Foucault, 1983) to one another. This similitude can be expressed in terms of common mathematical principles even though the detailed mechanisms differ completely.

ARCHETYPES AND PRIMITIVE TRANSFORMATION SETS

How does order or pure form manifest itself in the biological domain? This brings us to the problem of archetypes in biology. Cuvier and von Baer, some twenty years apart, independently distinguished four main structural archetypes among the great diversity of animal forms: radiate, longitudinal, massive (molluscan) and vertebrates. For Cuvier, 'type' was an expression of definite and basic constant relationships in the structure of living things that are fixed and unalterable, and upon which all knowledge of them depends. Similar explanations of type were adopted by von Baer.

For Goethe, however, the archetype was neither geometrical nor static, but dynamical through and through. The archetype was the eternal form that displays itself fully only in change. Form belongs not only to space but to spacetime (see Cassirer, 1950; Brady, 1987). Form is co-extensive with transformation as being is with becoming.

A particular 'form' is thus an instantiation of transformation; and different forms may be related by transformation from a common dynamical structure. Figure 3 is a collage of the range of larval forms obtained by exposing early *Drosophila* embryos to ether vapour. They are in effect snapshots of a transformation process which culminates in the formation of the normal number of body segments (Ho *et al.*, 1987a). Interrupting this process at different stages results in widely different segmental patterns. These patterns constitute a transformation set from a dynamical structure: each is a 'homeologue' equivalent to the others under transformation (see also Goodwin, 1988). What is the relationship between a transformation set and biological archetypes?

One of von Baer's important insights was that the type of organisation determines the manner of development, so classification of animals according to their mode of development should give the same divisions as the classification of adults. There are indeed, only a very few types of primary larvae in the entire subkingdom of multicellular animals. Most of the phyla can

Figure 3. The transformation set of *Drosophila* larva.

be allocated to one or the other of two superphyla on the basis of their larval forms: the trochophore larva of the annelids superphylum, which includes annelids, molluscs and arthropods; and the protochordates and chordates. The superphyla also differ in their mode of cleavage as well as in the development of the coelom.

With the general acceptance of evolution, archetypes lost their transcendental status and became incarnated as the common ancestors from which the major groups evolved. The different larvae are now generally considered to be recapitulations of some developmental stage in the ancestor of the different groups (Jagersten, 1972). However, the adults are so divergent in some cases, that the common larval forms could equally be the result of convergent evolution in the juvenile stages of unrelated classes of oranisms. The argument of homology versus analogy goes on at every level from anatomy to DNA sequences, simply because systematists confuse the tracing of genealogy with the rational taxonomy of forms.

Let me propose an hypothesis which is implicit in Goethe's theory of metamorphosis (see Cassirer, 1950): *archetypes are members of a primitive transformation set*. 'Primitive' in this context refers to the conditions of a relatively simple system. For example, in the origin of the metazoa, one might envisage the system as the first fertilised eggs — whatever they might be — developing in the most general unstructured environments to give rise to the primary larval forms. In other words, the primary larvae are archetypes interconnected by transformation.

If this hypothesis is correct, then among the primary larvae, cases of convergence should be expected as well as homology by descent, *simply because the different forms must have belonged to one transformation set at some time in the past.*

Goodwin and Trainor (1980) showed how the cleavage planes of holoblastic eggs correspond to the nodal lines of harmonic functions on a sphere selected by the simplest assumptions of minimisation of surface energy and a weak polarity. The spiral cleavage may be derived from the generalised pattern via appropriate transformational parameters.

Similarly, Jagersten (1972) notes that protostomian and deuterostomian larval forms have the same basic larval organisation, differing only with respect to the manner in which an original elongated blastopore fused along the midline. When fusion occurs from behind forwards, the remaining aperture becomes mouth. Conversely, when it occurs from the front backwards, the aperture becomes anus. Mouth and anus, according to Jagersten, are homologous and arose phylogenetically by the coalescence of the middle portion of the primitive mouth (Figure 4). The primary larvae therefore belong to a transformation set. This means that any form could have metamorphosed into another at some stage before the internal dynamic became too structured towards one particular transformation. So larval forms are not a sure guide to genealogy.

Løvtrup (1977) offers us the provocative hypothesis that molluscs, and not echinoderms, are the closer relatives to vertebrates, despite the fact that chordates (in which vertebrates are traditionally classified) and echinoderms share the same larval forms. His analysis is based on physiological, chemical and biochemical characters rather than morphological ones. This is corroborated by the amino acid sequence phylogenies of cytochrome C and haemoglobin obtained by other workers. If Løvtrup is right, it implies not only that the primary larval forms of chordates and echinoderms may have evolved in parallel, but that the supposed similarities between developmental stages in echinoderms and vertebrates may also represent convergent evolution. ((Løvtrup (1977) disputes both the classification of vertebrates within chordates and the developmental similarities between echinoderms and vertebrates.) This brings us to the fundamental question on the extent to which phylogenetic transformations are predictable on the basis of what we have discussed so far.

ON THE PROXIMITY OF EIGENFORMS

According to Thom (1975), there are formal structures which in a given

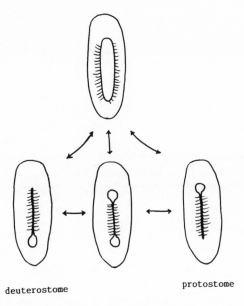

deuterostome   protostome

Figure 4. The primitive transformation set of metazoan larvae.

environment prescribe the possible biological forms (eigenforms) which are discrete by virtue of the fact that they are stable under different external parameters. If so, it would be possible to construct a 'phylogenetic map' which would represent the most probable evolutionary transformations or pathways of evolutionary transformations, at least at some local level. This implies that phylogenetic transformations would be determined largely by the proximity of eigenforms. Note that this does not mean there is an inevitable predetermined pathway; only that *for a sufficiently smooth change of external parameters, the given structures will undergo the most probable sequence(s) of transformations.* (It also implies that if there is a major environmental upheaval, many more transformations will be accessible including not only the most proximal but also more remote ones. I shall say more on this later.)

If Thom is right, one should expect parallelism and convergence in evolution (see also Saunders and Ho, 1981), and indeed they occur; so much so that Brundin (1968) is of the opinion that they are the rule rather than the exception. Parallel evolution can involve lineages that have diverged at some time in the past. The marsupials and the placental mammals have evolved separately since continental drift some 65 million years ago isolated one group of premammals in what would later become Australia and South Africa, and another in North America. Nevertheless, one finds among the marsupials, all the representatives of the major types of placental mammals such as wolves, cats, squirrels, ground hogs, anteaters, moles and mice (Simpson and Beck, 1965). Gardiner (1982) has found that in terms of physiological, biochemical and anatomical characters of the soft parts in the living species, mammals are most closely related, not to reptiles, but to birds. As with Løvtrup's suggestion that molluscs are the sister group of vertebrates, it too has aroused a great deal of heated controversy. But again, this is due to the inherent lack of necessary congruence between genealogical and rational taxonomical relationships.

Sometimes, similar characters appear not in different lineages, but in the same line in different epochs. This phenomenon is referred to as iterative evolution. In the Globigerinidae (planktonic forams), the ancestral group has persisted continuously over a long time, but two other major groups derived from it which exhibit different shell morphologies, were independently reiterated three times during different epochs (Cifelli, 1969).

It is from this same perspective that we should understand so-called mimicry: the resemblance in forms between species. the neo-Darwinian 'explanation' for mimicry is natural selection; in fact, mimicry tends to be regarded as primary evidence for natural selection itself!

But natural selection cannot work miracles, it must select what is already there: a convergence in wing pattern which reflects the existence of the same natural order that is responsible for the convergence between physicochemical and biological forms. This is brought home in the phenomenon of so-called *pseudomimicry*, the close resemblance between species which do not even occur in the same place (see Ho *et al.*, 1986). Pseudomimicry really represents cases of parallelism which is extremely widespread in the evolution of wing patterns, and is familiar to every field lepidopterist (see Shapiro, 1984). Many species of butterflies exhibit seasonal polyphenism with distinct cold and warm season forms. Different genera of butterflies inhabiting ecologically equivalent habitats (not necessarily sympatric) often exhibit parallel seasonal polyphenisms (see Ho, 1987b). Form convergence between species and genera is very common in many groups of animals and plants. They are referred to as *homeomorphs*. Figure 5 shows two pairs of homeomorphs among fossil brachiopods found in different deposits in different epochs.

Parallelism and convergence tell us that evolutionary transformations are far from arbitrary. Instead, they are repeatable and generic. In other words, there can be a map of 'eigenforms' based on which one could predict evolutionary transformations. This makes a strong case for a rational morphology which is independent of genealogy. But how far does such a map extend? Can a global map be constructed for *all* the *Bauplans* that characterise the different phyla, so that a completely rational morphology is realisable?

For the moment, that must remain an open question. My own intuition inclines towards the creation of real novelties in evolution. Dynamical structures have a fundamental uncertainty in their future evolution (see Prigogine, 1980; Ho, 1984a). Moreover, the openness of dynamic structures to contingencies results not only in transformations but additional enstructuring which in turn affects the future course of evolution. The possible histories are thus infinite, and the actual history cannot be described in advance. However,

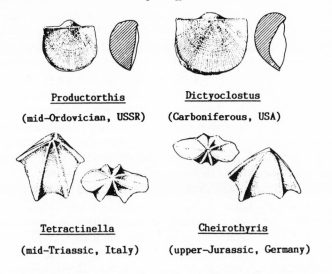

Productorthis

(mid–Ordovician, USSR)

Dictyoclostus

(Carboniferous, USA)

Tetractinella

(mid–Triassic, Italy)

Cheirothyris

(upper–Jurassic, Germany)

Figure 5. Homeomorphs among fossil brachiopods (redrawn from Jenkins, 1981).

the possible transformations *at any one moment* are likely to be finite, and may be specified given sufficient, relevant knowledge of the system. In other words, *repeatability and genericity apply at some local level.* The important corollary is that although organisms cannot foretell the future, it is active agent both in its own construction as well as in shaping evolutionary history (Jin and Hwa, 1982; Ho, 1984a). In this context, freedom may be said to consist in the conscious shaping of one's own destiny based on a clear understanding of the principles of structuring.

THE ELABORATION OF BIOLOGICAL FORM

How, then, are organisms put together? In the process view, one should ask how different life-histories evolve. I suggest that it is the sequential assimilation of experience that makes life-histories.

The primary larval forms are members of a primitive transformation set when conditions were relatively simple. But as successive generations experience life, they complexify their internal dynamic simultaneously as they complexify the structure of their environment (see above). Life-histories are therefore cobbled together out of certain past experiences, and organisms may indeed recapitulate or re-enact during development, some of the experiences of their ancestors. This may explain why life-histories are so bizarre. After all, how can it be possible to deduce a butterfly given a worm unless there is a very special dynamical structure built up by the accumulation of past accidents? This 'irrational' element of existence is related to creativity, and hence the unpredictable in evolution.

Is there any evidence that the internalisation of contingent transformations enstructures organisms in the course of evolution according to the scheme I have outlined in Figure 2? Let us restrict ourselves to a discussion on environmental contingencies for the moment, because unlike internal fluctuations such as random mutations, impulse, invention, or will, they are amenable to experimental investigation. (Though it is important to note that the same argument applies to each and every one of the factors mentioned.)

I have argued above that the operation of enstructuring principles enables us to predict locally the most probable evolutionary transformations. This implies that recently diverged species must belong to neighbouring 'eigenforms' accessible by manipulating the environment in which they develop *in an evolutionarily relevant way*. For example, geographic races of many butterflies exhibit differences in wing pattern, but each can be made to develop the pattern characteristic of any other race by simulating the special environmental conditions in which the other occurs. Towards the end of the last century, the lepidopterist Standfuss conducted an experiment in which he succeeded in reproducing the pattern characteristic of the geographic race of small tortoise shell endemic to Corsica from the typical form by rearing at high temperatures (see Figure 6). Similar homeological transformations have been demonstrated between related species (Shapiro, 1984). Note that in view of the discussion that has gone before, the presence of homeology does *not* prove genealogy, only that if an evolutionary transformation has occurred in that particular lineage, it will be in the direction indicated by developmental transformations between neighbouring forms. Thus, Arctic species of butterflies are often monophenic for the cold season form of their multivoltine relatives in the temperate regions (see Shapiro, 1984).

One special class of homeological transformations is represented by the phenomenon of *atavism*, so called because these transformation are believed to be 'throwbacks' to supposedly ancestral features. Examples are the five-digit forelimb in amphibians, the development of a hindleg in whales, and various conditions in humans such as extreme hairiness on the face and body, and the possession of a tail. Similar transformations are induced by experimental manipulations. Kollar and Fisher (1980) have induced the formation of teeth in chick dental epithelium by mouse mesenchyme. Alberch and Gale (1983) treated amphibian hindlimb buds with colchicine and reproduced the patterns of digit loss that distinguishes urodeles from anurans.

An experiment, perhaps demonstrating the absence of the converse of atavism, was performed by Dhouailly and Sengel (1973), who grafted lizard epidermis onto mouse dermis in different locations. In all cases, scales were induced whose pattern correspond to the pattern of the primary hair follicles characteristic of the location, but no hairs resulted. As we know, hairs are a new invention in mammals. It suggests , therefore, that hair development requires additional internalised contingencies which are not present in the lizard.

Particular contingent transformations become internalised via a process

Figure 6. Homeological transformation between geographical races of *Aglais urticae*. The race endemic to Corsica (bottom) is mimicked in a homeological transformation (middle) obtained by rearing the typical form (top) at high temperatures. (Courtesy of Dick Vanewright)

which Waddington (1957) divided into two stages. The first being *canalisation* — the intensification of the response to the original environmental stimulus, such that it increases in expression and/or appear earlier and earlier in ontogeny. Later, it becomes independent of the environmental stimulus. At that stage, it is said to be genetically assimilated. Note that the internalised response does lead to a reorganisation of development, and is not just a superposition.

A process very similar to the above has been identified by Jagersten (1972) in the evolution of metazoan life-histories. From comparative studies on metazoan larval forms, he proposed that the primitive life-history in the subkingdom consists of a free-floating larva phase followed by a bottom-dwelling bilaterally symmetrical adult phase. A survey of the metazoan larval forms reveals the widespread occurrence of adult characteristics 'accelerated' into the juvenile stages, by a process which he termed 'adultation'. An example is the veliger larva of molluscs which possesses a shell and a foot, but otherwise, shows a trochophore type of organisation. Another example is the echiurid *Branchiomma*, which develop adult tentacles in early larval life. The reorganisation that occurs subsequent to the internalisation of a novel transformation may be so drastic as to alter the entire life-history. Jagersten (1972) proposes that direct development evolved from indirect development by suppression of the free-living larval stages altogether in an extreme form of adultation.

What evidence is there that environmental contingencies could be involved in provoking novel transformations? Vrba (1984) shows how the global temperature fluctuations that affected rainfall and vegetation in many parts of Africa over the past five million years are correlated with simultaneous waves of speciations and extinctions for diverse groups of organisms including Bovidae, Hominidae, and other big mammals. Even more impressive are the large number of phylogenies in widely distinct taxa that are congruent with the 'area cladograms' of land masses involved in continental drift (Nelson and Platnick, 1984; Craw and Page, 1988). Major environmental upheavals are invariably accompanied by bursts of morphological evolution. This is consistent with the hypothesis presented here. During catastrophic disturbances (and barring extinctions), many more forms will be accessible in transformations: the neighbouring as well as the more remote. These may then be the forerunners of new species when the novel transformations become internalised, or assimilated.

A STRATEGY FOR RATIONAL MORPHOLOGY

Biological form is a synthesis of the rational and the existential. Whereas form and transformations can be understood in terms of a unity of generative process at some local level, as evidenced by the frequent occurrence of parallelism and convergence, the dynamical structures themselves evolve by the existential assimilation of accidents.

The course of evolution is therefore not predictable. The reasons for that may be restated as follows: dynamical structures have an inherent uncertainty in their future evolution, and moreover, the contingent conditions for realising various tra nsformations cannot be foreseen at every stage. In order to specify in advance, *all possible* transformations starting from a given dynamical structure, one must consider an infinite array of conjunctions of circumstances — a clearly impossible task. And all the more so when one takes into account the complexification of organismic structures themselves resulting from the assimilation of contingent experience which in turn shapes the future course of evolution.

However, it remains the case that a range of transformations can be circumscribed locally under relevant parameters, as a transformation set from a dynamical structure. This may include many of the evolutionary transformations that did occur. But there may also have been instances of actual evolutionary transformations that are unexpected on both empirical and theoretical grounds (see below). It will be of great interest to investigate where these 'unbridgeable gaps' are really situated in phylogeny.

The above deliberations provide the basis for a project in post-Darwinian rational morphology that combines both empirical and theoretical investigations.

As mentioned at the outset, one of the major sources of confusion for phylogenetic systematics is the implicit assumption that morphological relationships, or relationships of form, should be congruent with genealogical relationships. But whereas forms are subject to rational relationships, genealogies are anything but completely rational on account of the contingent, creative nature of evolution. The fundamental disparity between genealogy and the taxonomy of forms explains why genic evolution, or evolution of DNA, should appear decoupled from morphological evolution (see Ho and Saunders, 1979; Ho, 1987a). This immediately suggests that investigations on the taxonomy of forms are distinct from the reconstruction of genealogy.

A taxonomy of forms involves working out transformation 'distances' or transition probabilities between forms. Two lines of investigations may be pursued. The first consists of developmental studies of homeological transformations among related species under a range of relevant environmental conditions in order to establish *empirically* a map of the neighbouring forms, as well as the nature of the generative mechanisms themselves. In conjunction with the empirical studies, mathematical modelling of the generative process should be done with a view to reproducing the transformations observed.

Genealogy, on the other hand, is best traced by directly comparing as many DNA sequences as possible, preferably entire genomes (Sibley and Ahlqvist, 1983). On account of the conservative replication mechanism, DNA sequences are a much more reliable guide to genealogy than morphology, despite the recently uncovered fluidity of the genome. After all, genealogy is *defined* on genetic relatedness, in other words, on similarity of DNA sequences. (Morphological and other phenotypic comparisons have been used to make inferences of just that!) This principle is valid regardless of technical problems involved in determining average sequence similarities of genomes. Therefore, the objections raised by critics (e.g. Cracraft, 1987) are not really relevant to the issue. Many neo-Darwinian evolutionists are enthusiastic supporters of phylogenies, based on DNA sequence similarities over those based on morphological characters (e.g. Gould, 1985), because to them, the sole object of taxonomy is to establish genealogy. Not so for us who are concerned with articulating a project for a post-Darwinian rational taxonomy. Genealogy is only one aspect of the relationship between organismic forms.

Having established the genealogy, then one can begin to draw useful inferences concerning the kinds of morphological transformations that *did* occur in evolution. If evolution is governed primarily by dynamic expedience in the manner I have outlined here (see also Saunders, 1984; Ho and Saunders, 1984a), then a strong prediction would be that the frequencies of different morphological convergences would be directly proportional to their dynamic accessibility. In other words, if a particular transformation represents a strong attractor in a mathematical sense, then it would occur most frequently in evolution as convergences or parallelisms. Similarly, the sequence of transformations that did occur should also be one that could be predicted from a dynamical relationship of neighbouring forms. Thus, a rational taxonomic map need bear no simple relationship to genealogy or history, even though genealogy will be of help in its realisation.

The validity of the project proposed in no way depends on the total acceptance of the general framework presented in the rest of the paper. In particular, one could dissociate what some people fear to be 'Lamarckian' elements without affecting the main thesis. For my part, I prefer to take into proper account *all* contemporary findings in science in formulating a coherent view of evolution, in the hope that the tantalising mysteries of the evolution of biological form may finally be unveiled.

ACKNOWLEDGEMENTS

I am very grateful to Soren Løvtrup, Peter Forey, Brian Gardiner, Dick Vane-Wright, Guiseppe Sermonti, Gareth Nelson and Ron Brady for helpful comments on earlier drafts. An extended version was published in *Rivista di Biologia* 81, 11-55, 1988.

REFERENCES

Alberch, P. and Gale, E. A. (1983) Size dependence during development of the amphibian foot. *J. Embryol. Exp. Morph.* 76, 177-97.
Bateson, W. (1913) *Problems of Genetics*. Yale University Press, New Haven.
Brady, R. H. (1987) Form and cause of Goethe's morphology. In *Goethe and Sciences: A Reappraisal* (F. Amrine, F. J. Zucker and H. Wheeler, eds.). pp.257-300.
Brundin, L. (1968) Application of phylogenetic principles in systematics and evolutionary theory. In *Current Problems of Lower Vertebrate Phylogeny* (T. Orvig, ed.). Interscience, New York.
Burkhardt, R. (1977) *The Spirit of Systems*. Harvard University Press, Cambridge, Mass.
Cifelli, R. (1969) Radiation of cenozoic planktonic foraminifer. *System Zool.* 18. 154-68.
Conway-Morris, S. (1981) *Evolution S364: An Open University Course Unit 3.* Open University Press, Milton Keynes.
Cracraft, J. M. (1987) DNA hybridisation and avian phylogenetics. *Evolutionary Biology.* Vol. 21. 47-96.
Craw, R. and Page, R. (1988) Panbiogeography: method and metaphor in the new biogeography. In *Evolutionary Processes and Metaphors* (M.-W. Ho and S. W. Fox, eds.). Wiley, London. pp.163-89.

Dhouailly, D. and Sengel, P. (1987) Interactions morphogenes entre l'oiseau ou de mammifere. *C.R. Acad. Sci. Ser. D.* 277. 1221-4.

Foucault, M. (1983) *This is Not a Pipe Dream* (trans. J. Harkners). An Art Quantum, University of California Press, Berkeley.

Gardiner, B. (1982a) Tetrapod classification. *Zool. J. Linnaen Soc.* 74. 207-33.

Goodwin, B. C. (1988) Morphogenesis and heredity. In *Evolutionary Processes and Metaphors* (M.-W. Ho and S. W. Fox, eds.). Wiley, London. pp.145-62.

——and Trainor, L. E. H. (1980) A field description of the cleavage process in embryogenesis. *J. Theor. Biol.* 85. 757-70.

Gould, S. J. (1985) A clock of evolution. *Nat. Hist.* 94(4). 12-25.

Ho, M.-W. (1984a) Where does biological form come from? *Rivista di Biologia.* 77. 147-79.

——(1984b) Environment and heredity in development and evolution. In *Beyond neo-Darwinism: Introduction to the New Evolutionary Paradigm* (M.-W. Ho and P. T. Saunders, eds.). Academic Press, London. pp.267-89.

——(1986) Heredity as process: Towards a radical reformulation of heredity. *Rivista di Biologia.* 79. 407-47.

——(1987) Genetic fitness and natural selection: myth or metaphor? In Proc 3rd T.C. Schneirla Conference, Lawrence Erlbaum Assoc., New Jersey.

——(1988) On not holding nature still: Evolution by process, not by consequence. In *Evolutionary Processes and Metaphors* (M.-W. Ho and S. W. Fox, eds.). Wiley, London. pp.117-44.

——Matheson, A., Saunders, P. T., Goodwin, B. C. and Smallcombe, A. (1987a) Ether induced disturbances in segmentation in *Drosophila Melanogaster. Roux. Arch: Devl. Biol.* (1987) 196. 511-21.

—— and Saunders, P. T. (1979) Beyond neo-Darwinism: an epigenetic approach to evolution. *J. Theor. Biol.* 78. 573-91.

——and Saunders, P. T. (1982a) Adaptation and natural selection: mechanism and teleology. In *Toward a Liberatory Biology* (S. Rose, ed.). Allison and Busby, London. pp.87-104.

——and Saunders, P. T. (1983b) The epigenetic approach to the evolution of organisms — with notes on its relevance to social and cultural evolution. In *Learning, Development and Culture* (H. C. Plotkin, ed.). Wiley, London. pp.343-61.

——and Saunders, P. T. (1984a) Pluralism and convergence in evolutionary theory. In *Beyond neo-Darwinism: Introduction to the New Evolutionary Paradigm.* (M.-W. Ho and P. T. Saunders, eds.). Academic Press, London. pp.3-12.

——and Saunders, P. T. (eds.) (1984b) *Beyond neo-Darwinism: Introduction to the New Evolutionary Paradigm.* Academic Press, London.

——and Saunders, P. T. (1986) Evolution: natural selection or self-organisation? In *Disequilibirum and Self-organisation* (C. W. Kilmister, ed.). D. Reidel Publishing Co., Dordrecht, Holland. pp.231-42.

——Saunders, P. T. and Fox, S. W. (1986) A new paradigm for evolution. *New Scientist.* 27 Feb. 41-3.

——and Saunders, P. T. and Fox, S. W. (1987b) Through a neo-Darwinian Glass darkly. *Bio. Essays.* 6. 3-4.

——Tucker, C., Keeley, D. and Saunders, P. T. (1983) Effect of successive generations of ether treatment on penetrance and expression of the bithorax phenocopy in *Drosophila melanogaster. J. Exp. Zool.* 114. 257-368.

Jagersten, G. (1972) *Evolution of the Metazoan Life Cycle.* Academic Press, London.

Jenkins, G. (1981) *Evolution S364, an Open University Course Unit 8.* Open University Press, Milton Keynes, UK.

Jin, G.-T. and Hwa, G.-F. (1982) *Cybernetics and the Scientific method* (in Chinese). The Scientific Press, Beijing, China.

Løvtrup, S. (1977) *The Phylogeny of Vertebrates*. Wiley, London.

——(1985) On the classification of the taxon tetrapod. *Syst. Zool.* 34. 463-70.

Maynard-Smith, J. and Holliday, R. (1979) Preface to *The Evolution of Adaption by Natural Selection* (J. Maynard Smith and R. Holliday, eds.). The Royal Society, London. pp.v-vii.

Mivart, St. G. (1871) *On the Genesis of Species*. Macmillan, London.

Murray, J. D. (1988) How the leopard gets its spots. *Sci. Am.* 258, 80-88.

Nelson, G. and Platnick, N. (1984) Systematics and evolution. In *Beyond neo-Darwinism: Introduction to the New Evolutionary Paradigm* (M.-W. Ho and P. T. Saunders, eds.). Academic Press, London. pp.143-58.

Piaget, J. (1968) (trans. C. Maschler, 1971) *Structuralism*. Routledge and Kegan Paul, London.

Pollard, J. W. (1984) Is Weismann's barrier absolute? In *Beyond neo-Darwinism: Introduction to the New Evolutionary Paradigm* (M.-W. Ho and P. T. Saunders, eds.). Academic Press, London. pp.299-314.

Prigogine, I. (1986) *From Being to Becoming*. Freeman, San Francisco.

Riedl, R. (1977) *Order in Living Organism* (trans. R. P. S. Jefferies). Wiley, London.

Saunders, P. T. and Ho, M.-W. (1981) On the increase in complexity in evolution II. The relativity of complexity and the principle of minimum increase. *J. Theor. Biol.* 90, 515-530.

Shapiro, A. M. (1976) Seasonal polymorphism. In *Evolutionary Biology* (T. Dobzhansky, M. R. Hecht and W. C. Steere, eds.). Appleton Century-crofts, New York. pp.250-332.

——(1984) The genetics of seasonal polyrhenism and the evolution of 'general purpose genotypes' in butterflies. In *Population Biology and Evolution* (Wohrmann and V. Loeschcke, eds.). Springer-Verlag, Berlin. pp.16-30.

Sibley, C. G. and Alqvist, J. E. (1983) Phylogeny and classification of birds based on the data of DNA-DNA hybridisation.

Simpson, C. G. and Beck, W. S. (1965) *Life* (2nd ed.), Harcourt, Brace to World, New York.

Thom, R. (1975) *Structural Stability and Morphogenesis* (trans. D. H. Fowler). W. A. Benjamin, Reading, Mass.

Thompson, D. A. W. (1917) *On Growth and Form*. Cambridge University Press, Cambridge.

Vrba, E. S. (1984) Patterns in the fossil record and evolutionary processes. In *Beyond neo-Darwinism: Introduction to the New Evolutionary Paradigm* (M.-W. Ho and P. T. Saunders, eds.). Academic Press, London. pp.115-42.

Waddington, C. H. (1957) *The Strategy of the Genes*. George Allen and Unwin, London.

Webster, G. and Goodwin, B. C. (1982) The origin of species: a structuralist approach. *J. Soc. Biol. Struct.* 5.

Winfree, A. T. and Strogatz, S. H. (1983) Singular filaments organise chemical waves in three dimensions. *Physica* 8D, 35-49.

4. A Structuralist Research Programme in Developmental Biology

B. C. Goodwin

Structuralism is based upon the proposition that actual phenomena are particular realisations from a defined set of possibilities (Piaget, 1971). The set is intelligible because its members show a common order arising from the operation of the same generative principles. Applied to the biological realm as a whole, whose basic phenomenological context is the morphological diversity of organisms that have arisen in the course of evolution, the structuralist enterprise is to discover the unity of dynamic process that generates this ordered diversity of forms. This process is characterised by the properties of wholeness, regulation and transformation that are characteristic of organismic life-cycles (Webster and Goodwin, 1982; Hughes and Lambert, 1984).

Random variation (relative to states that persist) and natural selection cannot be the generators of this order, because a random process cannot produce an intrinsically ordered set. Furthermore, natural selection is strictly about dynamic stability, the capacity of entities to persist, and says nothing about their characteristic forms. Neo-Darwinism does not deal with the structuralist proposition about the biological realm; it does not, in fact, address the question of generative principles of form at all.

There is no guarantee that the structuralist quest in biology will be successful. But it is clearly well worth embarking on because science is committed to illuminating the conceptual darkness wherever possible. Searching the dim light of history for genealogical records that are covered with layers of contingent sediment can result in fascinating stories, but these are no substitute for an enquiry into the nature of the processes that are the generative source of the entities whose adventures constitute history itself. Since these entities, living organisms, are all about us still, the enquiry into their nature is something that can proceed using the principles of exact science, independently of the guess-work that is an inevitable part of an historical science such as the contemporary theory of evolution. Much of biology is in fact dedicated to this type of exact enquiry. But the subject as a whole still lives in the shadow of statements such as Dobzhansky's (1972) famous declaration: 'Nothing in biology makes sense except in the light of evolution'. Historical contingencies can indeed help us to understand aspects of organisms, as the phylogenetic history of the mammalian gut suggests why we still have dangerously ineffectual (apparently 'unfit') appendices. But this is a mere footnote to the problem of understanding how structures such as the gut are generated in the first place.

From a neo-Darwinian or functionalist perspective, most organismic characters are like appendices: they arise because they serve a purpose (confer increased fitness), such as the digestion of cellulose in herbivores; and if they persist in species where they fail to perform a useful function, they are relics, durable only because of the inertia of ancestral morphogenesis; i.e. they are frozen accidents, the sediments of previously useful contingencies. This context of enquiry does not address the questions: What properties of developing organisms make tubes (guts) and diverticuli (closed tubes such as appendices) *possible*? Are such structures a natural consequence of the dynamic order that underlies morphogenesis, as waves and spirals arise naturally in water? If so, then these forms are generic to developing organisms as dynamic structures of a particular kind. Once we know the type of generative order that characterises morphogenesis, we can define its generic forms and then ask the question: how much of the form observed in the biological realm is generic, to be expected as the high-probability states of the morphogenetic process?

In the context of population genetics, Kauffman and Levin (1987) put this question in relation to the properties of strongly epistatic genetic networks (which is a legitimate, if restrictive, way of looking at organisms). And their answer was: natural selection cannot drive organisms far from their generic states; i.e. most of the properties of organisms, described as genetic regulatory systems, occur because they are natural or generic to these complex systems, not because of natural selection. Applied to morphology, such a conclusion implies that what we see revealed in evolution is not the result of natural selection winnowing out high fitness, low probability states from a virtually unlimited set of possibilities, but the natural results of morphogenesis generating structures with high probability and intrinsic stability. Of course, these structures must satisfy dynamic stability criteria in relation to organismic life-cycles, as a gut contributes to the organism's survival and capacity to reproduce. But it is possible that the primary reason why guts occur in most animal phyla is because morphogenesis naturally and easily generates tubes. And we find this out by studying the development of actual, existing organisms, independently of their ancestries which are irrelevant to an understanding of the generative causes of form. Understanding morphogenetic principles will thus allow us to decide on the generic status of the different organismic forms and characters that have been produced in the course of evolution, and so to decide on the extent to which they are typical members of a restricted set produced by the same generative principles.

The study of ontogeny thus becomes the basis for understanding phylogeny and not the other way round. We then arrive at a reversal of Dobzhansky's statement: 'Nothing in evolution makes sense except in the light of biology' (Lambert, 1987). This biology is the structuralist kind, based upon an understanding of the generative principles that operate in all organisms.

METABOLIC AND DEVELOPMENTAL PATHWAYS

So much for the general programme of a structuralist biology. What about its detailed application to the study of development? Let me approach this question by comparing a very well-characterised area of biology, the study of metabolic pathways, with the study of development.

Both Goldschmidt (1938) and Waddington (1957), two eminent explorers of the causal relations between development and evolution, drew attention to the parallels between metabolism and development. I want to use the comparison to make a specific point about the relationships between general laws and their particular expression in organisms. What makes metabolic pathways *possible* is the differences in chemical potential between substrates and products. These thermodynamic relationships are measured under conditions of constant temperature and pressure, primarily by free energy differences. There is no way in which a metabolic sequence can run up a free energy gradient. Like the proverbial river that provides us with such a rich source of metaphors, metabolism always run downhill, products having less energy than substrates. A metabolic sequence is a series of such downward steps, from one or more (relatively) stable metabolite(s) to the next. The set of possible metabolic sequences is determined by these thermodynamic properties.

However, the rate at which different steps in a possible sequence occur is dependent not upon the free energy difference between substrates and products, but on the activation energy involved in converting one metabolite into another. In the real world of process, rates are where the action is, and organisms control them by enzymes' ability to influence these energies. There is thus a clear distinction between the laws of thermodynamics that make metabolic pathways possible, and gene products (enzymes) that alter rates of metabolic transformation. Consequently, gene products do not make metabolism possible; they stabilise particular expressions of the laws of thermodynamics in particular organisms by influencing specific rates in different pathways via control signals. The universal features of biochemistry are dependent upon basic chemistry and thermodynamics; the particulars arise from gene product specificities.

Now let me apply this argument to developmental pathways. Since I am concerned here with morphogenesis, it is the shape-determining aspects of development that I want to consider. I shall argue that, just as gene products do not make metabolism possible, this being a result of physical and chemical laws, so gene products do not make morphogenesis possible, this being also a result of the laws of physics and chemistry. But what laws, exactly? Clearly, if we knew this in detail, then we would have a knowledge of morphogenesis as exact and rigorous as that of metabolism. But we already know enough to give a general answer. Since morphogenesis is about making shapes, the laws (i.e. generative principles) on which it is based are those that describe how forms are initiated in systems with particular types of space-time organisation. Technically, these are the symmetry-breaking processes that result in the emergence of more complex from simpler (more symmetric) structures. In addition, it is necessary to have a general description of the basic building blocks out of which spatial forms are constituted, the analogues of metabolites which are the units of metabolic pathways. And finally, a complete description of morphogenesis requires some understanding of the energetic relations between these different building blocks, the spatial elements of morphogenetic sequences.

The first elements of a morphogenetic field theory are well characterised. Spontaneous symmetry-breaking or bifurcation is the process in which a spatially uniform state, subject to random perturbation, develops into a stable non-uniform pattern as a result of the balance of forces acting within the system, which make the initial spatially-homogeneous state unstable. The first demonstration of how this could occur in a biochemical system was given by A. M. Turing (1952) in his celebrated paper 'The Chemical Basis of Morphogenesis'. In this he showed how enzyme-catalysed biochemical reactions, together with diffusion, could result in an instability of spatially uniform states, which spontaneously transform into spatial patterns described by stationary waves of chemical concentration. This remarkable result showed how the laws of physics and chemistry, operating within a biological context, could generate patterns. The forces involved are those of chemical reaction together with diffusion. In relation to this theory, gene products (e.g. enzymes) do not themselves generate the patterns. They determine, in models of these processes, parametric values in the equations describing the potentially bifurcating system and so can determine whether or not bifurcations occur; and they influence the wavelengths and amplitudes of any spatial patterns that arise.

This brings us to the second component of a theory of morphogenetic pathways: the elements out of which a morphogenetic sequence is constructed. Like all theories dealing with spatio-temporal organisation, Turing's is a field theory, his equations describing the behaviour of a reaction-diffusion field. There are many different types of field in physics and chemistry, each characterised by different equations and describing spatio-temporal patterns with distinctive features of wave-form and rate of pattern initiation or transformation. But all field theories have certain properties in common: the solutions of such equations in their linearised forms are known as harmonic functions. These differ in wavelength, and any pattern of the field is initially described by some set of such harmonic functions. However, as pattern develops, the non-linear features of any particular field are expressed and distinctive wave-shapes emerge. In general this results in a discrete set of stable forms, solutions of the field equations, which characterise the set of possible spatial patterns which a particular system can display. In the case of Turing's equations, there are many solutions, and a variety of examples has been described by Murray (1977) and Meinhardt (1982) in their analysis of biological pattern formation based on Turing's theory. These are the elements out of which any morphogenetic sequence would be constructed, if it is based upon this particular theory. However, it is important to remember that there are other equally, if not more plausible, theories now available, a prime candidate being the mechanochemical model (Odell *et al.*, 1981; Oster *et al.*, 1983; Murray and Oster, 1984; Goodwin and Trainor, 1985). I shall return to this later.

Finally, what about the energetic relations between successive steps in a pattern-forming process? This is the least well characterised aspect of field theories, except in their simplest (linear) form, and in fact it is where the analogy with metabolic pathways begins to break down if taken too literally. However, there are interesting approaches to this problem that make use of what are called variational principles, in which different morphogenetic states are characterised by global quantities that are analogous to energies, and morphogenetic sequences tend to follow minimal 'energy' pathways (Goodwin and Trainor, 1980; Totafurno and Trainor, 1987).

In Waddington's (1957) visual metaphor, the epigenetic landscape, the valleys are precisely local minimal 'energy' pathways that the developmental process follows, leading to the morphological structures of the adult organism. In his description, genes influence the specific structure of the 'energy' surface that defines the landscape; but the general properties of the space-time process (field dynamic) are the assumed universals that make development possible. Waddington did not attempt to model this process in terms of morphogenetic variables, so his landscape has no generic features other than multiple 'energy' minima describing alternative branching pathways of development. D'Arcy Thompson (1917), on the other hand, used variational principles to characterise a variety of biological shapes as minimal energy surfaces, but he tended to ignore the particular influences of genes. The metabolic pathway analogy makes it clear that we must always consider both aspects of process, the general principles that operate throughout a set of phenomena and the particulars that are involved in realising a specific member of this set. The next step is to look in some detail at experimental approaches to this problem in relation to morphogenesis.

MORPHOGENETIC FIELDS AND AXIS FORMATION

The first stage of morphogenesis involves symmetry-breaking processes that result in the spatial axes of the developing organism. What variables are involved? Do they show the characteristic spatial patterns expected of field variables? Are their initial axis-determining harmonics followed by higher-order harmonics of the morphogenetic field, resulting in more detailed spatial patterns? The organism that is now providing answers to some of these questions is *Drosophila*, so let us look at some of the evidence.

Genetic studies of the antero-posterior axis in *Drosophila* have revealed a number of maternal effect mutants that result in characteristic types of disturbance, falling into three basic categories: (1) those that alter the extreme anterior and posterior poles; (2) those that disturb the formation of anterior structures (head and thorax); and (3) those that disturb the formation of posterior structures (abdomen). Cytoplasmic transplantation studies strongly suggest that the gene products are spatially localised to the regions affected, and this has now been conclusively established for the case of the *bicoid* gene product (category (2)). The use of ^{3}H-labelled cDNA probes to *bicoid* gene transcripts has revealed their presence only in the anterior region of the early embryo, while the protein product is distributed in a characteristic exponential pattern from anterior to posterior (Driever and Nüsslein-Volhard, 1988). This could be the result of a reaction-diffusion process with the protein as a morphogen, in the case of the lowest harmonic solution (a half-wave). Those genes that affect both anterior and posterior extremities appear to have their products distributed with peaks at both ends, a higher harmonic pattern of the morphogenetic field. And the gap gene transcripts (e.g. Krüppel and Hunckback), which are produced when the embryo is already axially organised by maternal gene products, show first gradients, then single peaks which go over to double peaks and a complex spatial pattern at the germ band stage (Jäckle *et al.*, 1986; Tautz, 1988).

But the most striking of the phenomena to emerge from the use of cDNA probes to monitor gene activity is the sequence of spatial patterns of pair-rule gene transcripts. The initial observations of Nüsslein-Volhard and Wieschaus (1980) on the segmentation genes had shown the startling characteristics of pair-rule mutants, revealing an unexpected 2-segment repeat unit prior to the final segmental pattern. The transcript patterns now reveal that a number of genes in this class pass through a complete series of harmonics of decreasing wavelengths, as shown for *even-skipped* (*eve*) and *fushi-tarazu* (*ftz*) in Figure 1. The sequence is: 1 band, 2 bands, 4 bands, 7 bands, with some members of this group (e.g. *paired*) then going to 14 bands at cellular blastoderm and others going later (e.g. *ftz*). The 1, 2 and 4 band patterns appear to be non-functional. So we seem to be seeing dynamic transient patterns that obey a wave doubling bifurcation sequence prior to the functional 7 band pattern, which is itself also transient, but longer-lived than the others. The different numbers of the pair-rule set follow similar though not identical patterns, with characteristic phase-shifts relative to one another. Such sequences are precisely what is to be expected from a morphogenetic field perspective. This does not, of course, prove that the patterns are actually field solutions. Meinhardt (1986) has argued that the pair-rule transcripts achieve their spatial patterns as a result of local induction by gap gene interactions. However, it is not at all evident how such a model can account for the distinctive sequence of bands shown in Figure 1 (Macdonald *et al.*, 1986).

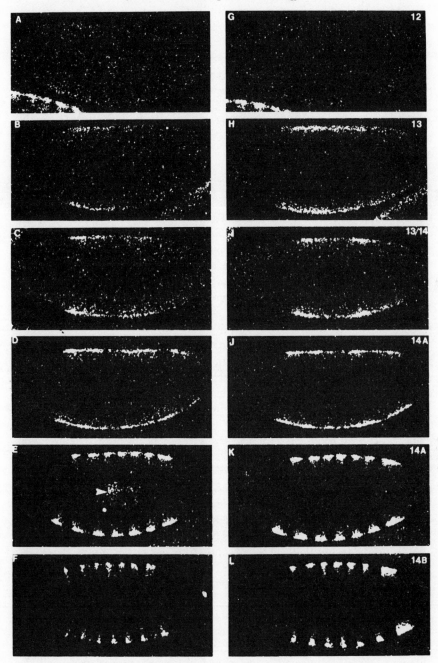

Figure 1. Transcript patterns at successive developmental stages of *Drosophila* embryos as revealed by ³H-labelled CD N A probes for *even-skipped* (left) and *fushi tarazu* (right) (from Macdonald *et al.*, 1986).

What is implied by a morphogenetic field interpretation of the harmonic sequence of Figure 1 is that there are global field variables that underlie the observed periodic spatial patterns. In general it is to be expected that such variables should show periodic patterns over the whole of the embryonic axis. The pair-rule transcripts appear, however, to be confined to about two-thirds of the embryo, there being a larger anterior and small posterior region without transcripts. It was therefore of considerable interest when Edgar *et al.* (1986) showed that cycloheximide treatment of embryos one hour before the normal striped pattern of *ftz* m R N A appears resulted in the emergence of two additional bands in the anterior region. This suggests that a periodic variable controlling *ftz* transcription extends into this domain, but a protein localised towards the anterior pole normally represses *ftz* gene activity. Cycloheximide stops production of the repressor, allowing the anterior periodicity to be revealed by the additional *ftz* bands. The normal pattern of gene expression at any stage of development is then a result of interactions between field variables and gene products, analysable into superimposed global harmonics of different wavelengths together with local inductive and repressive effects of gene products. An analysis of *Drosophila* data in these terms, providing a consistent interpretation of the observed gene expression hierarchy and the mutant data on deletions and mirror-symmetries, is given in Goodwin and Kauffman (1988).

However, it should be recognised that this is not the interpretation of the *Drosophila* data favoured by the majority of workers in this field. The dominant view is that global morphogenetic fields cease to play a significant role in development after the initial antero-posterior gradients of maternal gene products, all subsequent patterns being the result of local gene interactions (induction and repression). If this is the case, then there are no global morphogenetic field variables involved in what appear to be harmonic sequences, which become unexplained transients caused by local interactions between different gene products. Every embryonic transient would then be a result of the particular properties encoded in the genes and there would be a limited role for generative field principles in the establishment of gene patterns after the initial symmetry-breaking events that produce the embryonic axes in *Drosophila*. Further interesting observations relevant to this issue of the roles of gene products and field variables come from an examination of the dorso-ventral axis.

Eleven genes are currently known to be involved in the development of the dorso-ventral (D V) axis in *Drosophila*. One of these genes, called *Toll*, was regarded as a likely candidate for the role of primary determinant of the axis. This was because not only were there a series of mutant alleles whose phenotypes showed a loss of ventral characters (i.e. dorsalisation), but a dominant allel (*Toll^D*) resulted in ventral characters appearing around the whole D - V axis (ventralisation). The expectation was that Toll^+ product would be found distributed in a gradient from ventral to dorsal in the early embryo.

However, it turned out not to be so: the Toll$^+$ transcripts are uniformly distributed around the axis. And so are all the other gene products of the *dorsal* series that have so far been studied. Sooner or later a gene affecting this axis may be found to have the expected graded transcript distribution.

However, the perspective of gene activity within a dynamically ordered cytoplasmic context does not require this, and it may turn out that no gradient of gene transcripts will ever be found. The reason is perfectly simple. The variables of the morphogenetic field need not be gene products. In a reaction-diffusion model they can be small molecular weight morphogens (e.g. CAMP, serotonin, retinoic acid, peptides, etc.), while in a viscoelastic or mechanochemical model they are cytosolic free calcium and the mechanical state of the cytoskeleton ('strain'). Gene products (enzymes, repressors, calcium-binding proteins) affect the parameters of these fields, hence the bifurcation conditions that make spatial patterns possible, their wavelength, and amplitude. But the variables are diffusible molecules or ions and mechanical strain. Taking the mechanochemical field model as an illustration, it is perfectly possible that a gradient in cytosolic free calcium develops from ventral to dorsal either in the egg or the early embryo, and this is the primary determinant of the D-V axis. The gene products involved in consolidating this axis then act as amplifiers of the graded signal by a cascade mechanism that could be compared with the process of blood clotting, which is also triggered by calcium. The fact that one of the D-V genes, *snake*, codes for protein with the characteristics of a serine protease adds plausibility to this conjecture. This example makes more specific the concept of gene products as stabilisers and/or amplifiers of morphogenetic field patterns. The particular harmonic field solution of the mechanochemical model that could act as the primary gradient is a half-wave with maximum value of cytosolic free calcium and strain along the ventral mid-line, decreasing dorsally. This is likely to be rather labile and subject to particular types of disturbances during early development; i.e. there should be ways of phenocopying the effects of the dorsal genes by agents that disturb calcium distribution. The hypothesis that calcium, other ions, and the cytoskeleton may play such a role in the determination of the D-V axis comes from the work of A. Matheson in our laboratory (Matheson and Goodwin, 1988).

THE HIERARCHICAL NATURE OF MORPHOGENESIS

What emerges from this analysis of aspects of the current evidence relating to the roles of genes and morphogenetic fields in *Drosophila* development is the basic problem of identifying the full set of variables that is involved in specifying developmental pathways, and the dynamics that characterises the process. An effective strategy in studying this issue has always been to perturb the system and observe the effects. Genetic mutation is a precise and repeatable perturbation, but the effects are limited to those mediated by gene products. The problem is to identify the organised matrix of processes within which these products exert their influence, a matrix that includes the cytoskeleton, cell membranes, ion flux, second messengers and the whole organisation of metabolism. How does one tease out the contributions of these variables to morphogenesis, and so deduce the dynamics of the integrated structure? A procedure that complements the use of mutants is to perturb the developing embryo with stimuli that affect different components of the integrated system and observe the morphological consequences, which are often similar to those of morphological mutants and so have been called phenocopies (Goldschmidt, 1938; Ho et al., 1983, 1987). However, the two categories of perturbation are by no means identical and so it is better simply to regard the altered morphologies as transformations arising from disturbances to the normal morphogenetic pathway (Oyama, 1981). The frequencies of different classes of transformation give information about the proximity of alternative morphogenetic pathways in the epigenetic landscape, and so can be used to construct the stability surface. Furthermore, by using specific categories of perturbing agent (ionophores, ion channel blockers, metabolic inhibitors, cytoskeleton disruption, etc.) it should be possible to identify some of the variables of the dynamic context that is involved in generating the coherent global spatial order of the developing organism.

Morphogenesis particularly involves ion fluxes and those aspects of bioenergetics and metabolism that affect the state of the cytoskeleton. If there are generative universals that underlie the morphogenetic potential of the eukaryotes, they will be found in the properties of this ubiquitous dynamic structure. Its potential for shape generation in unicellular and multicellular eukaryotes, plants and animals, is being explored both experimentally and theoretically by many different groups. In the latter category of theoretical work, let me mention particularly the evidence for universal generative principles arising from studies of gastrulation (Odell et al., 1981), tetrapod limb formation (Shubin and Alberch, 1986) and plant morphogenesis (Green, 1987; Briere and Goodwin, 1988). Gastrulation, for instance, is a process that arises in a perfectly natural way in a system organised by minimal energy criteria that result in closed surfaces (spheres, ellipsoids) together with processes of contraction and relaxation organised by cytoskeletal strain fields and changing patterns of cell-cell adhesion (Mittenthal, 1983; Edelman, 1985). So organisms generate invaginations and tubes generically, producing guts, appendices, trachea, tubules, neural tubes and so on. The same processes within a changing context results in the passage from the large-scale order of gut, neural tube, and limb-bud to the local details of villi, nerves, and digits, with intermediate levels of structure in between. What we see operating here are principles of hierarchical order, morphogenesis proceeding from the general to the particular as progressively more localised detail emerges within an early-established global order. This has interesting consequences in relation to taxonomy.

HIERARCHICAL TAXONOMY

The body plans of organisms are determined by the number of broken symmetries that occur as bifurcations result in spatially-ordered asymmetries and periodicities, accompanied by the expression of non-linearities that give rise to fine local detail. Since there is a limited set of simple broken symmetries and patterns that are possible (e.g. radial, bilateral, periodic), and since developing organisms must start off laying down these elements of spatial order, it follows that these basic forms will be most common among all species. On the other hand, the finer details of pattern will be most variable between species, since the pattern-generating process results in a combinatorial richness of terminal detail and specific gene products in different species stabilise trajectories leading to one or other of these. Hence taxonomies based on morphology will inevitably be hierarchical, basic morphological patterns being common to many species while their differences are related to details of spatial patterning. In general, taxonomies need not be hierarchical, as shown by the periodic table of the elements. The properties of the elements are related to both their particulars of composition in terms of neutrons, protons and electrons (like details of species composition in relation to gene products) and to the principles of organisation as described by shells or orbitals (like the principles of morphogenetic field organisation), but there is no hierarchical order in terms of shared basic features and differences of detail over the elements as a whole.

Hierarchical biological taxonomies are often given an historical interpretation: the basic body plans of species are regarded as their more 'primitive' features, relating them to their common ancestors; while their more detailed characteristics, which distinguish them from others, are more recent. But any species must have both basic and detailed features. There is nothing intrinsically ancient about either. However, given that the exploration of morphogenetic potential takes place over evolutionary time scales, and that there is a much greater diversity of local detail available for evolutionary expression than of basic global patterns, it follows that the latter will have been fully explored and expressed in species early on in evolution, while exploring the enormous potential for morphological detail takes much longer, continuing to this day and beyond. The fact that virtually all the basic organismic body plans were discovered and established during an early evolutionary period, the Cambrian, is often remarked upon with surprise, but it is just what one would expect on the basis of the above argument. 'Ancient' and 'recent' morphological characters are secondary consequences of the hierarchical nature of morphogenesis and the exploration of its potential in time.

CONCLUSION

In conclusion, a structuralist research programme in developmental biology has as its objective the identification of those properties that are generic to living organisms, arising as inevitable consequences of the generative principles that operate in life-cycles. Once these are known, it will be possible to establish the extent to which the morphological and behavioural consequences of those principles, observed in different species, are generic and so establish them as natural kinds (Webster, 1984). The issue that is at stake here is that of intelligibility, of rational unification. A dominant objective in biology has always been to make sense of the vast sweep of organismic forms. Linnaeus regarded his taxonomy as a prologomenon to the understanding of the principles of biological creation. Darwin transformed this by taking the view that the reconstruction of actual, contingent genealogical succession was the procedure that would reveal the plan of creation, his vision resulting in an historical unification in terms of common ancestors. But the price paid for this was intelligibility. The question of a rational as well as an historical unification remains on the agenda in biology, and it is this which structuralism addresses in this context.

ACKNOWLEDGEMENTS

I am particularly grateful to M.-W. Ho, D. M. Lambert and A. Matheson for stimulating discussion and assistance in the clarification of numerous aspects of this paper, and to J. Mittenthal and L. E. H. Trainor for interactions that have helped to focus the arguments.

REFERENCES

Briere, C. and Goodwin, B. C. (1988) Geometry and dynamics of tip morphogenesis in *Acetabularia*. *J. theoret. Biol.* 131. 461-75.
Driever, W., and Nüsslein-Volhard, C. (1988) A gradient of *bicoid* protein in *Drosophila* embryos. *Cell.* 54, 83-93.
Dobzhansky, Th. (1973) Nothing in biology makes sense except in the light of evolution. *Am. Biol. Teacher.* march 1973. 125-29.
Edelman, G. M. (1985) Cell adhesion and the molecular processes of morphogenesis. *Ann. Rev. Biochem.* 54. 135-70.
Edgar, B. E., Weir, M.-P., Schubiger, G. and Kornberg, T. (1986) Repression and turnover pattern of *fushi tarazu* RNA in the early *Drosophila* embryo. *Cell.* 47. 747-54.
Goldschmidt, R. B. (1938) *Physiological Genetics.* McGraw-Hill, New York.
Goodwin, B. C. and Kauffman, S. A. (1988) Spatial harmonics and pattern specification in early *Drosophila* development. *J. theoret. Biol.* (submitted).
——and Trainor, L. E. H. (1980) A field description of the cleavage process in embryogenesis. *J. theoret. Biol.* 85. 757-70.
——(1985) Tip and whorl morphogenesis in *Acetabularia* by calcium regulated strain fields. *J. theoret. Biol.* 117. 79-106.
Green, P. B. (1987) Inheritance of pattern: analysis from phenotype to gene. *Amer. Zool.* 27. 657-73.

Ho, M-W., Bolton, E. and Saunders, P. T. (1983) Bithorax phenocopy and pattern formation. *Exp. Cell. Bio.* 51. 282-90.

——Matheson, A., Saunders, P. T., Goodwin, B. C. and Smallcombe, A. (1987) Ether-induced segmentation defects in *Drosophila melanogaster. Roux. Arch Dev. Biol.* 196. 511-21.

Hughes, A. J. and Lambert, D. M. Functionalism, structuralism, and 'Ways of Seeing'. *J. theoret. Biol.* 111. 787-800.

Jäckle, H., Tautz, D., Schuk, R., Seifert, e. and Lehmann, R. (1986) Cross-regulatory interactions among the gap genes of *Drosophila. Nature.* 324. 668-70.

Kauffman, S. A. and Levin, S. (1987) Towards a general theory of adaptive walks on rugged landscapes. *J. theoret. Biol.* 128. 11-46.

Macdonald, P. M., Ingham, P., and Struhl, G. (1986) Isolation, structure, and expression of *even-skipped*: a second pair-rule gene of *Drosophila* containing a homeobox. *Cell* 47, 721-734.

Matheson, A. D., and Goodwin, B. C. (1988) Ionic perturbations of axial order in *Drosophila* embryos (in preparation).

Meinhardt., H. (1982) *Models of Biological Pattern Formation.* Academic Press, London.

——(1986) Hierarchical inductions of cell-states — a model for segmentation in *Drosophila. J. Cell. Sci. Suppl.* 4. 357-81.

Mittenthal, J. E. (1983) A model for shape generation by strain and cell-cell adhesion in the epithelium of an arthropod leg segment. *J. theoret. Biol.* 100. 443-83.

Murray, J. D. (1977) *Nonlinear Differential Equation Models in Biology.* Clarendon Press, Oxford.

——and Oster, G. (1984) Generation of biological pattern and from. IMA J. *Maths in Med. and Biol.* 1. 51-75.

Nüsslein-Volhard and Wieschaus, E. (1980) Mutations affecting segment number and polarity in *Drosophila. Nature.* 287. 795-801.

Odell, G., Oster, G. F., Burnside, B. and Alberch, P. (1981) The mechanical basis of morphogenesis. *Devel. Bol.* 85. 446-62.

Oster, G. F., Murray, J. D. and Harris, A. (1983) Mechanical aspects of mesenchymal morphogenesis. *J. Embryol. exp. Morph.* 78. 83-125.

Oyama, S. (1981) What does a phenocopy copy? *Psychological Reports* 48. 571-81.

Piaget, J. (1971) *Structuralism.* Routledge and Kegan Paul.

Shubin, N. H. and Alberch, P. (1986) A morphogenetic approach to the origin and basic organisation of the terapod limb. *Evolutionary Biology.* 20. 319-87.

Tautz, D. (1988) Regulation of the *Drosophila* segmentation gene hunchback by two maternal morphogenetic centres. *Nature.* 332. 281-4.

Thompson, D'Arcy W. (1916) *On Growth and Form.* Cambridge University Press.

Totafurno, J. and Trainor, L. E. H. (1987) A non-linear vector field model of supernumerary limb production in salamanders. *J. theoret. Biol.* 124. 415-54.

Turing, A. M. (1952) The chemical basis of morphogenesis. *Phil. Trans. R. Soc. B.* 237. 37-72.

Waddington, C. H. (1957) *The Strategy of the Genes.* Allen and Unwin, London.

Webster, G. C. (1984) The relations of natural forms. In *Beyond Neo-Darwinism.* M.-W. Ho and P. T. Saunders (eds.). Academic Press. pp.193-218.

——and Goodwin, B. C. (1982) The origin of species: a structuralist approach. *J. Soc. Biol. Struct.* 5. 15-47.

5. Keywords and Concepts in Structuralist and Functionalist Biology

D. M. Lambert and A. J. Hughes

KEYWORDS

Twenty-three years ago at an international conference on elementary particle physics held in Kyoto, Japan, David Bohm (1965) reflected on the current state of his chosen science. He remarked: 'So physics is in a state of flux, in which the theories that will eventually emerge may well be as different from current theories as . . . those of the nineteenth century . . . a possible new line of development will be sketched, in which it is suggested that these problems can perhaps be resolved in terms of the notion of space-time as a discrete structural process.'

Bohm's attempt at a new resolution involved a rejection of the process of merely extending and modifying existing concepts. Rather, he argued that there is a great deal to be learned by thinking over familiar experiences in terms of new ideas. His recognition of the priority of the development of a new theoretical superstructure is clear. He said: '. . . when we have learned how a broad range of ordinary and familiar things can be comprehended in terms of new concepts of discrete order and structure, we will perhaps be ready to turn our attention more intelligently to the relatively technical kinds of information made available by recent experimental and theoretical developments . . . and perhaps eventually to raise entirely new kinds of relatively precise questions that could fruitfully be inquired into.'

Bohm (1965) claimed that the meaning of terms such as order, structure and process are tacitly presupposed in every word and sentence that we use. He argued that we must explicate what is usually hidden if we wish to make these common notions more precise.

In marked contrast to Bohm's view, it is sometimes claimed that words do not influence our perception of the world. This view is of course incorrect. As Schoofs (1987) says: 'Language dominates us least of all by explicitly logical argument. It effects its power primarily through the subliminal influence of rhetoric, through connotations and associations operating beneath our level of awareness.' In a purely *metaphorical* sense then, we are 'imprisoned' in a house of language. In their classic and useful book, *Teaching as a Subversive Activity*, Postman and Weingartner (1969) put it this way: 'We try to assess what is

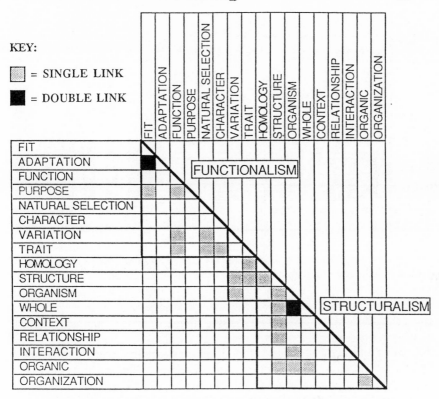

Figure 1. Matrix of keywords showing which words are defined in terms of each other. A single link indicates that one word of the pair is defined using the other, a double link indicates reciprocal definition.

outside the house from our position within it. However the house is oddly shaped and no one knows precisely what a normal shape would be. There are a limited number of windows. The windows are tinted and at odd angles. We have no choice but to see what the structure of the house permits us to see.' In other words our language is inseparable from our 'way of seeing'. However, we need to make the distinction between 'reality' and our 'knowledge of reality'. We contend that our language affects the processes whereby we understand the world, but this does not affect reality itself. Our language affects our 'way of seeing', but not the real world.

This relationship between language and our 'way of seeing' is of central concern in the book *Keywords — A vocabulary of culture and society* (Williams, 1976). Williams discussed how words appeared to be inextricably bound up with the problems that interested him. Certain words he heard again and again. He said 'I called these *Keywords* in two connected senses: they are significant, binding words in certain activities and their interpretation; they are

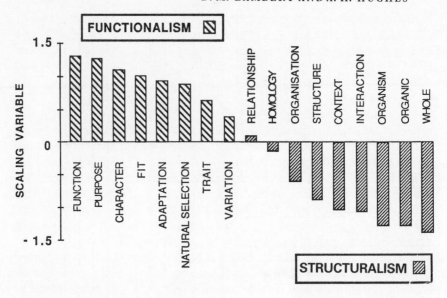

Figure 2. Values of scaling variables in dimension two from a multi-dimensional scaling analysis of word connections.

significant, indicative words in certain forms of thought. Certain uses bound together certain ways of seeing culture and society. . . .' The fact that words are connected by shared meaning was clearly recognised by Williams (1976) who emphasised the interconnections between words that formed a logical 'cluster'. Illich (1982) also recognised this and described such clusters as 'word fields'.

We will now discuss the meanings of some of biology's keywords and the dynamics of their associated word fields. Our analysis reveals a major schism between functionalist and structuralist sets. Using the Oxford English Dictionary, the pattern of relationships among keywords was investigated by recording which words were defined in terms of each other. A matrix of connections between keywords was constructed and is represented in Figure 1. Figure 2 illustrates the results of a multidimensional scaling analysis of connection information which presents the words as points in two-dimensional space. Dimension two clearly separates the words into two fields, again with a small degree of overlap between them.

An attempt was made to perform the same analysis using the same keywords as defined by dictionaries of biological terms. However, this proved impossible since only a fraction of them were listed. We suggest that this indicates an attitude amongst scientists that precision of meaning of technical terms is important but the same is not true of conceptual terms. We believe that this should not be the case and are reminded of the words of Ivan Illich (1982): 'Key words, then, are also more important for the formation of an industrialised language than creolisation by technical terms because each one denotes a perspective common to the entire set . . . and each modern language has its own set which provides that society's unique perspective on the social and ideological reality of the contemporary world.' In a similar manner Pörsken (1988) refers to the real problem of 'sphere confusion'.

FUNCTIONALISM

Functionalism: A framework of thinking in which parts of the whole perform functions and these functions represent 'biological significance'; and within an historical framework, leads to the notion of 'purpose'. Consequently functionalism represents the view that structures result from a 'need' posed by the environment.

The concept of function is ubiquitous in contemporary biology, in contrast to other fields of science (Lambert and Hughes, 1984). Howard Pattee (1969) put it well for physics, when he said: 'An electron has no function.' In biology it is not possible to define this important keyword, and to understand its many usages, independently of what Ivan Illich called the 'spider's web of keywords' within which it resides (Illich, 1982). It is also impossible to define other functionalist keywords independently, because it is the many connections between the words which actually embody this shared meaning. *Hence in biology we cannot use the word function without consequently committing ourselves to a host of associated keywords and concepts.*

The concept of function in biology is intimately connected to the metaphor of living organisms as machines which are constructed from separate parts. For Descartes organisms were composed of parts, whose functions could be reduced to mechanical operations, in order to show that living organisms were simply automata (Capra, 1982). Descartes said: 'I do not recognise any difference between machines made by craftsmen and the various bodies that nature alone composes' (Capra, 1982).

Machines operate as a linear series of causes and effects; in other words as a chain of one-way interactions. This general view has canalised thinking in biology for centuries and, for example, heavily influenced the early stages of molecular biology during which Crick developed the so-called 'central dogma'. This view holds that, generally, there can only be a one-way flow of 'information' from DNA to RNA to protein. However, this 'dogma' has been challenged by a number of biologists over a long period (e.g. Commoner, 1968; Wills, 1986) who have maintained that the biological specificity of inheritance is determined by a multimolecular network of interactions, in which various DNA, RNA and protein molecules participate. In reality there are few, or no, one-way processes in biology, rather it is characterised by continual feedback interactions.

In fact, functionalism canalises thinking in biology in at least two other important ways which are both consistent with the underlying metamodel of life as a machine (sensu Lewontin, 1982). First, it leads to an emphasis on parts of organisms, i.e. traits and characters, and not organisms themselves. Second, it leads to concepts of design, purpose and teleology.

Function when defined as 'purpose' has no place in biological discourse. For creationism, there is 'purpose' only because of a conscious designer. Darwin disposed of the conscious designer while retaining the concept of design. He rejected 'purpose' for whole organisms but retained 'purpose' for traits. This perspective also requires a quite inappropriate atomisation of the whole organism.

Consider now the keyword *adaptation* which is central to the keyword field of functionalism. The phenomenon of industrial melanism is *the* classic textbook example of adaptation in biology. According to traditional argument, the pollution of parts of Britain and Europe as a result of industrialisation was coincident with the rise in frequency of melanic forms of many species of animals at the expense of typical, or pale coloured individuals. In particular, many species of moths showed such a polymorphic condition. Natural selection was generally thought to be involved in the increase of the pigmented types and, in the case of the peppered moth, *Biston betularia*, evidence for this was produced by Kettlewell and his colleagues (see Kettlewell, 1973 for a review). They maintained that the results of a series of field and laboratory experiments illustrated that differential predation by birds of individuals resting on tree trunks was responsible for the different rates of survival of typical and melanic forms. The well-known photograph (Figure 3) which illustrates the crypsis of pale and melanic moths on unpolluted and polluted trees is powerful visual evidence for a 'fit' which was believed to represent an organismic 'solution' to an environmental 'problem' (for a contrary view, see Levin and Lewontin, 1985). The 'fit' between the melanic trait and the polluted environment is only 'appropriate', however, when viewed, not simply from a functionalist perspective, but from a *particular* functionalist perspective. In this case the functionalist 'eye' of the observer must be one of visual predation. However, in order to view the world in this way, it is necessary to separate radically the organism from its environment (since 'fit' is only possible between entities that can be separated in the first place) and then to argue that the postulated relationship between the organism and its environment is real. Unfortunately for such arguments, and despite claims in many textbooks, there is no evidence that individuals of *Biston betularia* ever regularly rest on tree trunks. For example, Clarke *et al.* (1985) found only two peppered moths resting on tree trunks despite twenty-five years of field collecting.

It is probably of some significance to note that the common photographs which purport to illustrate such a relationship are, in fact, 'constructed' in the sense that individuals were either pinned, glued or frozen, and placed on tree trunks for the purposes of photography. We have also argued elsewhere (Lambert *et al.*, 1986a; Millar and Lambert, 1988) that there is no convincing evidence for visual predation of *B. betularia* by birds. Hence the apparent 'fit' between this organism and its environment, which appeared real from a functionalist perspective, is, in fact, illusory. These well-known photographs,

Figure 3. Perhaps the best known visual metaphor of organism/environment 'fit'.

so common in biology textbooks (Lambert *et al*, 1986b) represent a kind of visual metaphor. However, this metaphor is quite misleading since the 'function' on which it is based, that of protective camouflage, has not been conclusively demonstrated. Yet, the example remains a powerful touchstone (Burian, 1983) throughout contemporary biology simply because of the power of the concept of adaptation and the dependent organism/environment dichotomy.

We agree with Ho (1984) that 'function' reflects an anthropomorphic perspective. Indeed, it appears from the *B. betularia* example that the 'way of seeing' is certainly concerned more with what we think nature *should* be doing than with what it *is* doing. It is perhaps tempting to believe that industrial melanism became a classic case because it most closely resembles the idea embodied in the phrase 'Nature red in tooth and claw'. After all, is not eating someone the ultimate selective force? However, the solution is probably deeper than this. We suggest that the case is a classic primarily because it appears to 'explain' an 'obvious' organism-environment 'fit'. That is, it is an answer to a question framed from a very specific perspective.

Since a central concern of functionalist theories is to explain such 'fit', it is not surprising that adaptation should remain central. However, if this problem is illusory then Gregory Bateson (1980) was quite correct when he said: 'If we come to regard the production of particular pieces of adaptation — the claw of the crab, the hand and eye of [humans] and so on — as central to the mass of problems that evolutionists must solve, we distort and limit our view of evolution as a whole'. We certainly agree with Gould's (1986) general argument that not only is adaptation a key and driving force for functionalist theories, but that 'our strong adaptationist biases have precluded proper attention to the important insights of structuralist thought'.

STRUCTURALISM

Structuralism: The doctrine that structure rather than function is important (Concise Oxford Dictionary, seventh edition, quoted in Hughes and Lambert, 1984). According to this viewpoint neither the elements nor the whole should be the focus of attention, but the relationship between them. Structuralism attempts to understand the laws and principles of organisation which represent the conceptual basis via which we can speculate about history (Webster and Goodwin, 1982; Goodwin, 1982).

Our keyword analysis reinforces the validity of this definition and properly recognises what structuralism *is* and what it *is not*. We suggest the definition also represents a lowest common denominator of views which comprise a range of interpretations of structuralism (Hughes and Lambert, 1984; Laughlin and d'Aquili, 1974).

Structuralist biology attempts to explain the generation of actual structures from the range of the possible (Webster and Goodwin, 1982). We suggest that, perhaps of equal importance, it can also explain stability in terms of the organisation of the structure itself (Thom, 1970). In this regard, it is important to realise that particular biological structures are not stable through generations. Real organisms die. The problem to be explained is how structures are produced regularly in different generations. Maturana (1980) makes exactly this point when he says that the phenomena of heredity and genetics occur as necessary consequences of reproduction. Moreover, Ho (1987) makes what we (Hughes and Lambert, 1988) consider to be an equivalent proposition with her emphasis on the need to recognise, within a 'structuralism of process', reproduction as a central property, in addition to 'wholeness', 'transformation' and 'self-regulation' (Piaget, 1971). As Thom (1975) reminded us, 'we must not forget that the essential object of study in biology is not the isolated individual but the continuous form in space-time joining parents to descendants'.

Darwinism considers variation of traits in space as given, and introduces a temporal aspect of the theory as a consequence of changes in the genetic composition of populations through generations. Acceptance of the structuralist view requires an elimination of this concept of time, *sensu* the succession of generations. Just as relativity forced physicists to abandon absolute time as a dimension separate from space, biological structuralism should force us to abandon 'generational time' and a static view of structures. Structuralism substitutes the same space-time conception which is already familiar to us in studies of development. In other words, there are no static structures in biology, there is only a stability of dynamic balance (Capra, 1982).

The appearance of similar structures in successive generations is not evidence for the 'fit' of the structure to prevailing or past conditions. Consider the following example which illustrates not simply persistence, but rather the increased frequency of a biological structure in the absence of any appropriate 'fit'. In various species of geometrid moths, Harrison (1928 see Lambert *et al.*, 1986 for a discussion) showed that pigmented forms can arise in laboratory culture when larvae are raised on plants containing certain pollutants. He showed that, through a number of generations, the proportion of melanic individuals increased despite pale or typical individuals being chosen as parents for the subsequent generation. Hence the increased penetrance of the melanic forms occurred, despite experimental selection *against* the character. In other words, this is a stable structure in the absence of any appropriate 'fit' with the experimental conditions.

Functionalism regards biological rationality only in terms of this 'fit' between 'organism' and its 'environment'. However, since ontogeny must always have environmental inputs, organisms can *never* be separated from their 'environment'. We agree with Gould (1986) that functionalists view adaptation as the cause of good design but disagree with him that structuralists view it as a fortunate side consequence. For structuralists 'fit' is meaningless — the rationality in biology lies in the underlying nature of ontogeny. This accounts for the equifinal nature of development (Bertalanffy, 1952), and also for the non-random nature of phylogeny. The actual results from the possible because of the operation of biological principles (Webster and Goodwin, 1982). That these principles exist cannot be denied as Schrodinger (1967) reminds us: '. . . from all we learnt about the structure of living matter, we must be prepared to find it working in a manner that cannot be reduced to the ordinary laws of physics'.

However, at a more fundamental and general level, similar structures may arise in different generations because of the nature of these principles governing biological structures *and* the contextual variables particular to each generation. Jantsch's (1980) concept of space-time structures is of value here in order to emphasise that such biological structures can never be regarded independently of time. He puts it as follows: 'What is meant here is not merely a spatial structure. In connection with dynamic systems, the notion of a space-time structure is in the focus, in other words, the arrangement of processes in space and time. Such a space-time structure includes the function of the system, and, thus, also its organisation and its relationship with the environment' (Jantsch, 1980).

Maturana (1980) stated that an autopoietic or self-renewing system is structure-specified. 'This means that at any instant of its operation the structure of an autopoietic system specifies into what structural configuration it goes as a result of structural transition, regardless of whether this results from its internal dynamics or from its interactions with the medium.' Therefore, the environment does not 'select' the structural configuration, but instead generates it by 'differential triggering'. We, therefore, reject the need for constructionist theories which attempt to unite incommensurable structuralist and functionalist methods of analysis and description, and to explain the stability of generated structures in terms of function (Piaget, 1971).

Structuralism is a 'way of seeing' biology in which structures have time-extended properties and in which their dynamics result, not simply from an 'internal' system, but also from 'external' forces which are intimately associated with the developing individual. Consequently we view structuralism as encompassing the processes leading to the generation of both 'deep' structure and 'surface' structure or form, and, in general maintain that it acts to break down conceptual dichotomies (Hughes and Lambert, 1984).

A DICHOTOMY?

Recently, Gould (1986) suggested that functionalism and structuralism represents one of the major dichotomies in biology and said: 'An adequate theory of evolution must meld both approaches . . . by recognising the strengths of each vision.' Gould (1986) argued for a pluralism in biology comprising both structuralism and functionalism, and illustrated his case by reference to the sutures in the skulls of young mammals. He suggested that Darwin and Owen were structuralists of a kind, because they both recognised that since birds and kangaroos possess sutures at birth, this cannot represent a character 'built' by natural selection to shape the foetal head and permit it to pass through the narrow birth canal. Since the egg protects the young bird at birth, and since kangaroos are born at an extremely small size, they cannot be under any pressure in this way. Instead, he argued that the sutures should be regarded as a constraint. Importantly, the example illustrates a preference for the primacy of functionalist explanations over others. Structuralism need only be invoked when functionalism has clearly failed. However, we contend that it is important to realise that when we reject a functionalist explanation, the interesting biology remains. The problems are not reduced in any way by their removal from the functionalist realm.

However, Gould does not wish to meld the components of the other major dichotomy which he recognises, namely that of evolution and creation. In fact he remarked: 'I have no objection to this division per se; scarcely anything else could be more fundamental.' Despite the fact that Gould says 'playing dichotomies' represents a favourite intellectual game whereby we simplify and caricature complex issues, he has no objection to this one. We agree with Gould that this division is fundamental for the same reason that the division between structuralism and functionalism is fundamental. Functionalism-structuralism and evolution-creation do not represent dichotomies at all but rather four different 'ways of seeing'. One cannot meaningfully force together such perspectives, since systems of thought have only an internally consistent meaning, and because this leads inevitably to what Bohm (1965) described as 'the confusion of trying to mix two sets of ideas that do not actually cohere. In other words, the "new wine" of discrete structural concepts should not be poured into "old bottles".' Moreover, it has been said that only a very intelligent person can hold within her or his head two contradictory ideas at the one time. We suggest that it would require a quite exceptional person to hold simultaneously two contradictory systems of thought. Structuralism and functionalism represent such systems of thought and are not simply opposite ends of a spectrum, which need to be merged into a middle ground, anymore than this is true of evolution and creation.

It is certainly true that dichotomies abound in biology. Elsewhere (Hughes and Lambert, 1986) we have illustrated that a resolution of inappropriate polar opposites in biology can best be achieved by first recognising the existence of complexity, and then by attempting to elucidate the nature of that complexity.

The fusion of distinct perspectives results in theories whose exact nature is unclear. It also becomes far more difficult to explicate the tacit component of the amalgam. We suggest that it is important for biologists to make their 'way of seeing' clear to others. This can best be done by attempting to build a structuralist 'house' with its own unique construction and consequently with its own perspective.

If we have the intention to communicate rather than to obfuscate, our views should not be shrouded in mysticism or difficult language, but clearly outlined in order that they can be best understood. If these are made clear, this consequently opens them, quite appropriately, to critical discussion.

SCHOOLS OF THOUGHT

Functionalism and structuralism represent two distinct systems of thought. We agree with Dwyer (1984), that these approaches entail vastly different *methodological* perspectives. It is our contention that this is so because, as Dwyer states, it is the questions we ask which do indeed 'guide us in our choices of methodologies'. However, the questions themselves are determined fundamentally by one's *theoretical* perspective. Theoretical perspectives are separated by 'a logical gap', and in such a situation language is of special importance. Polanyi (1958) speaks of members of new schools of thought as being separated from all those outside it. They think differently, speak a different language, live in a different world, and at least one of the two schools is excluded for the time being from the mainstream of science. 'Formal operations relying on one framework of interpretation cannot demonstrate a proposition to persons who rely on another framework. Its advocates may not even succeed in getting a hearing, since they must first teach others a new language, and no one can learn a new language unless they first trust that it means something' (Polanyi, 1958). In other words, we will not be able to convince others of the value of an alternative 'way of seeing' by conducting arguments within their word field, and we will certainly never be able to persuade them to alter their perspective. Pankow (1976) makes a similar point when he says that 'by definition, formal languages are incapable of recognising themselves and are, therefore, also incapable of recognising any other position. Thus, a formal language does not link positions, but constitutes itself a fixed position. It does not see the world beyond itself. It is not, like philosophy, an open eye to the outer world, but a closed eye which may also be called a logically isolated eye.'

Polanyi (1958) says: 'Different vocabularies for the interpretation of things divide [humans] into groups which cannot understand each other's way of seeing things and of acting upon them.' Hence one can easily see why there is such miscommunication between critics of functionalism and its defenders. The failure of these groups to make contact with each other's viewpoints is simply because they 'see' the world in a different way. Different methodologies then arise as a necessary consequence of the existence of different perspectives. It is important to emphasise that we are much more likely to persuade others to make the shift to a structuralist biology if we develop a consistent and parsimonious vocabulary which can be easily understood.

Functionalist biology consistently uses keywords (e.g. adaptation) in a variety of ways, and each change in meaning is usually only tacitly recognised. Michael Polanyi (1958) discussed a similar situation in physics. When heavy hydrogen (deuterium) was discovered by Urey in 1932 it was described by him as a new isotope of hydrogen. However, Frederic Soddy, the discoverer of isotopy, objected to this on the grounds that he had originally defined the isotopes of an element as chemically inseparable from each other, and heavy hydrogen was chemically separable from light hydrogen. No attention was paid to this protest, and a new meaning of the term 'isotope' was tacitly accepted instead. However, this resulted in heavy hydrogen being included among the isotopes of hydrogen, in spite of its unprecedented property of being chemically separable from its fellow isotopes. This new conception abandoned a previously accepted criterion of isotopy as superficial, and instead defined them only in terms of their nuclear charges.

· Our identification of deuterium as an isotope of hydrogen thus affirms two things. Firstly, hydrogen and deuterium are an instance of a new kind of chemical separability, pertaining to two elements of equal nuclear charge. Secondly, these elements are to be regarded as isotopes in spite of their separability, merely on the grounds of their equal nuclear charge.

Hence, the new observations resulted in conceptual and linguistic reforms. However, as Polanyi (1958) put it: 'The meaning of speech thus keeps changing in the act of groping for words without our being focally aware of the change, and our gropings invests words in this manner with a fund of unspecifiable connotations' (Polanyi, 1958).

We have previously argued (Hughes and Lambert, 1984) that all biologists, whether they appreciate it or not, have a 'way of seeing'. This can be either explicitly recognised or tacitly held. We have contrasted functionalism and structuralism as examples of two fundamentally different 'ways of seeing'. Each of these perspectives is fixed in place by largely independent keyword fields. The words which comprise the field can have tacit meanings, and as Polanyi's isotope example illustrates, there can be tacitly accepted changes in the meaning of such words through time. The keyword field itself, that is the complete set of relationships between the words, can also have tacit meaning and similarly change through time. A 'way of seeing' compounds these tacit components with those unique to the 'perspective' itself. Hence 'ways of seeing' are cognitive states whose existence is simply reflected by a distinct keyword field with its multidimensional tacit components. Confusion of such fields must result in the confusion of our whole thinking processes. This is difficult for many to recognise. As Schoofs (1987) pointed out, although westerners are able to recognise the tactics and strategies of rational discourse, we do not always appreciate other, more subtle, manoeuvrings. Clearly then, we are opposed to Wake and Larson's (1987) recent attempt to amalgamate functionalist and structuralist approaches. This paper also illustrates the vice-like grip which the organism/environment dichotomy has on thinking, where investigations of the organism are considered to be the domain of 'structuralism' and the study of the 'environment' is thought to be explainable through neo-Darwinism.

'Explanatory knowledge' (Bhaskar, 1978, 1979) can result only from a conceptual and linguistic framework that is, by its nature, directed towards the discovery of generative mechanisms, and one which is not 'confused' by the keywords from a different 'way of seeing'. Alternatively, 'taxonomic knowledge' (Bhaskar, 1978, 1979) is socially constructed and does not necessarily result in explanation. Functionalism, we contend, may generate knowledge but it does not attempt to discover the generative mechanisms of biology, and, owing to the nature of its keywords, does not express such knowledge in terms of definitions of natural kinds (Bhaskar, 1978; Webster, 1984). Functionalism does not even generate knowledge which is descriptive. In contrast structuralism acts to explain through knowledge of real processes and their generative mechanisms. Hence we suggest that keywords can play a central role in structuralist biology only when they represent real phenomena (Bhaskar, 1978, 1979; Lambert *et al.*, 1987). As Paul Weiss remarked: 'We cannot address biophysical or biochemical questions to words, but only to clearly described phenomena' (Grene, 1974).

Finally, a thorough understanding of keywords, their tacit components and our overall use of language should be a fundamental part of structuralist biology. We need to clearly delineate our language, with its keywords and thereby to reframe the issues from our perspective in order that we can think more clearly about the problems of biology. Unless we recognise the fundamental difference between functionalist and structuralist 'ways of seeing' subliminal confusion will remain. We need to separate the conceptual and linguistic characteristics of each system of thought in order to achieve clarity of thought.

Howard Pattee (1970) makes this point perfectly: 'A large part of what is called theoretical physics is a study of formal languages, searching for clear and consistent intepretations of experimental observations. Biologists have never paid this much attention to language, and even today most molecular biologists believe that the "facts speak for themselves". Hopefully, as these facts collect, biologists too will seek some general interpretations.'

ACKNOWLEDGEMENTS

We thank our colleagues in the Evolutionary Genetics Laboratory, in particular B. Michaux, C. D. Millar, R. D. Newcomb, C. S. White and P. M. Stevens, for their discussions over a long period. We are also particularly indebted to the participants to the workshop on Structuralism in Biology, held in Osaka, Japan (December 1986), for such a stimulating five days and for many helpful ideas. We thank C. S. White for the production of the figures and for his advice on methods of data analysis. The manuscript was improved by the comments of two anonymous reviewers and also by those from Edd Barrow and Ivan Illich. D. M. Lambert's research is supported by the Auckland University Research Committee, Grant No. 449.214. We thank Academic Press for permission to publish this modified version of an earlier paper of the same name.

REFERENCES

Bhaskar, R. (1978) *A Realist Theory of Science.* The Harvester Press Ltd., Sussex.
——(1979) *The Possibility of Naturalism — A Philosophical Critique of the Contemporary Human Sciences.* Humanities Press Inc., New Jersey.
Bateson, G. (1980) *Mind and Nature.* Fontana Paperbacks, New York.
Bertalanffy, L. von (1952) *Problems of Life.* Watts and Co., London.
Bohm, D. (1965) Space, Time and the Quantum Theory Understood in Terms of Discrete Structural Process. *Proceedings of the International Conference on Elementary Particles.* Oxford.
Burian, R. M. (1983) In *Dimensions of Darwinism* (Greene, M., ed.). Cambridge University Press, Cambridge.
Capra, F. (1982) *The Turning Point — Science, Society and the Rising Culture.* Flamingo, New York.
Clarke, C. A., Mani, G. S. and Wynne, G. (1985) Evolution in reverse: clean air and the peppered moth. *Biol. J. Linn. Soc.* 26. 189-99.
Commoner, B. (1968) Failure of the Watson-Crick Theory as a chemical explanation of inheritance. *Nature.* 220. 334-340.
Dwyer, P. (1984) Functionalism and structuralism: two programmes for evolutionary biologists. *Am. Nat.* 124. 745-50.
Goodwin, B. C. (1982) Development and evolution. *J. theor. Biol.* 97. 43-55.
Gould, S. J. (1986) Archetype and adaptation. *Natural History.* 10/86. 16-27.

Grene, M. (1974) *The Understanding of Nature*. D. Reidel Publishing Co., Dordrecht, Holland.

Harrison, J. W. H. (1928) A further induction of melanism in the Lepidopterous insect *Selenia bilunaria* Esp., and its inheritance. *Proc. Roy. Soc. B*. 102. 338-47.

Ho, M-W. (1984) Where does biological form come from? *Rivista di Biologia*. 77. 147-79.

——(1987) A structuralism of process. *Rivista di Biologia/Biology Forum*. 80. 183-4.

Hughes, A. J. and Lambert, D. M. (1984) Functionalism, Structuralism, and 'Ways of Seeing'. *J. theor. Biol*. 111. 787-800.

——(1986) Presented to the International Workshop on Structuralism in Biology, Osaka, Japan. December 1986.

——(1988) Sexual differentiation and mate recognition: the dynamics of structure. *Rivista di Biologia/Biology Forum*. In press.

Illich, I. (1982) *Gender*. Pantheon Books, New York.

Jantsch, E. (1980). *The self-organising universe*. Pergamon Press, New York.

Kettlewell, H. B. D. (1973) *The Evolution of Melanism*. Clarendon Press, Oxford.

Lambert, D. M. and Hughes, A. J. (1984) Misery of functionalism. *Rivista di Biologia*. 77. 477-502.

Lambert, D. M., Millar, C. D. and Hughes A. J. (1986a) On the classical case of natural selection. *Rivista di Biologia/Biology Forum*. 79. 117-23

——(1986b) Teaching the classic case of natural selection. *Rivista di Biologia/Biology Forum* 79. 117-23.

Lambert, D. M., B. Michaux and White, C. S. (1987) Are species self-defining? *Syst. Zool*. 36. 196-205.

Laughlin, C. D. and D'Aquili, E. G. (1974) *Biogenetic Structuralism*. Columbia University Press, New York.

Levin, R. and Lewontin, R. C. (1985) *The Dialectical Biologist*. Harvard University Press, Harvard.

Lewontin, R. C. (1982) In *Learning, Development and Culture* (Plotkin, H. C., ed.). John Wiley and Sons Ltd., New York.

Maturana, H. R. (1980) In *Autopoiesis, Dissipative Structures and Spontaneous Social Orders* (Zeleny, M., ed.). AAAS Selected Symposium, 55 Westview Press Inc., Colorado.

Millar, C. D. and Lambert, D. M. (1988) *Industrial melanism and natural selection*. Submitted for publication.

Pankow, W. (1976) In *Evolution and Consciousness — Human Systems in Transition*. (Jantsch, E. and Waddington, C. H., eds.). Addison-Wesley Publishing Co., London.

Pörksen, U. (1988) Unpublished manuscript.

Pattee, H. H. (1969) Physical problems of heredity and evolution. *Towards a Theoretical Biology*. 2. 268-284.

——(1970) The problem of biological hierarchy. *Towards a Theoretical Biology*. 3. 117-36.

Piaget, J. (1971) *Structuralism*. Routledge and Kegan Paul, London.

Polanyi, M. (1958) *Personal Knowledge — Towards a Post-Critical Philosophy*. Routledge and Kegan Paul, London.

Postman, N. and Weingartner, C. (1969) *Teaching as a Subversive Activity*. Penguin, London.

Schoofs, M. (1987) *New York Native*. 12. 17.

Schrodinger, E. (1967) *What is Life?* Cambridge University Press, Cambridge.

Thom, R. (1970) Topological models in biology. *Towards a Theoretical Biology*. 3. 89-116.

——(1975) *Structural Stability and Morphogenesis*. The Benjamin/Cummings Publishing Co., Reading, Massachusetts.

Wake, D. B. and Larson, A. (1987) Multidimensional analysis of an evolving lineage. *Science*. 238. 42-8.

Webster, G. (1984) In *Beyond Neo-Darwinism*. (Ho, M-W. and Saunders, P. T., eds.). Academic Press, London.

——and Goodwin, B. C. (1982) The origin of species: a structuralist approach. *J. Social. Biol. Struct.* 5. 15-47.

Williams, R. (1976) *Keywords — A vocabulary of culture and society*. Fontana, London.

Wills, P. (1986) Presented to the Workshop on International Structuralism in Biology, Osaka, Japan. December 1986.

6. A View of Species

Hugh Paterson

My predilection in biology is to search for an effective evolutionary synthesis and a credible biological world view. Though not consciously a structuralist, I appear to share aspirations and goals with at least some structuralists. For example, I feel empathy with the structuralists' concern for wholeness, the ideas of transformation and self-regulation, if I have conceived these abstract ideas in Piaget's way.

Evolution, particularly species theory, is a significant subject because it illuminates much of what we see in the living world and our own species. Such illumination can have far-reaching consequences not only in population biology, but for the way we see ourselves, as became obvious when society first realised that the human state was not the ultimate creation of a deity but the product of a process which had yielded millions of other such products, each remarkable in some way. This was a revolution in human thought appreciated by rather few other than philosophers. The pursuit of such an intellectual path is only possible for members of *Homo sapiens*, a fact which helps identify a more particular evolutionary perplexity: the achievement by humans of the conceptual powers which enable such a problem to be recognised.

In this chapter I shall consider from perspectives which may interest structuralists a number of evolutionary topics related to natural diversity, species and the origin of species. Although I retain common ground with the movement which led to the so-called 'modern synthesis' of evolutionary thought, I do not subscribe to a number of ideas and viewpoints which currently receive general support. My aim is to present a heterodox ordering of well-known information in order to provide a new perspective, rather than new facts. In particular, I wish to emphasise the fundamental importance of genetical species in evolution, despite their origins as serendipitous consequences or sex. I shall also draw attention to the evidence indicating that many of the transcending steps in the long story of life on earth have occurred by processes not encompassed by the 'modern synthesis'.

A VIEW OF SPECIES

'Man has always been fascinated by the great diversity of organisms which live

77

in the world around him. Many attempts have been made to understand the meaning of this diversity and the causes that bring it about. To many minds this problem possesses an irresistible aesthetic appeal' (Dobzhansky, 1951).

In 1952 I first read these words and became fully conscious of this irresistible appeal to the mind. This early interest in eukaryotic diversity, in turn, led to my interest in the genetic nature of species because species are the units of diversity. To address the problem of diversity from the basis of species it is evidently necessary to understand, at least in broad genetic terms, how new species might arise. Darwin failed to provide any answer which satisfies us today to the principal problem he addressed: the origin of species. It is now apparent that this is because he did not have, and, indeed could not have had at that time, a clear picture of the genetic nature of species. Therefore, he was unable to address the subject of his book in an adequate way. In fact, he conceived species morphologically, though through evolutionary eyes, and set out to answer his big question from this viewpoint. Now, however, we can see that an understanding of species diversity depends on a basic understanding of the genetics of speciation, which, in turn, is constrained by our view of species.

After some twenty years of rather unquestioning support for the prevailing Biological Species Concept (or, Isolation Concept), during which I applied it to the study of problem species in Diptera of medical importance (e.g. Paterson 1956, 1962, 1963, 1964a, 1964b, 1964c, 1970), the shortcomings of defining species in terms of their reproductive isolation from other species began to become manifest. The process of disillusionment was accelerated by my reading of George Williams' (1966) book *Adaptation and Natural Selection*, which upset my understanding of natural selection and which has continued to influence me to this day. In this work Williams set out to instil some discipline and rigour into evolutionary discussions involving adaptation through natural selection. Structuralists would probably wish to avoid this approach altogether, and I sympathise with this attitude to the extent of being interested in exploring the possibility of reducing my reliance on explanations involving the concept of adaptation through the differential transmission of alternative alleles.

In searching for a more satisfactory approach to species than in terms of reproductive isolation mediated by isolating mechanisms, I went back to first principles, in this case, sex, and asked the question: how, in general terms, is the inherently improbable process of fertilisation in biparental eukaryotes achieved?

A little exploration and a little thought revealed that every biparental organism must possess a set of characteristics which are effective in bringing about fertilisation under the conditions prevailing in the organism's normal environment. This is really axiomatic and applies to all biparental eukaryotic unicells, to fungi, plants and animals including *Homo sapiens*. The characteristics of these *fertilisation systems* vary with the ways-of-life of the organisms and with their normal environments, but in all cases known to me they are clearly necessary for the fundamental process of fertilisation to occur. In George Williams' terms, the function of the fertilisation system is the achievement of fertilisation under normal natural conditions, no more and no less. The fertilisation system as a whole can thus be regarded as a complex adaptation.

Before proceeding with this argument I should deal with a potent, all-pervading source of confusion. Darwin viewed species in morphological terms though he did this in quite a sophisticated way, using evolutionary explanations (Darwin, 1859: 423-4). He saw the 'fitness' of an organism in terms of its aptness for life in its normal environment. Accordingly, he saw the rather extreme secondary sexual characters of some species, particularly birds such as the peafowl, as leading to reduced fitness in his sense of the term. A peacock's train can hardly fit it for life in its normal wooded environment, and might well reduce its chances of surviving predation. To accommodate such situations Darwin introduced the concept of *sexual selection*. Instead of simply noticing that every biparental eukaryotic organism is necessarily equipped with a system which leads effectively to fertilisation, he believed that a further set of characteristics often evolved under the different selection pressure arising from either male/male competition for females, or, in some cases, inter-female competiton for males. Whether sexual selection in the strict sense really is a significant factor in evolution is still far from certain, despite the burgeoning literature which assumes it is (Halliday, 1983). In any case, it is seldom noticed that if it does exist it is an additional system (complex adaptation) to the fertilisation system, and that it has evolved under distinct selection pressures and had a distinct function. Thus, looking at reproductive systems of organisms like peafowl or birds-of-paradise, one needs to be very cautious in disentangling the fertilisation system characters from possible characters evolved in response to competition for mates. In studying particular species I believe that one needs always to ask: can the reproductive behaviour of members of this species be entirely accounted for in terms of the fertilisation system alone? If the answer is yes, it is clearly unjustified to believe that they evolved in response to competition for mates. A great clarification of the literature on reproductive behaviour would immediately result if this distinction were to be made consistently.

I return now to my main theme to consider a major consequence of any fertilisation system appropriate to the organism's normal environment and way-of-life. The consequence is that such a specific fertilisation system effectively constrains the exchange of genes so that exchange effectively occurs within the group which shares the same fertilisation system, the same normal habitat and the same way-of-life. Obviously, such properties are the same as those characterising any genetical species.

To sum up these points, one can define a species in genetical terms as that most inclusive population of individual biparental eukaryotic organisms which share a common fertilisation system. Every fertilisation system defines locally the field of gene recombination of a species. It is, perhaps, prudent to discuss this proposition briefly in order to provide a clear perspective. Fertilisation systems can differ markedly or only to a minor degree with the consequence that there is a continuum in difference between populations. At one extreme, two populations can comprise organisms with virtually identical fertilisation systems. At the other, we find organisms with fertilisation systems which are wholly different from each other, as between an ostrich and a ruby-throated hummingbird. Often, as in ducks (Lorentz, 1941) or Pelicaniformes (van Tets, 1965), components of the fertilisation system may be shared by different species with no loss of effectiveness.

Since my interest is in the understanding of the diversity in nature, I shall not be concerned with man-made situations. Lions and tigers do hybridize in zoos when confined to the same cage. However, the fertilisation system is here destabilised because it was not evolved to be effective in a zoo cage where no appropriate mates are present. Among plants a similar situation prevails in a botanical gardens where many species of related plants are artificially brought together. Another botanical example results from the destabilisation of fertilisation system through the disturbance of the environment (through human or natural causes) to such a degree that populations normally found in distinct environments are brought into proximity (Anderson's 1948 'hybridisation of the habitat').

A fertilisation system, I have already emphasised, is appropriate for the environment in which the organism normally lives and for its way-of-life (whether it is sessile or motile, diurnal or nocturnal, etc.). Under these circumstances the system is very stable. The individual characters are evidently subject to stabilising selection: aberrant individuals with inappropriate components to the fertilisation system will be less likely to fertilise or be fertilised. In motile animals, particularly, an important part of the fertilisation system is the specific-mate recognition system (SMRS) which serves to bring together potential mating partners. The SMRS characters are involved in the sending or receiving and processing of signals between mating partners or their cells (e.g. sperm and ovum, pollen and stigma). Sessile organisms, such as angiosperms or sessile molluscs, are much less dependent on the SMRS. Sessile organisms rely, inevitably, on vectors to transport their sex cells. These vectors are wind, water and animals (insects, birds and mammals). The signals between angiosperms and insects are not part of the SMRS, but are accommodations to a vector. Coadaptation between, say, a male signal and female receiver places a strong constraint on independent change in either the male or female component. The same is true for signals between a pollen grain and the stigma of the mating partner. SMRS signals, like the rest of the fertilisation system, are also usually apt for the organisms normal environment. Thus fireflies, moths and owls signal appropriately for nocturnal conditions. Forest birds and frogs are characterised by calls appropriate for transmission through dense vegetation (Morton, 1975). Birds of open grassland signal visually as well as by sound, as sound is readily disturbed by wind (Morton, 1975), etc.

Large population sizes of species make it nearly impossible to change a coadapted signal from one stabilised (coadapted) condition to another for the whole population. For this and other reasons, speciation is believed to involve small populations (see below), and the termination of speciation coincides with the growth of the daughter population following the switch from directional to stabilising selection.

Thus, for three independent reasons, fertilisation systems are stabilised: their relationship to the population's normal habitat, the coadaptation of signals and receivers (and other aspects of their fertilisation systems and biologies), and the stability of large populations.

SPECIATION

From this view of species, one can understand a little of what must occur during the formation of a new species. The difficult task to be accomplished entails the changing of critical characters, including the fertilisation system, from one stable state, appropriate to the parental environment, to a new stable state, appropriate to the new environment to which the daughter population has become restricted.

The stable state of a species in its normal habitat can be changed to a new one only if its stability is first disturbed. For example, a fertilisation system will be destabilised if a small population is displaced to a distinctly different environment in which the characters of the fertilisation system, etc., will not be fully effective. Stabilising selection on these characters will then be replaced by directional selection which will lead to the spreading of alternative alleles determining a new phenotype more effective under the new conditions. A small population will facilitate the fixation of the alleles determining a new stable state. This applies to other adaptive characters such as feeding and nesting habits, and predator avoiding behaviour as well. Achieving a new stable state involves the adjustment of all such characters of the organisms to a new stable state.

Since speciation entails small populations, the bottleneck probably facilitates the fortuitous fixation of certain alleles and chromosome arrangements at the same time. Of course, the genetic variation fuelling the selective process may involve pleiotropy.

Thus, the 'normal habitat' of a species is thought to approximate in key features to the one in which speciation occurred. Changing habitat is a major revolution for organisms, and available evidence convinces me that it corresponds with a speciation or subspeciation event.

In the normal habitat all environment-related characteristics of members of a species are under stabilising selection, not just the fertilisation system including the SMRS. Thus, for effective development to occur, fertilised eggs of fish, frogs, or mosquitoes, for example, must develop within certain limits.

The development of the eggs of the subarctic mosquito, *Aedes stimulans*, normally occurs at low temperatures. If the eggs are kept at higher temperatures, development is aberrant (Horsfall and Anderson, 1963). Similarly, organisms in their normal habitats are efficient in feeding, avoiding the predators with which they are in contact, and, in some cases, nidification. This efficiency is seriously disrupted if organisms are displaced into effectively different habitats. Judging by the prevalence of simplistic models for how habitat change might occur, it is not well appreciated that change of habitat for any group of organisms requires a major genetic revolution. Mayr (1963) and others have drawn attention to the fact that speciation entails many changes in ecological characteristics, but this has not always been understood.

The work of Coope and his colleagues (Coope, 1979 for review) on Quaternary fossil beetle assemblages in peat bogs in Europe and America has provided much telling support for these points. His demonstration of the stability of organism-habitat relationships despite the overwhelming environmental changes due to advancing or retreating ice is of fundamental importance in understanding why species are so stable and must be taken into account in formulating any views on the diversity of the living world. Coope has pointed out that speciation is not a common outcome of such catastrophic environmental events. For it to occur, organisms must be 'trapped' in front of a mountain range, for example, so that retreat ahead of the change by the organisms and their environment is blocked. Even then extinction is a more general outcome than is speciation or subspeciation.

Restriction of organisms to new environmental conditions as a necessary prelude to speciation can occur in many ways. Relic populations can commonly be observed today telling of former wider distributions under different climatic regimes. These provide us with illustrations of what Coope is saying. Increased aridity and cooling seem to be particularly effective in restricting organisms to new habitats through the progressive degrading of relic communities. Of course, islands at appropriate distances from continents provide other possible conditions which lead to speciation through destabilising the species which invade them adventitiously. Other possibilities exist as well.

OTHER PROPOSED MODES OF SPECIATION

Many other modes of speciation have been proposed (White, 1978; Mayr, 1963, 1987), but they have all been conceived with the constraints of the isolation concept in mind. It should therefore be noted that the model of speciation which I call allopatric speciation is genetically different from the well-known model of geographic or peripatric speciation long advocated by Ernst Mayr (1942, 1954).

Mayr's model and mine share common ground in requiring the physical isolation of small populations for sufficient time for speciation to occur, but differ because Mayr was obliged by his species concept to rely on pleiotropy to modify the existing 'primary' isolating mechanism (usually some form of postmating isolating mechanism). He believed that other isolating mechanisms often evolved later under natural selection when daughter and parent populations again met (Mayr, 1963: 551). I have previously provided details of the difficulties existing for the various models generated by the isolation concept (Paterson, 1978, 1982a, 1985), and have argued that no *prima facie* evidence exists to show that any species has ever arisen by any model of speciation other than some form of allopatric speciation (Paterson, 1981, 1985, 1987), and that substantial difficulties confront models invoking selection for reproductive isolation (Paterson 1978, 1985).

It should be reiterated that models of speciation are logically derived from concepts of species so that when a concept of species is abandoned, all its dependent speciation models must be discarded with it.

CONSEQUENCES

Interesting genetic and ecological consequences flow from the picture of species in terms of specific-mate recognition, and how they are likely to arise. These consequences lead us to look at the data of nature with different eyes. The prevailing concept of species, the isolation concept of Dobzhansky and Mayr, defines one species in relation to other species, which leads to many problems which I have outlined before (Paterson, 1978, 1980, 1981, 1982a, 1985, 1987). Derived consequences from the isolation concept are quite different from those from the recognition concept, despite Mayr's (1987) assertion that the two concepts can be seen as 'the two sides of a single coin'. It is not possible to compare the consequences of the two concepts here, but some consequences of the recognition concept will be discussed.

Although natural selection is invoked as part of the process of speciation, it is merely part of the process of organisms adapting to new conditions. If speciation results from this it is fortuitous, and is an extreme of a continuum in degrees of divergence. In George Williams' terms species are not 'adaptative devices' but incidental consequences of adaptation ('effects'). This is a fundamentally important insight. Darwin reached a similar conclusion but with a limited understanding of species and speciation. To many this conclusion is unacceptable when applied to our own species (Paterson, 1982b, 1985, 1987). However, it has a far wider significance than this. For example it affects fundamentally our views on ecology and the causes of biological diversity (Paterson, 1985, 1986; Walter *et al.*, 1984; Hulley *et al.*, 1988).

The model of speciation which follows from the recognition concept also directs thinking in particular directions and has important implications. It very firmly invokes speciation in small populations, despite population genetical reservations on the subject. This is in keeping with empirical evidence from actual speciation events of the past, and it provides a better understanding of why 'punctuation' should be a feature of the fossil record (Eldredge, 1971; Eldredge and Gould, 1972). The recognition concept is also important in understanding the assembly of ecosystems and communities, and in interpreting biogeographical data.

The three reasons for the stability of species provide insights for the understanding of a number of aspects of evolution. They provide a clear explanation of the 'equilibrium' phase of Eldredge and Gould's 'punctuated equilibrium' view of the fossil record. Species homeostasis has also an important bearing on the long and drawn out debate on sympatric speciation. Member organisms of a species in their normal habitats are subject to mainly stabilising selection. There is no pressure to speciate under such conditions because there is nothing to disturb the existing stable state. This view contrasts with the view of species as 'adaptive devices', which diverge in order to exploit more fully natural resources by occupying 'unoccupied niches'. Under the recognition concept this viewpoint is wholly unjustified. The niche occupied by the organisms of a species is not a property of the environment but is largely a reflection of their genotype (Paterson, 1973; Walter et al., 1984). Once this is understood it is no longer a puzzle why species do not occupy 'niches' which appear to ecologists as so temptingly 'vacant'. Expectations are likely to remain unfulfilled if they stem from inappropriate analogies with human economic systems.

When species are understood to be extreme incidental consequences of adaptation to new environments, hybrids and hybridisation are seen in quite new ways. As J. L. Crosby (1970) once warned, the consequences of hybridisation may be good or bad and are decided by natural selection, not by our biases and idealistic preconceptions. Once the preservation of 'species integrity' or 'species purity' is seen to involve deep cultural preconceptions (Paterson, 1982b, 1985, 1987) we stop expecting hypothetical 'isolating mechanisms' to be 'reinforced' by selection, and expect natural selection simply to act to maintain viability. A full understanding of what is occurring in hybrid zones or in hybrid populations demands a proper understanding of the nature of species.

Species integrity is conventionally seen as being protected from destruction by so-called 'isolating mechanisms'. Few pause to wonder why these 'isolating mechanisms' are often protecting hybrid genomes as in the case of polyploid species of plants. These are widely accepted as generally being allopolyploids (Amphiploids). Are the isolating mechanisms in such cases still protecting 'species integrity'?

Some authors (Scoble, 1985; Templeton, 1987) criticise the recognition and isolation concepts for not covering uniparental organisms. Both Dobzhansky and I have accepted that this desire for generality has its roots in taxonomy (see Mayr's 1963: 28 approach), but reject it because our aim is to understand natural diversity, not to classify organisms. Most eukaryotes are biparental, or are at least facultatively biparental, and so are to be understood in terms of a genetical concept. A few primary uniparental eukaryotic organisms may exist (amoebae, euglenoids) but most are derived from biparental organisms.

Widening a species concept in order to cover these secondarily uniparental organisms destroys the explanatory power of a genetical concept, and involves the conflation of concepts of species from two quite distinct fields of scientific endeavour (Taxonomy and Evolutionary genetics) (Paterson, 1981). Rather than attempting to devise a concept that brings 'chalk and cheese' under one heading, I prefer to account for the secondarily uniparental eukaryotes by trying to understand their origin. Understanding that they very generally bear signs of a hybrid origin, uniparental eukaryotes, e.g. allopolyploid plants, can often be recognised as examples of organisms which have 'escaped from hybridity' (Darlington, 1958; Grant, 1971; Paterson, 1981, 1985, 1987). This alternative viewpoint is in accordance with the idea that, as usual, natural selection acts on hybrids by selecting for viability (Paterson, 1978).

This brief catalogue is not comprehensive in listing the important new insights deriving from the adopting of the intuitively appealing and evidently effective recognition concept of species. Active application of the ideas will readily reveal many more.

DISCUSSION

'The thesis that new facts are always responsible for the ultimate clarification of scientific problems is becoming increasingly questionable' (Mayr, 1976: 331).

Mayr is here drawing attention to the fact that the way we look at problems in science is often more critical in clarifying them than is the provision of yet more empirical data.

Some evolutionists still feel happy with the 'evolutionary synthesis'. This is depressing to me and, I am sure, to many others, in the face of the remarkable empirical and theoretical advances of this period. In fact, I believe the advances made in the last forty years have revolutionised our evolutionary view of life, and what is new should be reflected in our synthesis. On the other hand, it would be surprising if nothing remained of the very impressive edifice erected in the thirties and forties. Perhaps reformatting our views on evolution should be our aim rather than debating whether a new synthesis is required or not.

To many the core of the evolutionary synthesis is the biological species concept. Certainly much in the synthesis is related to species theory. It follows, therefore, that a significant change in viewpoint on the genetic nature of species is likely to be an important reason to reformulate the evolutionary synthesis. As the outline provided above will have demonstrated, the Recognition Concept does constitute a new way of looking at species in genetic terms, and its adoption will thus ensure that any evolutionary synthesis built around it will be significantly new.

Besides, we must also incorporate the appreciation that so transcending a step as the evolution of the eukaryotic cell entailed a process not envisaged under the world view of the evolutionary synthesis: symbiosis. Today we appreciate that symbiosis involves a radical form of genetic and systems recombination quite unimagined, or, at least, unconsidered in 1942. The evolutionary synthesis has never provided a satisfactory explanation of the evolution of sex. The cannibalism theory of the evolution of sex (Margulis and Sagan, 1986) provides a reasonable scenario of how sex might have evolved. This model cannot be considered part of the evolutionary synthesis despite it having been considered seriously by Maynard Smith in 1958. We might eventually achieve a more credible and general understanding of the evolution of sociality when we rethink it in comparable stochastic terms, and abandon the procrustian task of forcing the problem into a neo-Darwinist framework. The neutral theory of molecular evolution (King and Jukes, 1969; Kimura, 1969) has provided many insights which would not have been forthcoming in the light of the evolutionary synthesis, and I am sure there are more insights to come from it.

Although I have not exhausted the revolutionary ideas outside the evolutionary synthesis, enough examples of major consequence have been cited to illustrate the fact that we now have at our disposal the elements of a quite radically different view of evolution than was available in the thirties and forties. A synthesis of these elements has not yet been made, because, besides it being a formidable task for which few are fitted, I believe few have attempted to think through the consequences. Or perhaps those who have done so have drawn back in awe at the picture partially glimpsed.

Much of this modified world view will be acceptable to structuralists, but probably not all. At present I still retain a place for functionalist explanations, though I check their credentials individually. But I certainly do not exclude the explanatory explanations of physical scientists or structuralists (Rosenberg, 1985). I don't believe this stand constitutes fence-sitting, as that has not really been my style in the past; rather I think it is because both kinds of explanation can, at times, provide understanding. A hope we might cherish in support of Mayr's statement with which we began this discussion is that scientists will in future spend more time in considering theory instead of generating more and more empirical data in attempting to answer inappropriately posed questions.

REFERENCES

Anderson, E. (1949) *Introgressive Hybridisation*. John Wiley, New York.
Coope, G. R. (1979) Late Cenozoic fossil Coleoptera: evolution, biogeography, and ecology. *Annual Review of Ecology and Systematics*. 10. 247-67.
Crosby, J. L. (1970) The evolution of genetic discontinuity: computer models of the selection of barriers to interbreeding between species. *Heredity*. 25. 253-97.
Darlington, C. D. (1958) *Evolution of Genetic Systems*. Oliver and Boyd, Edinburgh.
Darwin, C. (1859) *On the Origin of Species by Means of Natural Selection*. John Murray, London.
Dobzhansky, T. (1951) *Genetics and the Origin of Species* (3rd Ed.). Columbia University Press, New York.

Eldredge, N. (1971) The allopatric model and phylogeny in Paleozoic invertebrates. *Evolution.* 25. 156-67.

——and Gould, S. J. (1972) Punctuated equilibrium: an alternative to phyletic gradualism. In *Models in Paleontology* (T. J. M. Schopf, ed.). Freeman, Cooper and Company, San Francisco. pp.82-115.

Grant, V. (1971) *Plant Speciation.* Columbia University Press, New York.

Halliday, T. R. (1983) The study of mate choice. In P. Bateson (ed.): *Mate Choice.* Cambridge University Press, Cambridge. pp.3-32.

Horsfall, W. R. and Anderson, J. F. (1963) Thermally induced genital appendages on mosquitos. *Science.* 141. 1183-4.

Hulley, P. E., Walter, G. W. and Craig, A. J. F. K. (1988) Interspecific competition and community structure, I. *Biology Forum/Rivista di Biologia.* 81. 57-71.

Kimura, M. (1968) Evolutionary rate at the molecular level. *Nature.* 217. 624-6.

King, J. L. and Jukes, T. H. (1969) Non-Darwinian evolution: random fixation of selectively neutral mutations. *Science.* 164. 788-98.

Lorentz, K. (1941) Vergleichende Bewegungsstudien an Anatinen. *Journal für Ornithologie* (Suppl.). 89. 194-294.

Margulis, L. and Sagan, D. (1986) *Origins of Sex.* Yale University Press, New Haven.

Maynard Smith, J. (1958) *The Theory of Evolution.* Penguin Books, Harmondsworth.

Mayr, E. (1954) Change of genetic environment and evolution. In J. S. Huxley, A. C. Hardy and E. B. Ford (eds.): *Evolution as a Process.* Allen and Unwin, London. pp.157-80.

——(1963) *Animal Species and Evolution.* Harvard University Press, Cambridge.

——(1976) Sibling or cryptic species among animals. In E. Mayr (ed.): *Evolution and the Diversity of Life.* Harvard University Press, Cambridge.

——(1987) The species as category, taxon, and population. In J. Roger and J.-L. Fischer (eds.): *Histoire du Concept D'Espèce dans les Sciences de la Vie.* E. J. Brill, Leiden. pp.303-20.

Paterson, H. E. H. (1956) Status of the two forms of housefly occurring in South Africa. *Nature.* 178. 928-9.

——(1962) Status of the East African Salt-water-breeding variant of *Anopheles gambiae* Giles. *Nature.* 195. 469-70.

——(1963) Species, species control and antimalarial spraying campaigns. Implications of recent work on the *Anopheles gambiae* complex. *South African Journal of Medical Science.* 28. 33-44.

——(1964a) Saltwater *Anopheles gambiae* on Mauritius. *Bulletin of the World Health Organisation.* 31. 635-44.

——(1964b) Population genetic studies in areas of overlap of two subspecies of *Musca domestica L.* In D. H. S. David (ed.): *Ecological Studies in Southern Africa.* W. Junk, The Hague. pp.244-54.

——(1964c) Direct evidence for the specific distinctness of forms A, B, and C of the *Anopheles gambia* complex. *Rivista di Malariologia.* 43. 192-6.

——(1973) Animal and plant speciation studies in Western Australia: Animal species studies. *Journal of the Royal Society of Western Australia.* 56. 31-6.

——(1978) More evidence against speciation by reinforcement. *South African Journal of Science.* 74. 369-71.

——(1980) A comment on 'mate recognition systems'. *Evolution.* 34. 330-1.

——(1981) The continuing search for the unknown and the unknowable: a critique of contemporary ideas on speciation. *South African Journal of Science.* 77. 113-19.

——(1982a) Perspective on speciation by reinforcement. *South African Journal of Science.* 78. 53-7.

——(1982b) Darwin and the origin of species. *South African Journal of Science.* 78. 272-5.

——(1985) The recognition concept of species. In E. S. Vrba (ed.): *Species and Speciation*. Transvaal Museum, Pretoria. pp.21-9.

——Environment and species. *South African Journal of Science*. 82. 62-5.

——(1987) On defining species in terms of sterility: problems and alternatives. *Pacific Science*. 42. 64-70.

—— and Norris, K. R. (1970) The *Musca sorbens* complex: the relative status of the Australian and two African populations. *Australian Journal of Zoology*. 18. 231-45.

Rosenberg, A. (1985) *The Structure of Biological Science*. Cambridge University Press, Cambridge.

Scoble, M. J. (1985) The species in systematics. In E. Vrba (ed.): *Species and Speciation*. Transvaal Museum, Pretoria. pp.31-4.

Templeton, A. R. (1987) Species and speciation. *Evolution*. 41. 233-5.

van Tets, G. F. (1965) *A Comparative Study of Some Social Communication Patterns in the Pelecaniformes*. American Ornithologists Union.

Walter, G. H., Hulley, P. E. and Craig, A. J. F. K. (1984) Speciation, adaptation and interspecific competition. *Oikos*. 43. 246-8.

White M. J. D. (1978) *Modes of Speciation*. W. H. Freeman, San Francisco.

Williams, G. C. (1966a) *Adaptation and Natural Selection*. Princeton University Press, Princeton.

7. Structuralism as a Non-vitalistic Alternative to Reductionism

David Elder

THE CONCEPT OF LOGICAL RESTRICTION

The molecular biology revolution in the decade after 1953 is often portrayed as a simple and straightforward victory of reductionism over an earlier tradition of 'vitalism'. Certainly it is most impressive to observe the way in which the invisible entities of the atomic world were shown to underlie the visible phenomena not only of the inorganic but of the organic realm as well. So we must indeed pay reductionism its due. In saying this one is not making sweeping philosophical statements about 'life, the universe and everything', but simply acknowledging that molecular biology effectively abolished the need to invoke anything as overtly vitalistic as Driesch's entelechy to explain the phenomena with which technical biology is concerned.

Yet there has been a persistent tradition of scepticism towards the out-and-out reductionism which molecular biology encouraged, and these sceptics were rarely as extreme as Driesch. But the molecular biologists often gave them short shrift, placing them in the same category as Driesch; if this charge of gross vitalism was denied, the molecular biologist tended to take the line that the critic was either just woolly-minded or else engaging in fruitless quibbling over terminology. Ironically, many of the founders of the field have had second thoughts in the wake of the many chastening complexities that their subject has encountered of late. But what exactly is it that is wrong with their original position? Surely the powerful concepts of molecular biology are more than adequate to provide a basis for the outstanding problems in biology?

It seems to me that the expression 'more than adequate' is the crux of the dilemma. The concepts of molecular biology are in a sense *too* adequate. They can provide such a wealth of possible explanations for a problem like development, given a modicum of ingenuity, that one is soon confronted with an embarrassment of riches. It is not at all easy to resolve the many possibilities by experimental means because of the complexity of the system, and it is rarely possible to discriminate among them from theoretical constraints at the molecular level itself. So if we are to find the sort of constraints or logical restrictions from which a genuinely powerful theory could emerge, we will have to seek them at a higher level — that of the organisation or structure of the system as a whole (Elder, 1986).

SOME CLASSICAL EXAMPLES

Let me illustrate this point by examining the way in which molecular biology itself developed after the discovery of the double helix in 1953. Watson and Crick had succeeded in finding a DNA structure which was attractive not only on stereochemical grounds but also because it provided a basis for the crucial biological process of gene replication. It seemed reasonable to suppose that the genetic code relating nucleic acid and protein sequences could also be solved by this stereochemical approach. But the only success which resulted was Crick's adaptor hypothesis — which had the consequence that there is no stereochemical relationship between a nucleic acid codon and its corresponding amino acid. So stereochemical considerations generated a large, amorphous and ill-defined set of possibilities, no one of which had anything to specifically recommend it.

Nevertheless, the code did prove to have some well-defined properties, most notably the fact that all the codons are triplets. But this was first demonstrated not by biochemical studies on protein synthesis but by purely genetic experiments using frameshift mutations (Crick et al., 1961). One or two frameshifts resulted in a non-functional gene, but a third frameshift restored the proper reading frame. This classic work is notable not for its emphasis on molecular detail but rather for its deft avoidance of unnecessary entanglement with such details, and its incisive concentration on the overall logic of the process.

Why does this triplet regularity exist? Partly of course it is for the reason familiar from textbooks, namely, that to code 20 amino acids with four nucleic acid bases we need at least three bases in a codon. However, that is not the whole story, because in some codons the third base makes little or no contribution to coding: why then is it present at all? And why did one not get a 'messy' code like the Morse code, where some code groups contain one element, some two, some three, four, five and so on? The answer evidently is that all the codons have to be standardised to the same size to allow the decoding machinery of the ribosome to handle them. I feel that it is this logical restriction which was revealed by these elegant frameshift investigations.

Clearly, then, the style of thought which ushered in the molecular biology revolution was considerably less reductionist than is generally supposed. Indeed, one dreads to think what could have happened had this subject fallen into the hands of conscientious and literal-minded exponents of the 'molecular approach'. One can see a whole generation of workers earnestly sequencing the innumerable components of the ribosome, trying to obtain its tertiary structure, etc. — and missing the real point. The solving of the genetic code was in many ways more akin to Mendel's lonely triumph of a century before.

Mendel's great discovery is unfortunately also often misrepresented today: it is often seen merely as a stepping stone to the reductionist triumph of the double helix. Its true significance again resides in the overall logic of a process. In this case the process concerned is sexual reproduction.

In sexual reproduction two individuals combine their genomes, and a new and potentially more favourable gene combination can result. But if this continues in every generation, the level of ploidy will increase to two, then four, then eight, and so on, and will soon become prohibitive. Hence, as Weismann saw in the 1880s, this must be counteracted by a special type of cell division — the first meiotic division, in which the chromosome number is reduced from the diploid to the haploid level prior to gametogenesis in each generation. In the process, the maternal and paternal copies of each gene are segregated from each other, and this is the essential point of Mendel's laws. None of this has anything particularly to do with DNA. It is rather a matter of nature imposing a logical restriction on the gamut of possible ways in which genes could be combined in sexual reproduction.

It might be objected that such constraints are dependent in turn upon the nature of lower levels. However, many lower level scenarios will often *converge* upon the same restriction. For example, the restriction which underlies Mendel's laws would hold regardless of whether the gene was DNA or protein or something else again. Now convergent dependence is for practical purposes equivalent to independence; so logical restrictions at higher levels, though not absolutely autonomous, can often be treated as if they were so.

I believe that if breakthroughs of the order of those we have been considering are ever made in the remaining problems in biology — development, the brain and so on — these breakthroughs will involve logical restrictions of this type, operating at higher levels than that of genes and molecules.

DEVELOPMENT

Molecular biologists were initially very confident that work at the molecular level would soon provide all the answers to the age-old problem of development. Unfortunately recent advances in molecular biology all too often have resulted only in the discovery of new problems within its own discipline — split genes for instance — without throwing very much light on the classical problems at all. Why has molecular biology proved relatively impotent here?

Sydney Brenner (1975) points out that molecular biology originally made rapid headway because DNA is a rather simple molecule; there are only a certain number of things it could do, and only a limited number of things one could do to it. This situation provided useful constraints for theories of genetic coding. But genes control development through proteins, and the 'strong principle' about proteins is that they can do practically anything. So molecular biology can only make vague and nebulous predictions about development, and holds out no better prospect than an exhaustive descriptive cataloguing of molecules and mutations. There is no guarantee that such approaches will provide any insight into the 'deep structure of organisms' (this is Brenner's own expression).

Surely then it is at higher levels that we must seek the constraints or structure that could restrict the amorphous set of possibilities arising from molecular biology, and so give the insight that molecular considerations alone are unable to provide. One thinks for example of the geometrical constraints which were explored by D'Arcy Thompson (1942), and which are now enjoying a renaissance. It is often possible to deduce constraints of this type which would be common to a wide variety of mechanistic scenarios (Saunders, 1984). For example, the logarithmic spiral appears in many systems — the shells of foraminifera, of molluscs and cephalopods, and in the horns of mammals — because it arises from a simple geometrical condition, namely, that the spiral expands at a rate proportional to the distance from the centre.

I also suspect that quite a deal of structure (especially in more complex organisms) lies at a still higher level, that of genetic regulatory networks. The concept of the binary epigenetic code is an example (Garcia-Bellido, 1975; Kauffman, 1975). Codes of this type exhibit a number of interesting logical constraints (Elder, 1984 and in preparation).

EVOLUTION

These structural restrictions incidentally have interesting implications for evolutionary theory. For example, they are very relevant to the debate on 'punctuated equilibrium'. Many authors have pointed out that structural principles are often intrinsically conducive to discontinuous change. Indeed, there is a predisposition to this even just in a pattern with a defined and integral number of elements, as in the digits of the vertebrate limb.

On the other hand, I wonder whether these epigenetic structures could be the sole basis of punctuated equilibrium, since not all developmental systems are so directly conducive to it. Consider for example those spiral forms in shells and horns. Here the generative conditions allow a range of forms which grade into one another in a continuous fashion. This does not appear to provide any robust basis for long periods of stasis; yet some of the best documented cases of punctuated equilibrium involve these spiral patterns (Raff and Kauffman, 1983; Vrba, 1984).

It appears that a specifically populational theory involving some form of stabilising selection is required to give a general explanation of the phenomenon. However, this need not invalidate the structuralist approach in the wider sense. Saussure's original version of structuralism involved a constraint which was populational in nature, namely, consensus in the choice of signals as the basis for linguistic communication. And I feel that Saussure's ideas are in certain respects similar to the explanation of punctuated equilibrium which Paterson (1985) has advanced on the basis of his Recognition Concept of species. 'Recognition' here refers to the signals which individuals use to communicate with potential mates. (The horns of Vrba's antelopes fall in this category.) Alteration of this code of recognition will generally entail reduced reproductive capacity and will be strongly opposed by selection; hence stasis emerges in a particularly direct and natural way.

Thus form can be constrained not only by epigenetic but also by populational structures.

THE NERVOUS SYSTEM

There was a time when molecular biologists felt that neurobiology was another area which would soon yield to the molecular approach. They delighted in naive speculations about memories being carried by specific molecules and so on; but this reductionist enthusiasm has long since waned. It is now accepted that the nervous system has to be addressed at its own level and on its own terms. In a general article on this subject Francis Crick (1979) observed that this system is so complicated that there is little hope of understanding it by a naive empiricist approach of painstakingly analysing each part of it. One must try to deduce the nature of the flow of information through it. The problem is that there are so many ways in which this could occur; and basic considerations like neurophysiology do not supply enough constraints to discriminate among them. So again reductionism fails in practice, not because the lower levels cannot supply a possible basis for a solution, but because they allow so many possibilities, each as plausible as the next.

Crick suggests that the best level of attack may be the highest level of all: the integration of the brain's numerous areas and functions to yield a unified conscious experience. He draws the analogy with Mendel's approach, which yielded information at a relatively high level of organisation, that of the chromosome (and, we might add, of the whole system of sexual reproduction).

At present we have little idea of what kind of structure to look for in the brain. However, I would like to mention certain insights which have been gained, and which may be of general interest to structuralists. Here I would like to refer to an article by Sibatani (1985) in which he distinguished two versions of classical structuralism, which he called St I and St II. St I can be exemplified in linguistics by Saussure's concept that the assignment of words to objects (semantics) is arbitrary, and depends purely on consensus. St II in linguistics corresponds to Chomsky's conception of generative grammar — intrinsic rules which govern the ordering of words into sentences (syntax).

Now neurologists have found that there are two different areas in the cortex of the human brain that are especially important in language production (Geschwind, 1979). One centre was discovered by the Frenchman Broca in the 1860s; the other was described by the German investigator Wernicke in the following decade. Both centres generally reside in the left hemisphere of the brain, but they lie in quite different parts of it. Broca's area is in the frontal lobe, whereas Wernicke's area lies toward the rear of the brain, in the temporal lobe; and the two centres play substantially different roles. Damage to Broca's area results primarily in grammatical defects: speech has a jerky 'telegraphic' style, and complex grammatical constructions present particular difficulty. By contrast, with damage in Wernicke's area it is the proper choice of words that is most severely impaired. The patient uses inappropriate words, and even nonsense syllables and words.

So Wernicke's aphasia, with its predominantly semantic errors, corresponds rather well to St I; and Broca's aphasia, with its predominantly syntactic disorders, corresponds of St II. This non-trivial correspondence suggests that these structures are not merely subjective fancies, but do relate to something objective in nature. It also constitutes a vote of confidence for the structuralist method as a whole.

CONCLUSION

The general problem with which we have been concerned is the logical relationship of structuralism to the molecular basis of biological processes. Many would argue that reduction to that basis is the essence of progress in biology, and that concern with higher levels of biological organisation is either just a temporary expedient or a manifestation of 'woolly-minded vitalism'. I have tried to show that the truth is just the opposite — that these logical structures are the real core of biology, and that naive reductionism is inadequate to discover them. This is not because the lower levels cannot provide a basis for the higher ones (as a thoroughgoing vitalist like Driesch would have argued); on the contrary, the problem is that the lower levels provide too many possibilities to have any real predictive power. Hence it it ironically the reductionist who ends up making vacuous, woolly statements; and his programme tends to degenerate into an indiscriminate accumulation of experimental findings in which vital clues become buried and obscured.

In conclusion, biological structures do not involve mysterious additions to the laws of physics and chemistry, but rather impose logical restrictions upon the rich array of possibilities allowed by those laws. The same applies at each successively higher level of biological organisation, which always represents a logical selection from the many possible constructions that could be generated from the elements of the level below it. Thus the concept of logical restriction provides a justification for structuralism as a non-vitalistic alternative to reductionism in biology.

REFERENCES

Brenner, S. (1975) The genetic outlook. In *Cell Patterning*. *CIBA Symposium*. 29. 343-5.
Crick, F. H. C., Barnett, L., Brenner, S. and Watts-Tobin, R. J. (1961) General nature of the genetic code for proteins. *Nature*. 192. 1227-32.
Crick, F. H. C. (1979) Thinking about the brain. *Scientific American*. 241 (3). 181-8.
Elder, D. (1984) Theory of epigenetic coding. *J. theor. Biol.* 108. 327-32.
——(1986) Structuralism and reductionism. *Riv. Biol./Biol. Forum.* 79. 75-81.
Garcia-Bellido, A. (1975) Genetic analysis of wing disc development in *Drosophila*. In *Cell Patterning*. *CIBA Symposium*. 29. 161-78.
Geschwind, N. (1979) Specialisations of the human brain. *Scientific American*. 241 (3). 158-68.

Kauffman, S. A. (1975) Control circuits for determination and transdetermination: interpreting positional information in a binary epigenetic code. In *Cell Patterning*. *CIBA Symposium*. 29. 201-14.

Paterson, H. E. H. (1985) The recognition concept of species. In *Species and Speciation*. Vrba, E. S. (ed.). Transvaal Museum, Pretoria. pp.21-9.

Raff, R. A. and Kauffman, T. C. (1983) *Embryos, Genes and Evolution*. Macmillan, New York and London. pp.39-42.

Saunders, P. (1984) Mathematics in biology. Where quantitative can be just poor qualitative. *Rivista di Biologia*. 77. 325-41.

Sibatani, A. (1985) Molecular biology: a structuralist revolution. *Rivista di Biologia*. 78. 373-97.

Thompson, D'Arcy W. (1942) *On Growth and Form*. Cambridge Univ. Press. 2nd edition.

Vrba, E. S. (1984) Patterns and processes in the fossil record. In *Beyond Neo-Darwinism*. Ho, M. and Saunders, P. (eds.). Academic Press, London. pp.115-42.

8. A Formalism Linking Structure with Function

René Thom

The problem of morphogenesis in biology concerns two very different domains — that of the cell, on one hand, and that of pluricellular organisms on the other. In spite of the traditional reductionist argument which holds that the smallest component is necessarily the most simple, there is good reason to believe that the morphogenesis of Metazoa, in particular, is in some ways *simpler* than the internal organisation of the cell. Descriptions of the organisation of animal anatomy in particular have been around for a very long time (the oldest goes back to Aristotle). Now if you ask the most expert of contemporary cytologists to describe the structure of the cytoplasm of a cell, you will get the most varied and the most incoherent answers. They will tell you about tubules, saccules and membranes, all steeped in some juice, and it will not be clear whether this composes a single compartment or several. This means that there is no real theory of intra-cellular structure in existence. Unlike the case of the genome, which has been the object of attention bordering on fascination, very little is actually known about cytoplasmic structures. It was only very recently that the concept (important, it is true) of cytoskeleton made its appearance; but even the way the membrane grows around a cell is far from clear (be it Prokaryotis or Eukaryotis), and the mechanisms of mitosis have not yet been properly understood. The formalism we present here, therefore, concerns only pluricellular beings. Animals, to be even more precise. Why animals? Because dynamics for animals involves far greater constraint: they have to feed themselves by capturing prey from outside. The plant draws nourishment from an external environment rich in diffuse chemical energy, or, by photosynthesis, from light energy. The 'prey' of plant life is not individuated (leaving aside, needless to say, the exceptional phenomenon of carnivorous plants). This has important consequences in plant morphology. As the plant has to occupy a volume wherein it diffuses its structure, its most typical form is that of ramification, where a morphogenetic field (structure isomorphic to the model) is re-implanted in itself over and over again; i.e. a plant is, basically, the sketch of a 'fractal' in Mandelbrot's sense of the word. (Fractals do not exist in nature, the self-similarity of the generating process having to stop somewhere.) This quasi-fractal character of plant

96

morphology is likewise apparent in sessile marine animals, such as corals, which filter their prey (plankton) from a current which they can themselves initiate. (Eighteenth-century naturalists, as we know, called these animals Zoophyta.) In the same way, the leaf of a chlorophyll-containing plant is an organ which, perpendicular to the rays of the sun, derives energy from them. Plant morphology then is governed by the laws of reinsertion of a field into itself, which may give rise to interesting mathematical structures. There is an abundant literature on these models (Phyllotaxis, Lindenmayer models), even though the problem has not been fully solved. As a result, botanists cast *a priori* a more favourable eye upon attempts to mathematise plant form — which cannot always be said of animal specialists.

ANIMAL ORGANISATION

The model I am going to talk about touches upon an old problem, that of the general plan of animal organisation (Bauplan). I shall evoke eventually the classic controversy between Cuvier and Geoffroy Saint-Hilaire as to the presumed oneness of this (or these) plan(s).

Before broaching the model itself, I must say something about a concept which is now very much in fashion, that of 'self-organisation'. It is obvious that if there is no constraint, no law, imposed on a process of self-organisation, then the door is left wide open to the arbitrary, and we would see no reason for not starting to believe once more in spontaneous generation, given a suitable environment. Here again, we come upon the ambiguity of the Prigoginian notion of 'dissipative structures'. If we look at the example (quasi-unique in fact) of the Rayley-Bénard phenomenon, we find ourselves dealing with the following situation: a fluid, spread in a thin horizontal layer, is heated from underneath. So long as the difference in temperature between the top and bottom levels, $\triangle T$, remains below a certain threshold A, nothing happens. We have a stationary system with zero current involving heat conduction alone. If $\triangle T$ goes above A, then suddenly a new stationary system is established, involving the subdivision of hexagonal convection cells, with the current rising at the cell-centres and falling down the walls (for example). What characterises this type of 'order' as it is called is:

1. The presence of an invariant stratified subset left invariant by the flow (the cell-walls in fact). Here, more precisely, there is in the substrate space M an invariant foliation into circles (with singularities).

2. The presence of singularities forming hexagons (the axes of convection cells).

These phenomena are comparable with the facts of symmetry breaking. Instead of the full displacement group of the two-dimensional plane, we have a configuration invariant under the subgroup which leaves the hexagonal lattice of the cells invariant. Here we touch on a major problem: namely, the approximation of a zero function by a non-zero function. When the underlying dynamics of molecular interaction is invariant under a dynamic group G, one may expect the approximation by a subgroup $\phi \subset G$ to remain invariant. On the real line, we will have periodic functions, the simplest of which is the sinusoid. On a bounded segment, we will have approximation by a Chebychev polynomial (whose critical values are two in number: such a polynomial tends towards the sinusoid when the segment length tends to infinity). We have to admit that symmetry-breaking phenomena are *global* phenomena. From this point of view they differ from the phenomena of 'phase' in matter: the latter have a local symmetry (crystals, for example) but are propagated *locally* in the milieu, under the effect of a purely local determining field. The conclusion to be drawn is that these broken-symmetry phenomena can be considered as due to a variational principle (of the type $| \triangle f |^2 da$ minimal for $| f |^2 da = 1$) for a given (compact) boundary condition.

This has important consequences for the application of a formalism of the catastrophe theory type (or of the Ruelle-Takens model). In this last case we have a flow in a function space X, usually the space X of vector fields on a given spatial domain D, and we want to 'bifurcate' the zero field in X supposedly an attracting singular point. The theory predicts Hopf's bifurcation, i.e. a periodic regime and thus an action of S^1 in X. The 'miracle' is that, in certain cases, this action of S^1 takes place in the base M (at least in so far as M admits an invariant foliated structure). In each convection cell there will then be a field having locally, in the substratum space, properties of invariance supporting an action of S^1. A later bifurcation into a torus T^2 will translate by a periodic deformation the initial invariant structure. The big problem raised by this theory lies precisely in how to characterise the local invariant structure in the substratum space: is this phenomenon a general one? Here the hypothesis of the homogeneity of the underlying dynamics always intervenes and it is this hypothesis that the biological situation forces one to abandon. The longitudinal subdivision of an animal in metameres (segments) — as in Myriapoda — thus appears as a symmetry breaking due to the preceding global mechanism. Yet in practically all metameric animals there is no perfect periodicity modulo a segment translation. Each segment is 'modulated' according to its global function in the whole. A cephalic segment is not identical with a caudal segment. We are therefore justified in simultaneously considering processes of global symmetry breaking and local variations (modulations) linked with certain 'morphogenetic gradients'. The model we shall look at answers this requirement. In every point x of an animal we have a fibre-bundle dynamical system F_x, an 'attractor' of a local metabolism. Global symmetry breakings are made manifest in periodic variations of this attractor (according to time and space); these variations can perhaps lead to bifurcations and to 'catastrophes', resulting in tissue dissociation and the differentiation of parts.

THE MODEL

The model is directly inspired by catastrophe theory. At every point x of an organism, we designate by F_x the space of possible local metabolisms in x. The global metabolic state of the organism will be characterised by a section of σ of the fibre-bundle $\pi : F_x \times B \xrightarrow{\pi} B$, that is $\sigma : B \to F_x$. This section is generally continuous on the organic base B. We suppose that it allows discontinuities on certain surfaces ρ in B. These surfaces ρ are the support of functional variations: for example, the intestinal mucosa separates the digestive juices from the blood and from the flesh in general; the pulmonary membrane of the lung separates blood from air drawn into the alveoli from outside. If we add the spatial position to the space F, the section σ can also describe the movements of internal fluids in the organism, as well as the relative movements of bones at an articulation. Those versed in Aristotelian biology will recognise here the classic distinction drawn by Aristotle [DPA] in his treatise 'On Animal Parts' between homogeneous or homoeomeric components and the surfaces of conflict, called anhomoeomeres. The homoemeric parts are the strata made up of regular points in the sense of Catastrophe Theory. For Aristotle, the anhomoeomeric parts are the organs, seats of function, parts in *act*. The homoeomeric parts are 'potential' with respect to the anhomoeomeric ones.

That being so, the problem is to describe the chief processes of embryology by means of a global dynamical model. To this end, we shall start from the quiescent egg endowed with a stationary punctual regime α. After fertilisation, the metabolism is set in motion; new degrees of freedom appear. The fundamental idea is that local metabolism of a cell bifurcates from α, and, right from the blastulae stage, develops into an attractor A whose geometric form *stimulates* the totality of the physiological functions necessary to the survival and reproduction of the adult animal. But this attractor A will implode locally into different sub-attractors corresponding, at different points, to different specialisations. Here the main morphogenetic gradients intervene:

1. the cephalo-caudal gradient proceeding from the animal-vegetative gradient of the egg

2. the left-right gradient

3. the exterior-interior gradient (distal-centripetal).

Now let us describe the passage from α to A. We start with a cusp catastrophe leading to a bimodality zone between two punctual attractors (figure 1). In the u-v plane we have a (Maxwell) separatrix which will separate the ectoderm from the endoderm. This is gastrulation. The mesoderm has a metabolism represented by the hysteresis cycle associated with the cusp (Figure 2). This cycle can degenerate into a point circle through the classic transformation of Van der Pol's equation: the cusp must then be 'unfolded' into a vertical flux point curve of the type $v = x^3$ (Figure 2) (a return to the organising centre $u = v = 0$). The mesoderm 'pumps' inner energy in order to bring the prey to the point of capture. The idea is that this singularity will later

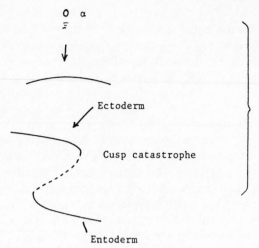

Figure 1.

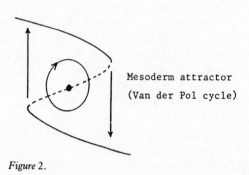

Figure 2.

degenerate into a singularity $v = x^5$, the deformation of which will give rise to a staircase curve (Figure 3).

Here we postulate the coincidence of the 'cofold' points, as we did in the situations of instrumental morphogenesis [Thom OT]; the two associated hysteresis cycles (in vertebrates) are realised in the lateral mesoderm: the dorsal cycle by the somatopleure and the ventral cycle by the splanchopleure.

A subsequent splitting of these hysteresis cycles leads to the staircase figure (a model of the global attractor A) that I have called *physiological blastula* (Figure 4).

The upper path IS T F O G L A describes the trajectory of the prey, first outside then inside the organism. Localisation of the prey is described by IS T; pursuit of the prey by TF; capture by GO; mouth by O; digestion in the stomach by OG; and intestinal digestion by GL. The point of bifurcation at L describes a part

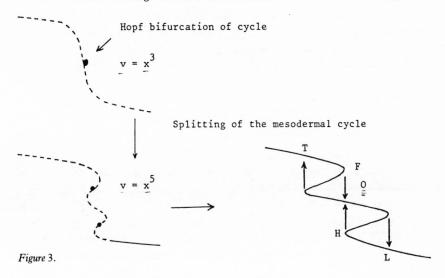

Figure 3.

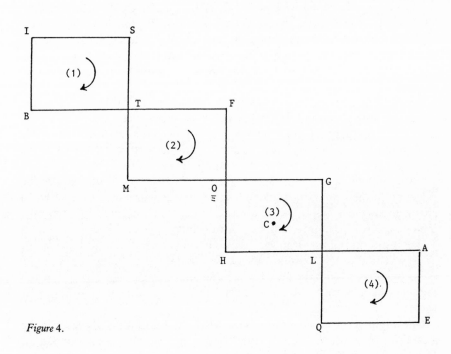

Figure 4.

of the substance of the prey being assimilated according to LH and going into the blood. The other part will be directed towards the caecum LA and subsequently eliminated from the interior by the anus (AE).

The hysteresis cycles associated with the rectangles 1234 have the following functional signification:

1.   Sensory search for a prey leading to its recognition and localisation.

2.   Capture of the prey in space after motor pursuit.

3.   Cardiovascular cycle with centre C (heart).

4.   Cycle of excretion. This has three organic realisations: kidney, large intestine, lung — according to the phase of the waste matter to be eliminated (liquid, solid, gas).

The physiological blastula is organically constructed only step by step. Induction phenomena, in Spemann's sense [1], play an essential part in this organogenesis. They are represented in the physiological blastula diagram by movements which are spatial in ontogenesis and become functional in the adult animal.

Now let us see how we can use this model to interpret neural induction in amphibians. Following invagination, the cephalic part of the prechordal mesoderm enters into contact with the underlying ectoderm and there induces the formation of the neural plate, then of the neural groove which will be formed in the spinal cord. The ectoderm has an attractor which comes from the physiological blastula by implosion: it is practically reduced to the stable TF ridge which represents the prey in the throes of being captured. The mesoderm has a complicated attractor derived from the coupled hysteresis cycle (△) (Figure 5).

It will be granted that the ectodermic attractor has a vanishing cycle at the vertex T left over from the ISTB circuit, a cycle whose presence characterises neurogenic capacity. Upon contact with the prechordal mesoderm, this vanishing cycle will come into resonance with the partial cycle ISTB of the rectangle △, synchronising at their common vertex T. The ridge MT has in △ TB as its functional prolongation (Figure 5). Resonance will thus realise the ridge TB in the ectoderm, prolonged later by the neural cycle BIST, which characterises the neural tissue. However, the cycle TFOM which represents the motor capture of the prey subsists as a vanishing cycle attached to the vertex T. Later on, during maturation of the central nervous system, this vanishing cycle will find a new existence in the functional cycle (Figure 6) linking a motory centre μC with the muscles M commanded by the motor axon NM and the cenesthetic nerve N_c. Action of M is in fact the virtual centre of the capture cycle (2) TFOM of the physiological blastula.

One might of course object to this model on the grounds that there are many material agents which induce neural tissue in a suitable dorsal ectoderm. Minerals like chalk of Kieselguhr, for example. No doubt we can see here the fact that the ectoderm represents not only the prey but also predators close

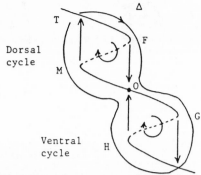

Dorsal cycle

Ventral cycle

Figure 5.

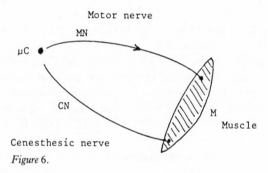

Motor nerve

MN

μC

CN

Cenesthesic nerve

Figure 6.

M

Muscle

enough to adhere to the skin. Next to the capture cycle, the nervous system (and the spinal cord in particular) has the job of eliminating these foreign bodies which perhaps constitute a menace. This is realised in the diagram (Figure 7) where SP, like SI, symbolises the outside world.

In this case, induction gives rise to the cycle STFP, rejection of a foreign body, which in turn sets off (by symmetry with respect to STM) the cycle ISTB, creator of the nervous system (see Thom [ET] for details).

I believe these examples will suffice to show how the functional structure of the physiological blastula is reconstituted after a period of dissociation due to implosion into distinct attractors. Note that the cardiovascular cycle, symbolised by OGLH, in fact irrigates the whole system. Its centre is the heart, the first organ to be formed by ontogenesis, according to Aristotle [DGA].

THE PLANS OF ORGANISATION

The diagonal VSOIE describes the path of the prey inside the organism. For most animals (terrestrial vertebrates, insects, etc.) it is the cephalo-caudal axis.

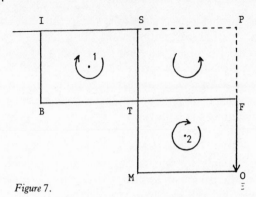

Figure 7.

This is not so, however, in the case of Mollusca: Cephalopoda like the Octopus, Gasteropoda like the Helix. Indeed, the latter's digestive tube is so folded as to place the anus close to the mouth. Here we have to bring in another axis: in Vertebrates, the spinal axis appears by 'blowing-up' the central point O (in the figure) — the phase known as elongation of the embryo. So there is a growth axis which does not necessarily coincide with the trajectory of the prey. Note that in terrestrial vertebrates, the digestive tube presents numerous circumvolutions around this axis, by internal breaking of the external bilateral symmetry. With Gasteropoda, this axis often takes a spiral form perpendicular to the axis of the animal's movement on the ground (or on the sea bed). Thus we see that the Bauplan of an animal depends almost wholly on three functional gradients: that of normal movement (generally the cephalo-caudal axis), that defined by the prey trajectory, and finally the growth axis. These axes have positions defined in relation to the physical gradients of the environment: the vertical direction of gravity, sometimes practically nil, as in a marine environment, due to Archimedes' thrust; contact interfacing between elements, like the ground (earth-sea interface) or sea surface (sea-air interface).

. The relative correlation of functional gradients is a considerable factor in the variation of organisation plans. In bipeds such as Man, the cephalo-caudal axis coincides with the vertical; in Tetrapoda it is perpendicular to it. There the organic effects of human two-leggedness have been relatively discreet; the annihilation of weight in marine animals has resulted in a wide variety of plans. The octopus, the oyster and the amphineura (bilateral symmetry) all have very different plans. The attractor of the simple diploblastic system (a hollow sphere) plays a part in this case (Cnidaria). (In Echinoderms, the rotational symmetry around the vertical axis undergoes a breaking into a discrete subgroup or order five.) The constancy of the physiological blastula schema is perfectly compatible with the most varied ontogenetic plans, for the attractors which define the broad embryological layers can implode according to very diverse chronologies and quantitative modalities. The phenomenon of insect metamorphosis, where one has a larval stage followed by the adult imago stage, may be interpreted as a partial return to the initial organising centre α of the structure. There also exist partial organising centres to which the organism may regress pathologically (the case of cancers?). But the identification of the main morphogenetic gradients (animal-vegetative, then external-internal, growth axis, etc.) with the physical gradients of the environment is a decisive factor in the determination of the Bauplan.

A FEW HISTORICAL CONSIDERATIONS

At this meeting which aims to rehabilitate structural biology, it is not inappropriate to evoke the personality of Etienne Geoffroy Saint-Hilaire and his relationship with G. Cuvier. Taken in its strictest sense, the principle of the unity of the organisational plan finds its origin in German Naturphilosophe (of which Goethe is a well-known representative). It could be expressed in its strict form by saying that there exists a universal model consisting of a stratified catastrophe set K in an auxiliary euclidean space U such that the ontogenesis of every animal (from the egg to the adult stage) may be described by a well-defined application $F_t: B \times T \to U$ transversal on the set K. The counter-images $F_t^{-1}(K)$ would thus define the arthomoeomeric parts (in Aristotle's sense) i.e. the surfaces where functional changes take place between homoeomeric tissues, hence organisation at every moment t and its variations in time. If this application F_t were unique (up to topological type) we would then have the strict correspondence given by Geoffroy Saint-Hilaire: homology of all organs to the masterplan and also homoeomorphism of their ontogenesis through embryology. The 1830 controversy between Cuvier and Geoffroy Saint-Hilaire was essentially a question of semantics: Geoffroy recognised the necessity of making geometric transformations in one Bauplan to render it isomorphic to another. (Thus the Mollusc was identified with a vertebrate folded in two, the insect with a vertebrate turned upside-down with respect to a horizontal axial section.) Unfortunately the terminology used by biologists of that time in the matter of geometric transformations was very uncertain (I am not sure that it is any more precise today . . .). As Geoffroy was unable to specify, in his 'Principle des Analogues', what types of transformation he would allow in the Bauplan, Cuvier was not wrong in criticising the conceptual vagueness enveloping Geoffroy's principle (see P. Tort). Cuvier was certainly not wrong either in insisting on the rôle of the function in the transformation of organs. As it was, much of Geoffroy's principle could have been salvaged if it had been seen, as suggested by the catastrophist point of view, that on the catastrophe set $K \subset U$ the metabolism attractors jump from one to the other, i.e. hence the set $F^{-1}(K)$ characterises the surfaces of functional discontinuity. For instance, a surface articulation between two contiguous bones (such as the humerus and radius) is functional; on the contrary, when the bones are practically welded together like those of the dome of the skull, it is not. Then these non-functional anatomical separations should not be taken into account for the principle of correspondence. As I see it, all one can do is to admit that there is a universal functional plan, the physiological blastula. But the sequence of implosions defining local attractors in ontogenesis, although very permanent, nevertheless varies a great deal. Here the identification of morphogenetic gradients with external physical gradients plays a key part; this identification itself involves a choice in a finite set (3^2). It is a fact that there are hardly more than eight or nine basic Bauplans for animal organisation.

This problem of transcendent anatomy which so fascinated biologists at the beginning of the nineteenth century is now coming into a phase where it is at least possible to propose a formalisation which, through the dynamic continuity suggested by the CT model, goes much further than a simple description. But in order to appreciate this gain in intelligibility, we need quite a deep knowledge of qualitative dynamics, which is, of course, inclined to scare off the contemporary biological community.

REFERENCES

Aristotle, [DPA] *De Partibus Animalium* 646a. 22-23.
——[DGA] *De Generatione Animalium* 741c. 15-20.
Thom, R. (1975) [ST] *Structural Stability and Morphogenesis*. Pergamon.
——(ETA) *An essay in transcendent anatomy* (to appear).
——(1986) [OT] *Organs and Tools: A Common theory for Morphogenesis, in Complexity, Language and Life*. Publ. IIASA, Biomathematics Series No. 16. Springer Verlag.
Tort, Patrick (1983) *La querelle des analogues*. Editions d'Aujourd'hui Plan de la Tour (Var), France.

9. Mathematics, Structuralism and the Formal Cause in Biology

Peter T. Saunders

In any discussion in which structuralism features, it is necessary first to agree how the term is to be understood, for there is no canonical definition. Even in linguistics it can be used in more than one sense, and as the idea has spread into other fields it has acquired correspondingly more shades of meaning. The best known description is probably that given by Piaget (1968): the study of systems which concentrates on wholeness, on transformations and on regulation, but even this does not cover all structuralist work well enough to be acceptable as a definition. Nor, indeed, did Piaget claim it as such.

It is clear, however, that the distinguishing characteristic of a structuralist approach is that phenomena are to be considered as wholes and that it is the relations between the units, i.e. the structure, that is of primary concern. For example, Lyons (1973) writes that the central thesis of structuralist linguistics is that we cannot determine the units first and then inquire what are the relationships between them; units can only be identified in terms of their relationships with other units. Whatever else may be involved in any particular version of the approach, the essence is the stress on wholeness and structure, and this will be taken here as the defining property.

Structuralism is thus seen not as a single programme but as a class of related approaches which share a basic principle while differing considerably in their details. The approach of Saussure and his successors is the modern form of a point of view which has existed for centuries, not something which has appeared relatively recently and without warning. It is only fitting that this should be so, for if we believe that transformation and regulation are crucial properties of systems, then we may expect the system of thought within which we hold this view to exhibit those properties as well.

That the emphasis on structure is the core, and properties such as regulation and transformation more recent developments, is also consistent with the common usage of the word 'structure' in the English language. According to the *Oxford English Dictionary*, it originally meant something static, like a building. Only later did it acquire a more dynamic connotation as well, as in an organism or a society. Significantly, there has been a similar shift in the scientific concept of equilibrium: whereas most work was previously concerned with steady states, of which a ball at the bottom of a cup is the archetypal example, there is now far more interest in the dynamic equilibria that are characteristic of open systems and in which regulation and transformation are important.

STRUCTURALISM AND SCIENCE

In many cultures, including our own for much of the time, science has been essentially structuralist. We do not find in Greek or mediaeval science the concentration on mechanism that dominates the modern approach. The aim was more to show how phenomena fitted into the pattern of the universe. And because mathematics is the study of patterns, many of the accounts were in mathematical terms. The motion of heavenly bodies was supposed to be on spheres. Kepler tried to account for the distances between the successive planetary orbits in terms of quantities derived from the regular polyhedra. There was a great deal of numerology, from the four elements and the four humours to the intricate arguments of the Cabbalists, who made great play of the fact that in Hebrew the letters of the alphabet are also used as numbers.

The justification for using mathematics was, however, quite different from the one we would give today. Spheres were chosen because they were seen as perfect forms, the regular polyhedra because there are only five of them (whereas there are infinitely many regular polygons). In both cases it was assumed that if these objects are special in mathematics they must also be special in science, mathematics itself being considered at the time to be a science.

Note that this was essentially a synchronic structuralism; the heavenly bodies obviously moved but there was no idea of an evolution of the orbits themselves.

Everything changed with the Newtonian revolution. Explanations were now supposed to be in terms of mechanisms. Planets went around the sun in elliptical orbits not because conic sections are especially simple or important mathematically, but as a consequence of Newton's inverse square law of gravity. Significantly, gravity was held to be a force, just like a pull on a string, despite the objections of those who refused to accept the idea of a force that acts at a distance.

As structuralism was replaced by a reductionist mechanism, mathematics lost its primary place. It was still important, and indeed there was a tremendous development of the subject to meet the needs of science, but it was no longer a source of explanation in itself. Its role was to assist in the working out of the consequences of the laws of physics. One result of this was that much of the great progress that was made in mathematics was in those areas that are well suited to the reductionist approach. The branch of the subject which gained the most was analysis, which is based on what happens in the neighbourhood of a single point. This of course increased the power of reductionism, and so even further contributed to the weakening of structuralism.

Biology too eventually moved away from the structuralist point of view. The rational morphology of the eighteenth century gave way to the Darwinism and cell theory of the nineteenth and the neo-Darwinism and molecular biology of the twentieth. Structure and form were no longer primary; they became secondary phenomena to be explained in terms of function through the mechanism of natural selection. Darwinism is not part of the Newtonian theory but it is part of the Newtonian paradigm, and indeed many biologists have seen physics as the model science to which their own should strive — though they generally have in mind the physics of the last century rather than the quite different contemporary paradigm of quantum mechanics and relativity.

Both these subjects have much in common with the pre-Newtonian structuralism. For example, in general relativity the force of gravity, with which so many earlier workers were uncomfortable, vanishes from physics. The universe is considered to be a four-dimensional curved space-time along whose geodesics move any particle moving under no forces — bearing in mind that gravity is not considered to be a force.

Thus the planetary orbits again depend not on forces but on the structure of the universe. This in turn is essentially specified by the metric tensor, whose components are determined by a set of partial differential equations which are known as the field equations and are of the form $R_{ab} - \frac{1}{2}Rg_{ab} = \kappa T_{ab}$. Here the left-hand side is a shorthand for a complicated combination of the metric tensor and its partial derivatives up to second order, while the right-hand side is made up of terms representing the velocity, density and pressure of the matter and energy in the universe.

To compute the orbit of a planet around the sun, we make the assumption that if the only massive body in the universe is a static sphere then the universe should be spherically symmetric and static. We solve the field equations subject to this condition, and then solve the geodesic equations. At no time do we introduce the idea of a force, and the mass of the sun enters into the problem only as a constant of integration which is fixed by comparing a limiting case of the equations of radial geodesics with the Newtonian law of attraction.

Thus while there is still a connection between the material in the universe and the paths of particles, there is no causal relation in the sense that is familiar to us from Newtonian mechanics. The field equations are not derivable (as Laplace's and Poisson's equations are) from a hypothesis about the forces between individual masses. They are equations which have been arrived at by largely heuristic arguments to describe the structure of space-time, and while they have been chosen to reflect certain ideas of what physics should be like and also to reduce to the classical equations in a suitable limit, they are essentially mathematical statements rather than translations into mathematics of physical ones.

Note how the whole idea of force as a fundamental concept is thus being eroded. In some cases it may still be appropriate, and in others it may serve as a convenient approximation, but just as we no longer think in terms of a gravitational force so it is too simplistic to see the interaction between an organism and its environment in terms of a single force, natural selection, which for all practical purposes may be considered to be exerted by the larger entity on the effectively passive smaller one.

Physics is now far less mechanistic and reductionist than it used to be and than most biologists probably still think it is. Even classical physics now includes such topics as co-operative phenomena and chaos. Hence if physics is to be thought of as setting the pattern for biology, that does not mean that biology should become more reductionist. On the contrary, the experience of physics suggests that structuralism may have much to offer, though of course it must be a modern structuralism. No one is advocating a return to epicycles and Platonic solids, at least not unless they can be justified on rigorous scientific grounds. The aim is not to throw away the accomplishments of the Newtonian paradigm, but to move beyond it.

MATHEMATICS AND BIOLOGY

Since mathematics is the study of patterns, we would expect it to be involved in much structuralist work, as in fact it is. What is less obvious, however, is that it can also be applied directly to the study of biological phenomena, and not only through the analysis of physical and chemical models or even of particular models at the levels of biological systems themselves (as, for example, in population biology). For there are in biology, and indeed in the study of all complex systems living or not, many forms and patterns about which much can be said on almost wholly mathematical grounds, with very little in the way of knowledge or hypotheses about the underlying processes.

An important clue to this has been known for a long time. It is well known that the same patterns often occur naturally in quite different situations. D'Arcy Thompson (1917) gave some striking examples in *On Growth and Form*: recall how closely a drop of fusel oil which has been allowed to fall into paraffin can resemble a medusoid.

Now such parallels can arise either because the underlying processes are essentially the same, which may well be the case in the above example, or because different processes can be described by the same mathematical equation. The wave equation, for example, arises in many different contexts, and all the various processes which give rise to it share certain important features. This in itself brings mathematics into prominence, because the wave equation and its properties acquire an importance far greater than if they only applied to one particular situation. The same applies to other mathematical structures; the more contexts in which they appear the more they become objects for study in themselves, with the applications to real phenomena to be considered later.

In most cases, however, the role of mathematics is still limited, because we must have a model of a system before we know that any particular equation is involved. There is growing, however, a new approach in which mathematics plays a central role and can be applied directly to biology without the intermediary of a model.

The clearest example of this, though by no means the only one, is catastrophe theory, the aim of which is to 'construct an abstract, purely geometrical theory of morphogenesis, *independent of the substrate of forms and the nature of the forces that create them*' (Thom, 1972, p.8). This might seem, as Thom acknowledges, hard to believe, but in fact Thom and other mathematicians have derived some remarkable theorems that have enabled at least one part of his programme to be carried out.

Imagine an aeroplane flying at above the speed of sound. The sky around it can be divided into two distinct parts, that ahead of the aeroplane in which there is no sound from the aeroplane, and that behind it in which there is sound, first loud and then dying away. The boundary between the two regions is the shock wave, heard as the sonic boom, and it has the form of a cusp, or if drawn in three dimensions, a sort of cusped cone.

Now think of light falling onto the surface of a cup of coffee. Again there are two regions, one dark and one light, and a very bright boundary between them, called a caustic. The caustic too is cusp shaped.

When *Dictyostelium discoideum* amoebae feed on *E. coli* in a continuous flow vessel, their specific growth rate exhibits abrupt changes. If these changes are plotted on a graph with time as one axis and bacteria/amoebae ratio as the other, they lie on a cusp (Bazin and Saunders, 1978). We also see cusps in the plots of the imperfection sensitivity of beams (e.g. Thompson and Hunt, 1973) in the regions of bimodal responsiveness as a function of hormone concentrations in the study of thyrotropic response (Seif, 1979) and in many other situations.

The processes involved in these examples are quite different, but it is no mere coincidence that they all produce cusps. For it can be proven that the range of forms or patterns that can be produced by a very wide range of mechanisms is remarkably small; they can all be found in the famous list of seven elementary catastrophes. In particular, if there are only two control variables, i.e. two parameters which are crucially involved in producing the discontinuity (which in the case of forms means the boundary), then the cusp is the most complicated shape that can appear, at least locally. The range of mechanisms referred to includes almost anything that can be described by any differential equation or set of differential equations that any biologist and most physicists would be likely to write down.

This gives the elementary catastrophes a special status in explanation, just like spheres and dodecahedra and so on had in the past. There is, however, an important difference. We have not abandoned the idea of mechanism. On the contrary, the choice of these preferred forms, these archetypes, one might say, has been made consistent with the idea that forms and patterns arise through the sorts of physical and chemical processes which are studied by conventional modern science. We do not, however, need to know the particular process which operates in any given situation; granted some quite weak hypotheses about what is going on, the rest follows mathematically. It is not magic; it is true because our results apply not to individual mechanisms but to large classes.

This sort of result is not peculiar to catastrophe theory, although that is probably the most striking example and one of the few for which there are theorems which specify the complete range of preferred forms. For example, much work is being done following Turing's (1952) discovery that reaction-diffusion equations can produce patterns out of an originally uniform region of tissue. It turns out that many of the properties of these patterns are not very sensitive to the particular choice of reaction scheme. The subject may not have the theorems that catastrophe theory does, but there are still good grounds for seeing certain properties of the solutions of a whole class of parabolic differential equations as characteristic of real phenomena in nature.

As long as we accept that the phenomena with which we are concerned can be suitably modelled using mathematics, statements about classes of processes, including statements about the patterns (in the most general sense of the word) they can generate, are in effect statements about classes of mathematical models. Conversely, some mathematical theorems translate into statements about the real world almost directly, and mathematics effectively regains the position in scientific explanation that it lost with the Newtonian paradigm.

Thus we are almost back to the days when mathematics was a science and objects that were special mathematically were believed to be special scientifically as well. It is how we decide what is special that has changed. We choose the seven elementary catastrophes instead of the five regular polyhedra for good scientific reasons related to the sort of analyses which have been carried out for many years. This is surely as it should be; one cannot imagine that the new structuralism and the new importance of mathematics would have gained nothing from the many years of successful mechanistics and reduction.

THE FORMAL CAUSE IN SCIENCE

With the rise of the Newtonian paradigm, the fourth of Aristotle's causes, the final cause, was apparently banished from science. To assert that stones fall to earth so as to achieve their proper positions strikes most of us not just as wrong but as a totally inappropriate account. Yet, as Lankester (1888) pointed out, Darwin's theory of natural selection 'refounded, reformed and rehabilitated' teleology, so that explanation in terms of function became acceptable again, at least within the context of evolution theory. If we ask why *Camarhyncus psittacula* (one of Darwin's finches) has a peculiarly shaped beak, we can accept as a sensible answer that it is to allow the bird to take insects from the bark of trees. This may not be a complete explanation, it might even be a wrong account of the origin of the shape, but at least we do not see it as an explanation outside the scope of modern science. Instead, we accept it as a shorthand for a more complicated argument in terms of processes such as heredity, variation and selection, all of which are known to occur. Seeing the final cause in this way may reassure even the most conventional scientist that it is a legitimate form of explanation, but does not deny it a distinctive role. For by leading biologists again to enquire about the functions of things, the rehabilitation of the final cause has had a profound effect — many would argue too profound an effect — on the direction of research.

The final cause was not, however, the only one of Aristotle's causes to fall into disfavour. It would be an overstatement to claim that only the efficient cause remained, even though such an eminent figure as Lord Kelvin (1884) could write: '. . . the test of "do we understand a particular subject in physics?" is "can we make a mechanical model of it?".' Certainly the material cause remained important, though it can be argued that the aim of such disciplines as the physics of solids and the atomic theory of matter was to reduce it to the efficient cause. But the formal cause did lose its former status, driven first out of physics and then, with the decline of the school of rational morphology and the rise of Darwinism, out of biology as well. It is ironic that it was the return of the final cause that destroyed one of the last remaining bastions of the formal cause.

The use of mathematics in biology in the way outlined in the previous section brings back the formal cause as a proper mode of explanation. It accomplishes this in a way which is analogous to the rehabilitation of the final cause by Darwinism, i.e. by demonstrating how explanation in such terms can be consistent with our current ideas of science yet at the same time be worthy of consideration on its own terms, not as a trivial consequence of other aspects of explanation.

For we are discovering that it is quite common for a large number of mechanisms to map into a much smaller number of patterns. These patterns then become significant in their own right, and this together with the extreme difficulty in so many cases of elucidating the mechanism, gives the formal cause the status of a proper and effectively independent mode of explanation.

In fact the formal cause has a stronger claim for independent consideration than does the final cause. For because neo-Darwinism is unfalsifiable (Saunders and Ho, 1982), adaptive explanations can be found for any phenomena. They are therefore seldom convincing unless they are supported by evidence as to how selection operated. Hence a satisfactory account in terms of the final cause generally requires an explanation in terms of other causes. In contrast, mathematics can make it possible to predict in advance what the preferred forms will be, so that there is no need to appeal to the efficient and material causes in the same way.

It is, however, important not to carry the argument to the point of insisting that only the formal cause matters. This view is often ascribed to structuralists in many fields, and not always without justification, but it is to be avoided. To adopt it would be to make the same mistake as is made by neo-Darwinists, i.e. to place too narrow limits on what is required by way of explanation. Darwin began by rehabilitating the final cause, but he and his successors eventually reached the point where the final cause was seen as being the only proper form of explanation in evolution.

This is because the variations on which natural selection acts are taken by neo-Darwinists to be random. There is consequently nothing that need be or can be said about them (save, possibly, for a vague appeal to 'developmental constraints' in cases of great difficulty). As a result, while no one argues that there are no formal, material and efficient causes in evolution, for neo-Darwinists the burden of explanation falls almost entirely on the final cause.

The new role of mathematics brings the formal cause back into biology, but only as a part of explanation. It is important to realise that we can make progress towards understanding morphology independently of the 'substrate of forms and the nature of the forces that create them', but that is not to claim that a knowledge and understanding of the substrate and of the nature of the forces are not also important (cf. Gierer, 1981) nor to deny that selection has an effect. The aim should be to expand the means of explanation, not artificially to restrict them, as the Darwinists have done.

Finally, while it should be obvious from what has been discussed so far, it is perhaps worth emphasising that to stress the importance of the formal cause does not imply anything along the lines of of Sheldrake's (1981) morphic resonance hypothesis. Were Sheldrake to be proved correct, then the formal cause would certainly be important, but the converse does not follow. The question is whether part of explanation in biology can consist of the identification and study of certain preferred patterns, whether we accept Sheldrake's hypothesis or whether — like most scientists — we are confident that patterns ultimately arise through conventional chemical and physical processes.

AN EXAMPLE

To see how structuralism can actually be useful in biology, we now turn to an example in which both the mathematical and non-mathematical aspects of it were used. These arose in the course of investigations into the development of the fruit fly *Drosophila melanogaster* (Ho *et al.*, 1983a, 1983b). The aim has been to learn about normal development by studying what happens when it goes wrong. Most studies of this kind are done on mutants, such as the well-known *bithorax*, in which what ought to be the metathoracic segment develops partly or entirely into the mesothoracic segment. The same effects can be achieved in genetically normal flies by exposing them to ether vapour at an early stage of development; this gives what are called *phenocopies*. Ho *et al.* have chosen to work with these because they involve a better defined perturbation of the system than mutations.

Now *Drosophila* development is comparatively simple, which is one of the reasons it is being so extensively studied. At an early stage the larva divides into segments, of which three will form the thorax, nine the abdomen, and the rest (and there seems to be some disagreement about how many one should count) the head. Also comparatively early on (by comparison with most organisms) each segment appears to be divided into compartments, such that each cell within a given compartment will give rise to cells which will ultimately form a certain structure.

Figure 1 is a sketch of the metathoracic segment in the embryo and the same segment in the adult of a fruit fly exhibiting the complete *bithorax* transformation. The letters indicate which regions of the so-called 'imaginal disc' will give rise to which parts of the developed segment. The same compartments in the imaginal disc of a normal fly lead to related but different structures in the adult. Instead of a wing there is a haltere, a sort of balancing device, and the other parts look different enough to be distinguished under a microscope. The effect of either the mutations or the ether treatment is to cause some or all of the compartments on the metathoracic segment to develop not as they should but into the corresponding structures on the mesothoracic segment, the one on which a normal fly has its only pair of wings.

If all transformations were complete, the story would be less interesting, although we would still hope to learn something about the effect of the structure of the organism and its epigenetic (i.e. developmental) system on the possible variations. Usually, however, only some of the compartments within the segment are transformed, and we can gain additional information by noting which compartments tend to transform together and which do not.

The conventional explanation of the transformations is that the fate of a compartment is determined by a hierarchy of gene switches. A change in any gene will cause the transformation of all compartments below it in the hierarchy. This allows us to predict which compartments should transform together; for example on the generally accepted pattern of switches (Garcia-Bellido *et al.*, 1973) the co-transformations should be

$$ABCDEF \quad ABDE \quad AB \quad A \quad B$$
$$DE \quad D \quad E$$
$$CF$$

In fact the pattern observed by Ho *et al.* was quite different. Out of the 2^6-1 = 63 possible co-transformations the only ones that occurred with a frequency of more than 2 per cent were

$$A \quad AB \quad ABC \quad ABCF \quad C \quad ABCDEF \quad B \quad ABCDF \quad ACF \quad ABCD$$

and together these accounted for 86.8 per cent of the total. This pattern can be shown not to be consistent with any model based on a hierarchy of gene switches. What is more, the transformations do not respect compartmental boundaries, as they ought to on the conventional model in which the compartments are specified as clonal units. The pattern is, however, consistent with simple physical contiguity: nearby compartments tend to transform, or

Figure 1. (a) Compartments in the metathoracic segment of a transformed fly. From Saunders and Ho (1985).

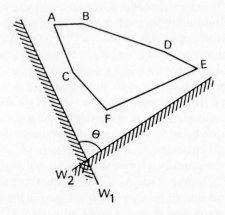

(b) Relative locations of the same compartments in the imaginal disc of a *Drosophila* embryo. The lines marked W_1 and W_2 indicate the orientation of the two waves referred to in the text. From Ho *et al.* (1983b).

not, together. And it is not too difficult to see that the pattern can be explained simply by assuming that two plane waves pass through the region almost at right angles to each other. The idea is that the first wave sensitises the cells and the second desensitises them. Only if the ether is applied between the passage of the two waves is the cell diverted to the 'wrong' state.

Not only does this model fit the pattern of co-transformations, it is also consistent with the observation that the transformations do not respect compartmental boundaries. On the other hand, it requires two waves passing through a region, and we have to explain where these waves could come from, and how they could be co-ordinated with the right sort of interval between them. Otherwise our explanation of the phenomenon is almost as complicated as the phenomenon itself, and we are not much further ahead.

Not enough is known about the processes that are going on in the embryo at this stage to allow us to make a convincing case for any particular mechanism to produce the waves. We can, however, still solve the problem in the following way (Saunders and Ho, 1985).

We know that at early stages in development the cells of an organism are not determined: depending on environment and stimulus they can develop into different final forms. Later on, however, they are committed to become bone, muscle, cartilage or whatever, providing only that they survive at all.

A simple way in which this transition can occur would be that there is some biochemical reaction within each cell which, once it is triggered, moves from one equilibrium state to another. If we also suppose, as seems reasonable, that the system can be diverted from its normal development only if it is perturbed while it is not at or very close to equilibrium, this explains why transformations occur only if the ether treatment is applied during a relatively short interval.

We next have to consider how the reaction can be initiated. It might be by direct genetic pre-programming with a sort of alarm clock in each cell, but this must be implausible. Much more likely is a signal which either passes through the region, or at least triggers the cells at one end which trigger those next to them and so on. In either case, there will be a wave of cells starting to become committed. The chemical reaction that does this will not be instantaneous, so there will be a second wave of cells actually becoming committed. The idea that changes of this kind happen in apparent waves is due to Zeeman (1974), though he did not envisage the origin of the second wave in quite the same way.

Now we know from catastrophe theory that the simplest mechanisms that will give us a transition from one equilibrium to another must have two control variables, which here means two parameters of the reaction. How these affect the reaction depends on the model, but we can say in general that two cells which are disturbed from equilibrium at the same time will not reach the new equilibrium at the same time. It follows that the second wave will not follow directly behind the first; it can be slower, faster, in the opposite sense, or in a different direction altogether. So here are the two non-parallel waves we need.

While this general argument is sufficient for our purposes and has the great advantage that the result does not depend on a particular choice of model, it may be helpful to see an example of an equation that will accomplish what is required. One that has been proposed in a somewhat different context is (Lewis, Slack and Wolpert, 1977):

$$\frac{dg}{dt} = S + \frac{g^2}{K+g^2} - Dg.$$

Here g is an (unspecified) gene product, S is the concentration of some 'signal substance' (also unspecified, but possibly calcium ions or CANP), K is the second parameter as mentioned above (possibly the concentration of some other substance which competes for binding sites) and D is the rate of degradation of g. But while it may be reassuring to know that even such a simple equation can produce two waves at the sort of angle that is required (see Saunders and Ho, 1985, for details), the whole argument goes through without any equations. We now know that if we observe a certain pattern of phenomena, here an apparent transition from one equilibrium to another, then consistent with this pattern — and the not unreasonable assumption that the mechanism that drives it is no more complicated than it has to be — we may expect to observe other phenomena, in this case the two waves.

Finally, we may ask what is the trigger that sets the whole process off. Here we apply a structural argument to the organism instead of to the mathematics. The process we have been describing occurs shortly after segmentation. Since segmentation is likely to involve waves moving longitudinally along the organism (Zeeman, 1974; Cooke and Zeeman, 1976), and since that is the direction of the first of our two waves, it seems likely that there is a link.

CONCLUSIONS

In mathematics and science as in other fields, structuralism tends to arouse controversy. A common criticism is that it provides at best a description, not an explanation, and contributes nothing to our understanding of phenomena. Now it should be clear from the specific biological example given above that this need not by any means be so, though it is not possible to defend every structuralist argument against the charge, any more than one can defend every application of any mathematical technique. Moreover, any serious discussion of this point runs into the problem that it is not at all obvious what we really mean by the word 'explanation'. It was, after all, a physicist, Max Planck (1925), who wrote: 'As long as Natural Philosophy exists, its ultimate aim will be the correlating of various physical observations into a unified system and, where possible, into a single formula.'

All the same, there is in structuralism a danger, not always avoided, of setting up empty formalisms and barren analogies. But there is also an important weakness in the mechanistic approach, which structuralism allows us to see clearly. Suppose it can be demonstrated on structuralist grounds that a certain phenomenon should occur. This implies that there is a large class of mechanisms each of which would produce the same result. Hence that a particular mechanistic account makes a prediction which accords with the observations is nowhere near as strong a verification as it is likely to be taken to be. So we are in danger of coming to wrong conclusions about mechanisms — quite apart from the tendency of some reductionists to be content with *ad hoc* equations with no theoretical justification whatsoever.

Consider, for example, the elementary derivation of Snell's law of refraction by the determination of the least-time path from source to observer. Anyone who takes this seriously is left wondering how the photon knows what the shortest path is, especially before it sets out on the journey. Eventually, of course, one learns that is has nothing to do with photons trying to save time. It is instead a matter of a stationary path length being necessary to avoid destructive interference.

While this situation is sufficiently well understood to cause no real problems, there are others which are not so clear, such as the use of game theory to explain certain aspects of animal behaviour, for example, foraging patterns or the tendency of many animals to decide conflicts by harmless means like displays, rather than actually resorting to violence. The problem is that it can be very hard to distinguish between a genetically programmed game-theoretic solution to a problem and the possibility than an animal is learning from experience.

In this case the difference between the two approaches is important, because the apparent success of game theory is taken by many workers as evidence that much of the behaviour of animals, including of course humans, is under direct genetic control, with particular patterns having been created by natural selection. The other hypothesis implies a much less precise innate specification of behaviour; all that is required is an ability to learn from experience.

To adopt a structuralist approach in biology is not to argue for a form of old-fashioned vitalism, or to deny that biological phenomena are ultimately due to physical and chemical interactions. But organisms are so complex that the reductionist programme is often quite impracticable; indeed one unfortunate feature of the programme is that it leads biologists to concentrate their attention on those phenomena that can be explained by reductionist techniques rather than those which are intrinsically the most interesting (cf. Dawkins, 1982, p.24).

The structuralist approach has much to contribute to biology, as to the study of all complex systems. But the structuralism will be not that of the pre-Newtonian era, nor exactly that of Saussure. It will not be opposed to or ignorant of mechanism; on the contrary, what we know of mechanisms must be incorporated into our models. Moreover, while concentrating on the synchronic may have been a natural reaction to the reductionist diachronic approach that preceded it, it is essential to include transformations in time. This is certainly true in biology, in which evolution is such an important feature. It is also true in linguistics: it may be wrong to track the change in one word as though it had nothing to do with the rest of the language, but that does not mean we should not be trying to understand how entire languages have been transformed over the centuries. We began with unchanging structures, we went on to changing particles, now the challenge is to cope with changing structures.

Mathematics, structuralism and biology are coming together again, but each of the three is different from what it was two millenia or even two centuries ago. There is no question of an attempt to return to an outmoded paradigm, neglecting all that has been learned in the meantime. On the contrary, we are seeing a return of interest in questions that have been asked many times before, but with the difference that we now have at our disposal some of the tools we need to begin to answer them.

REFERENCES

Bazin, M. J. and Saunders, P. T. (1978) Determination of critical variables in a microbial predator-prey system by catastrophe theory. *Nature.* 275. 52-4.

Cooke, J. and Zeeman, E. C. (1974) A clock and wavefront model for the control of the number of repeated structures during animal morphogenesis. *J. theor. Biol.* 58. 455-76.

Dawkins, R. (1982) *The Extended Phenotype.* W. H. Freeman, Oxford.

Gierer, A. (1981) Generation of biological patterns and form: Some physical, mathematical and logical aspects. *Prog. Biophys. molec. Biol.* 37. 1-47.

Ho, M-W., Bolton, E. and Saunders, P. T. (1983a) The *bithorax* phenocopy and pattern formation. I. Spatiotemporal characteristics of the phenocopy response. *Exp. Cell Biol.* 51. 282-90.

——Saunders, P. T. and Bolton, E. (1983b) The *bithorax* phenocopy and pattern formation. II. A model of prepattern formation. *Exp. Cell Biol.* 51. 291-9.

Kelvin, Lord (William Thomson) (1884) *Lectures on Molecular Dynamics and the Wave Theory of Light.* Johns Hopkins University, Baltimore.

Lankester, E. R. (1888) Zoology. In *Encyclopaedia Britannica.* (9th edn.). p.806.

Lewis, J., Slack, J. M. and Wolpert, L. (1977) Thresholds in development. *J. theor. Biol.* 65. 579-90.

Lyons, J. (1973) Structuralism and linguistics. In *Structuralism: an Introduction* (D. Robey, ed.). Oxford University Press, Oxford. pp.5-19.

Piaget, J. (1968) *Le Structuralisme.* Presses Universitaires de France, Paris.

Planck, M. (1925) *A Survey of Physics* (trans. R. Jones and D. H. Williams). Methuen, London.

Saunders, P. T. and Ho, M-W. (1985) Primary and secondary waves in prepattern formation. *J. theor. Biol.* 114. 491-504.

Seif, F. J. (1979) Cusp bifurcation in pituitary thyrotropin secretion. In *Structural Stability in Physics* (W. Guttinger and H. Eikemeier, eds.). Springer, Berlin. pp.275-89.

Sheldrake, R. (1981) *A New Science of Life.* Blond and Briggs, London.

Thom, R. (1972) *Stabilité Structurelle et Morphogénèse.* Benjamin, Reading.

Thompson, D'A. W. (1917) *On Growth and Form.* Cambridge University Press, Cambridge.

Thompson, J. M. T. and Hunt, G. W. (1973) *A General Theory of Elastic Stability.* Wiley, London.

Turing, A. (1952) The chemical basis of morphogenesis. *Phil. Trans. R. Soc. London.* B237. 37-72.

Zeeman, E. C. (1974) Primary and secondary waves in developmental biology. In *Some Mathematical Questions in Biology VIII. Lectures on Mathematics in the Life Sciences.* Vol. 7. (S. Levin, ed.). American Mathematical Society, Providence. pp.69-161.

10. Dynamical Levels in Developing Systems

L. V. Beloussov

The concept of levels is undoubtedly central for a structuralist approach. However, the mere statement that living, and particularly developing, systems consist of different levels sounds today almost trivial. It becomes largely non-trivial if multilevelled organisation is ascribed not only to statical structures but primarily to the processes underlying organic development, and if multilevel analysis is used as a methodological basis for understanding the behaviour of self-organising biological systems. Up to now only a few, though highly significant, steps have been made in this direction (Weiss, 1969; Thom, 1972; Goodwin, 1976). In this chapter I shall try to follow this line. First I would like to discuss the main manifestations of self-organisation in organic development and how they are connected with the concept of dynamical levels and their interactions.

SELF-ORGANISATION PHENOMENA IN BIOLOGICAL DEVELOPMENT
AS OPPOSED TO DETERMINISTIC 'ONE CAUSE-ONE EFFECT'
RELATIONS

Self-organisation can be defined as a process by which a structure A transforms itself into a spatially more complicated structure B without requiring any internal or external blueprint homeomorphic to B. In somewhat more precise terms, self-organising systems are those capable of spontaneous symmetry-breaking (reduction in symmetry order) without requiring an external influence. In embryonic development there are many such transformations, beginning with the first steps (the egg's capacity to polarise and establish a plane of symmetry even in isotropical conditions, for example in some kinds of parthenogenesis) up to organogenesis (metamerisation of mesoderm, formation of brain vesicles etc. in the absence of homeomorphic prepatterns). It seems also impossible to trace any homeomorphism between the structures of embryonic inducers and the induced rudiments; the latter structures are almost always more regular and complicated than are the corresponding inducers.

The existence of self-organisation phenomena in organic development largely undermines the effectiveness of a classical approach of linear uniform determinism, with its 'one cause-one effect' rule. In each case of a self-complication (symmetry-breaking) this uniformity is indeed lost and a given 'cause' (which could be as a rule only conditionally distinguished from the whole set of accompanied events) leads to more than one effect (for example, morphological structure). It would be proper to go even further and to claim that the developmental events which are postulated to be causes and their effects are as a rule completely non-comparable at least quantitatively and in some cases also qualitatively. In a number of developmental events (partheno-genesis is one of the most well-known examples) the 'small' cause leads to great results whereas in others (canalised, equifinal developmental trajectories) considerable disturbances do not lead to any measurable final changes. The most important case of a qualitative non-comparability of the postulated causes and the observed effects is obviously the genotype-phenotype relation, that is the relations between the genotype and the spatio-temporal succession of developmental events. How can a stable chemical structure equally represented in all or almost all the embryonic cells serve as a homeomorphic blueprint for spatially heterogeneous developmental processes?

The above certainly does not mean that I consider development as a non-regulated process having no relation to the genotype. What I would like to argue is that organic development even in its general outlines cannot be studied and understood in the framework of a philosophy of a linear uniform determinism and requires quite another non-linear ideology in which the concept of dynamical levels is central. Let us follow this ideology employing some simple mathematical examples.

PARAMETRIC AND DYNAMIC REGULATION: MATHEMATICAL FORMALISMS AND BIOLOGICAL PARALLELS

One of the simplest cases of self-organising systems may be exemplified by a non-linear third-order differential equation

$$\dot{x} = kx - k_1 x^3 \ (k_1 > 0) \tag{1}$$

It is easy to show that at $k < 0$ it has only one real stable solution, $x_1 = 0$ whereas at $k > 0$ this solution becomes unstable and two new real stable solutions appear, $x_{2,3} = \pm \sqrt{(k/k_1)}$ (Figure 1). That means that by changing k values from negative to positive the system (1) becomes self-complicating.

How is the behaviour of this system regulated? We can see here two principally different regulatory pathways. The first and the most important one is parametric: there are changes in k parameter values which determine a set of solutions and make the system capable or incapable of self-complication. Another kind of regulation, dynamic, is related to the values of the dynamic variable x and decides which one of the two available stable solutions is actually realised: with $k > 0$ all $x > 0$ lead to the positive and all $x < 0$ to the negative solution. Therefore, dynamic regulation is:

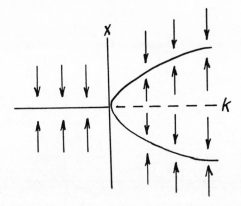

Figure 1. A diagram of stable (solid lines) and unstable (dashes) solutions of eq.(1). Horizontal axis: parameter k, vertical axis: dynamical variable x. When the value of k parameter passes from the negative to positive area the solution $x_1 = 0$ becomes unstable and instead two new stable solutions $x_{2,3} = \pm \sqrt{k/k_1}$ appear. Such a bifurcation of the initially stable solution may be considered as one of the simplest cases of the parametrically regulated self-complication of a non-linear system.

1.   Parametrically dependent (since it works only under the definite parameters values), and

2.   Highly degenerate (or, in biological terms, largely non-specific).

Parametric regulation is much less degenerate (more specific) since both solution values are uniformly dependent upon the values of the parameters k and k_1.

It should be stressed now that the dynamical variable x and each of the parameters k and k_1 differ from each other by their characteristic times, that is by their reverse rates of change. The changes of the dynamical variable x are ex definitio of an order more rapid than those of the parameter k which are in their turn infinitely greater than those of the k_1 parameter (the latter is considered as constant).

Let us define variables with different characteristic times as belonging to different levels, the greater the characteristical time T_{ch}, the higher the corresponding level. Thus, system (1) is three-levelled. One can see that parametric regulation acts from (a) higher level(s) and the dynamical one from the lowest level of a system.

If a process is assumed to occur not only in time but also in space, the different levels may be distinguished one from other not only by their T_{ch} but also by the characteristic space dimensions L_{ch}. As a rule, L_{ch} are proportional to T_{ch}: the greater is a given level's T_{ch} the more extended and spatially delocalised are the space events belonging to this level.

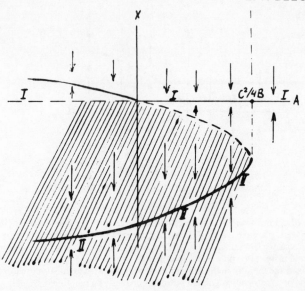

Figure 2. A diagram of stable (solid lines) and unstable (dashes) solutions of eq.(2). Same co-ordinates as in Figure 1. With the change of parameter A value from $+\infty$ to $A<C^2/4B$ the previously unique stable solution I becomes metastable (at $A>0$) and then unstable (at $A<0$). In the area $0<A<C^2/4B$ a finite perturbation is required in order to transfer the dynamical variable into the attractor's basin (dashed) of a new stable state II. This scheme illustrates some classical embryological concepts. Namely, the acquiring of competence may be interpreted as a parametric (horizontal) shift to the left from the point $A = C^2/4B$; determination is the vertical downward transfer of the dynamical variable to the attractor's basin of a new stable state II; differentiation is a final reaching of this state. The external influences promoting the acquisition of competence, determination and differentiation may all be designated as inducers.

Another kind of differential equation, namely

$$\dot{x} = -Ax - Bx^2 - Cx^3 \tag{2}$$

illustrates the biologically important concept of metastability and attraction basins. A solution $x_1 = 0$ is unique and stable in the parameter range $A>B^2/4C$, metastable in the range $0>A>B^2/4C$ and unstable in the range $A<0$. In the metastable range a finite dynamic perturbation is required in order to shift the dynamical variable x from the attraction of I solution to the basin of II solution (Figure 2).

Finally, let us briefly discuss a well-known system of two coupled differential equations with a so-called 'small parameter' ϵ (see for example Zeeman, 1972):

$$\begin{aligned} \dot{x} &= y - kx^n - b \\ \epsilon\dot{y} &= -(y^3 + ay + x) \quad (n\geqslant0; \epsilon\to0) \end{aligned} \tag{3}$$

This system contains the dynamical variables and the parameters of two different order values (or, in other words, the parameters and the 'slow' (x) and 'rapid' (y) dynamical variables). It is at least three-levelled. The analysis shows that depending upon the relative values of the parameters k, n, b and a the system (3) exerts three qualitatively different kinds of behaviour:

1. A unistationary, or waiting behavioural regime, characterised by a return after perturbation to the same point of phase space;

2. A bistationary, or trigger behaviour characterised by the existence of two alternative stable points;

3. An auto-oscillatory behaviour with non-damping oscillations of a period T_{ch} intermediate between the parameters and dynamical variables T_{ch}. If it is space-dependent (by means of diffusion-like short-range interactions) this regime produces waves of length L_{ch} which is also intermediate between L_{ch} of the parameters and of the dynamical variables.

The above examples illustrate clearly the dualistic subordination of self-organising systems to parametric and dynamic regulation. It is parametric regulation which determines the set of potentially achievable stable solutions and, so to say, the very nature of a system's behaviour (seen most clearly in the last example). The role of dynamic regulation is to select a specific solution from a given set. Let us stress once again the property that is at first glance paradoxical but actually typical for self-organising systems: the specific solution is selected by a largely non-specific (degenerate) dynamic agent.

It is also clear that the above discussed examples give just those self-organising capacities which are inherent in biological development. In particular, its capacity to undergo spontaneous symmetry-breaking corresponds to the parametrically regulated transition from a unistationary to bistationary state. The 'small causes—great effects' situation corresponds to that typical for instability (or 'strong' metastability) domains whereas the reverse situation prevails in the attractor basins of stable solutions. We may go even further and 'translate' into mathematical language those genuinely biological concepts as competence, determination (commitment), differentiation and embryonic induction. Those developmental systems may be defined as competent which have, for given parameter values, more than one stable state; systems with no more than one stable state are non-competent. Hence the establishment of competence should be a purely parametric event. Determination (commitment) may be defined as the shift of a dynamical variable into the basin of attraction of the next (or final) stable state and differentiation as the ultimate reaching of this very state. Therefore both determination and differentiation (taken as processes) are dynamical events. As to induction, it seems appropriate to define it as any influence (either parametric or dynamical) upon a certain part of of an embryo which promotes its movement to the final developmental state. I hope that the definitions proposed may be of heuristic value. For example, in order to reach a better understanding of inductive phenomena it might be useful to study whether they have some parametric and/or dynamical components. A suggestion can be made that the so-called directive inductions are mainly parametric whereas the permissive ones are dynamical (see Beloussov *et al.*, 1985 for more details).

Another general and important property of self-organising systems is their capacity to generate new intermediate levels by interactions of the pre-existing higher and lower levels. This is illustrated by equations (3) in which the new level of auto-oscillations (and, in the space-dependent case, corresponding wave solutions) intermediate between those of parameters and dynamical variables is formed. Such a formation requires a non-closed interaction loop, containing two branches: the first one is exemplified by the downward parametric influences from the upper level to that of dynamical variables whereas the second one is exemplified by the upwardly directed dynamical influences (exerted by the latter level) just generating the new level. More precisely, the dynamical influences play the role of initial conditions in creating a new intermediate level. As we shall see in the next section, similar loops occur in biological development. But before coming to the particular examples we must investigate what may be the main dynamical levels of the developing systems and how can they interact with each other.

DYNAMICAL LEVELS AND THEIR INTERACTIONS IN DEVELOPING SYSTEMS

Modern achievements in cell biology make it possible to outline a set of interrelated processes which are the direct motive forces of morphogenesis and may be hence defined as its dynamical variables. These are the cytoskeleton and membrane transformations (CMT), that is the conformational changes of actin and tubulin structures, lateral mobility of plasma membrane components, exo-endocytosis and others. Their average T_{ch} do not exceed, as a rule, a few minutes and their L_{ch} is of nannometer range. CMT are often affected by even more rapid electrochemical processes (on and off switching of ionic currents) with T_{ch} of about $10^{-3} - 10^{-1}$s. The latter may relate to CMT as a rapid variable y from equations (3) to the slow variable from the same equations. Such a relation offers extensive possibilities for generating, under the appropriate values of higher level parameters, auto-oscillating, trigger or waiting (unistationary) regimes with T_{ch} and L_{ch} much greater than those of CMT, but smaller than those of the uppermost parameters.

What are these slowly changing or constant biological parameters? Following the insights of Goldschmidt (1955) and Waddington (1957) and the direct suggestions of more recent authors (such as D. Chernavskii — see Romanovskii, Stepanova, Chernavskii, 1984) I propose that the role of the highest parameter is played by the genome and particularly by its relatively non-specific loci which control the synthesis of cytoskeletal and membrane proteins and the enzymes involved in energetic metabolism.

The possible parametrising function of the low-specificity parts of the genome remains almost unexplored in modern biology. Both theoretical considerations and some experimental data suggest that it may play a powerful role in generating new intermediate levels and in preparing, in some cases, the initial conditions for the local spatio-temporal expression of more specific genes. For example (Romanovskii *et al.*, 1984) in the case of a non-linear cross-inhibition of two genetically determined synthetic processes it is the value of a non-specific rate parameter (probably related to energetic metabolism) which determines whether both syntheses are evenly balanced or one of them becomes inhibited whereas the other is activated. After exceeding a certain threshold the rate parameter forces the system to select one of the previously coexisting synthetic pathways (which one will be selected degeneratively depends, as usual, upon the relative values of the dynamical variables). Thus the system reduces its symmetry order and segregates into synthetically different territories of the new, non-pre-existing spatial (and possibly also temporal) dimensions. In each of these territories one of the two alternative specific genes is expressed whereas another is inhibited.

This scheme may be used for a better understanding of how specific genes come into action in the course of development. Instead of the widespread belief that all they need to be activated are 'strong' specific inducers acting on this spatio-temporal point of development, one may suggest that the activation depends upon some relatively non-specific parametric shifts that make gene-regulated specific synthetic pathways unstable or metastable and thus open to certain relatively weak and not too specific dynamical perturbations. The latter may well be related to CMT. Their role in promotion of the expression of specific genes has been demonstrated in several cases (e.g. Nielsen *et al.*, 1983).

It should be remembered that the increase in the rate of cytoskeletal protein synthesis and/or of membrane fluidity almost inevitably leads to clustering of cytoskeleton or membrane components and thus to the generation of local mechanical and/or electrical forces (e.g. Larter and Ortoleva, 1982). The latter should generate some spatial and temporal structures with T_{ch} and L_{ch} greater than those of CMT but certainly much smaller than those of the genetic parameters. For genetic parameters T_{ch} may be taken as the reverse mutation frequency which Dobzhansky's (1970) estimations exceeds by 5-6 orders the average life cycle duration. L_{ch} for the same parameters should be formally estimated as the total physical volume of a genetically homogeneous population. Whatever the importance of the new data and suggestions on genome fluidity, somatic mutations etc., it can hardly be denied that the genome remains the most conservative among life cycle parameters.

Let us specify these suggestions taking as an example some aspects of morphogenesis of two remote groups of animals, amphibians and hydroid polyps. In early amphibian development, from late blastula up to neurula, several regular mechanically stressed cell patterns successively exchanging each other can be traced (Beloussov *et al.*, 1975). Each of them consists of a domain of polarised epithelial cells flanked by elasticity stretched and tangentially flattened parts of epithelia. The average life-time T_{ch} for these structures is a few hours and their diameter L^{ch} is about 10^2–10^3 μm (the best known example of such a domain is the neural plate). All these domains arise by a common process, namely by the movement of a cell polarisation wave with a rate of several microns per minute (which means that the polarisation of an individual cell takes several minutes). In the model elaborated by Belintzev et al. (1987) the formation of the polarised cell domains in a coherent epithelial layer with fixed edges is a self-regulated process since the domain's enlargement is limited by the tangential stretching of the flanking layer's regions caused by cell polarisation. In terms of interaction levels the model may be formulated as follows.

A certain generalised mechanochemical parameter M is introduced which is the same for all the cells of a layer and depends upon their biochemical and mechanical properties, in the latter instance genetically determined. Hence, T_{ch} and L_{ch} for this parameter level largely exceed those for the domains to be generated. If M does not exceed a first threshold value, a cell layer will have only one stable state in which it remains homogeneous and non-polarised. By M passing the first threshold the homogeneous state becomes metastable: a layer acquires a competence for cell polarisation and after a certain finite local polarising perturbation(s) segregates to the polarised and tangentially stretched domains, their relative lengths depending upon the parameter, but not the local perturbation(s) values. The model implies also a second threshold, after passing which the homogeneous cell state becomes completely unstable and the layer must be segregated after infinitesimal perturbations. This scheme (experimentally proved in some crucial respects) clearly demonstrates that the downward parametrising influences leading to the meta- or instability of a lower level together with the dynamical perturbations arising from this very level generate a new intermediate 'cell domain' level with its own non-pre-existing T_{ch} and L_{ch} specific for morphogenesis in the given species. Being generated by the initial meta- (in-) stability, this level acquires its own structural stability and may play the role of a new parametrisor for the lower level and of initial conditions for the same or upper level processes (see Beloussov *et al.*, 1985, for more details).

In hydroid polyps, growth and morphogenesis of vegetal generation is closely related to so-called growth pulsations (GP), cell reorientations of several minute periods caused by a complicated net of contractile, osmotic and electrochemical events (Beloussov *et al.*, 1984, 1988). The GP 'profiles' (their internal frequency-amplitude characteristics) are specific to species and clones and hence are genetically determined. As such, they represent an extremely clear example of genetically parametrised auto-oscillations based upon rapid electrochemical dynamics. GP create thus a new intermediate level with T_{ch} of several minutes order and L_{ch} corresponding to the distance passed by the 'cell reorientation wave' (Zaraisky *et al.*, 1984) within each GP. This distance is from 200 to 500 μm in length. Hydranth dimensions are of the same order of magnitude in the species studied.

Such a self-complicating interplay of different levels including the formation of new levels seems to be a fundamental property of biological development. Being well aware that the proposed list of developmental levels may be incomplete and even partially wrong I suggest nevertheless that the distinction of a limited number of discrete levels is a necessary condition for the adequate analysis of development including its genetic aspects.

The main general importance of the multilevelled approach is for me a direction of escape from the vicious circle of specificity, characteristic of modern biology. It needs, perhaps, a certain intellectual effort to accept that the highly specific and regularly localised events of biological development can be generated by interactions of vaguely spread, almost or completely constant parameters with some quite degenerative, occasionally localised dynamical perturbations, rather than by any strictly specific and precisely located events. However, such an effort seems to be necessary if we want to extricate ourselves from the preformistic and linearly deterministic deadlocks. The proposed approach should not be necessarily linked with the invention of mathematical models and may well be used by the classically minded biologists, either experimental or descriptive. All that is required is to address new questions to the age-old events, such as: What are the main levels of the process under study? What are the characteristic temporal and spatial dimensions of the level of particular interest? By what other level processes is it parametrised and/or dynamically perturbed? What are the spatio-temporal regions of its stability and instability? and so on. Even if the answers are rough and tentative they will manifest themselves in the attainment of a new level in our biological cognition.

REFERENCES

Belintsev, B. N, Beloussov, L. V. and Zaraisky, A. G. (1987) Model of pattern formation in epithelial morphogenesis. *J. theor. Biol.* 129. 369-94.
Beloussov, L. V., Chernavskii, D. S. and Solyanik, G. J. (1985) Applications of synergetics to ontogenesis (on parametric control of development). *Ontogenez (Sov. J. Develop. Biol.).* 16. 213-28.
——Dorfman, J. G. and Cherdantzev, V. G. (1975) Mechanical stresses and morphological patterns in amphibian embryos. *J. Embryol. exp. Morph.* 54. 553-74.
——Labas, Ju. A. and Badenko, L. A. (1984) Growth pulsations and rudiments shapes in hydroid polyps. *J. Obsch. Biol.* (Russ.) 45. 796-806.
——Labas, Ju. A., Kazakova, N. I. and Zaraisky, A. G. (1988) Cyrophysiology of growth pulsations in hydroid polypes. *J. Exp. Zool.* (in press).
Dobzhansky, T. (1970) *Genetics of the evolutionary process.* Columbia University Press, N.Y.-L. p.505.

Goldschmidt, R. (1955) *Theoretical Genetics*. University of California Press, Berkeley, Los Angeles. p.546.

Goodwin, B. (1976) *Analytical physiology of cells and developing organisms*. Academic Press, L., N.Y., San Francisco. p.287.

Larter, R. and Ortoleva, P. (1982) A study of instability to electrical symmetry breaking in unicellular systems. *J. theor. Biol.* 96. 175-200.

Nielsen, P., Goelz, S. and Trachsel, H. (1983) The role of the cytoskeleton in eukaryotic protein synthesis. *Cell Biol. Intern. Repts.* 7. 245-54.

Romanovskii, Ju. M., Stepanova, N. V. and Chernavskii, D. S. (1984) (Russ.). *Mathematical Biophysics*. Nauka, Moskva. p.304.

Thom, R. (1972) Structuralism and biology. In *Towards a theoretical biology*. C. H. Waddington, ed. Edinburgh University Press, Edinburgh. 68-82.

Waddington, C. H. (1957) *The Strategy of Genes*. Allen and Unwin, London. p.262.

Weiss, P. (1969) The living systems: determinism stratified. In *Beyond Reductionism; New Perspectives in the Life Sciences*. A. Koestler (ed.). J. R. Smythies, London. 3-55.

Zaraisky, A. G., Beloussov, L. V., Labas, Ju. A. and Badenko, L. A. (1984) Studies of cellular mechanisms of growth pulsations in hydroid polypes. *Ontogenez Sov. J. Develop. Biol.* 15. 163-70.

Zeeman, Ch. (1972) Differential equations for the heartbeat and nerve impulse. In *Towards a theoretical biology*. C. H. Waddington (ed.). Edinburgh University Press, Edinburgh. 8-67.

11. Structuralism in Evolutionary Biology and Systematics

Leendert van der Hammen

The results summarised in the present chapter are based on studies of the comparative morphology, systematics and evolution of Chelicerata (see Van der Hammen, 1979, 1982, 1985a, 1985b, 1986b, 1986c, 1988b). The choice of this group appeared to have a number of important advantages: Chelicerata are segmented animals, of which the postembryonic development is characterised by moulting and the occurrence of a series of separate instars; besides that, parthenogenesis is found in several groups of mites. The origin of segmentation (a key event in the evolution of the Metazoa) must be partly connected with a repeated manifestation of the same genotypic information; it is often followed, in the course of evolution, by the superimposed manifestation of divergency (probably as a result of specific genetic and developmental interactions). A postembryonic development which is characterised by moulting, has the advantage that a restricted (and often fixed) number of levels of transformation can be distinguished (the manifestation of changes is concentrated at distinctly separated levels, by which an analysis is facilitated). The occurrence of parthenogenesis, finally, has the advantage that the manifestation of certain variations can be analysed not only in bisexual populations, but also in clones; in the case of the present research, this analysis has led to the concept of evolutionary potentiality and the concept of probability of manifestation (see Van der Hammen, 1981b; 1988a, 23-63).

Simultaneously with my practical investigations in the fields of morphology, systematics and evolution, I have made studies of certain theoretical aspects of these disciplines (Van der Hammen, 1978, 1981a, 1981b, 1983, 1985c, 1986a, 1986d; a revised version of these papers is now included in Van der Hammen, 1988a). One of these studies pertained to the eighteenth- and nineteenth-century type-concept, which I developed into a hierarchic model of the evolutionary potentialities of a group (this type represents, in fact, the model of a structure in the structuralist sense).

EVOLUTION

The results of the investigations, which are the subject of this section, have from the outset been at variance with the current views on evolution. For this reason, it is inevitable to start the evolutionary part of the present chapter with some remarks on the theory of evolution (these remarks do not constitute an explanatory theory, but the theoretical framework necessary for a structuralist approach). The deep structure underlying evolution must be regarded as a growing structure, of which the manifestation at the surface ('self-expression') has various aspects, among which, e.g. conformity to the type of organisation inherited, determination by certain fundamental properties of matter and life, and 'adaptation'. 'Adaptation' is defined here as the condition of an organism (or an organic structure), of being adapted, of showing particular fitness for particular situations which are part of its environment. The manifestation of evolution at the surface is the result of a co-ordination of internal and external factors, i.e. genotype and environment. The laws of transformation, however, are in the genotype which is consequently characterised by the possession of evolutionary potentialities. It may be remarked here that, in this connection, the genotype is interpreted cybernetically as a programme of action and reaction. The essential elements of this theoretical framework were introduced more than a century ago by the philosopher Teichmüller (1877). It arose from his discussions with K. E. von Baer (whose evolutionary views are expounded in Von Baer, 1876; 49-105, 170-480; and Stölzle, 1897; 195-289). Teichmüller remained unknown in evolutionary biology until he was rediscovered by me some years ago (see Van der Hammen, 1981a; 28; 1983; 1987-8; 1988a; 10, 126). The philosophical roots of a structuralist approach in the study of evolution, however, reach back to antiquity (see Van der Hammen, 1988a). They include Aristotle's form concept, the Scholastic concept of substantial form, Leibniz's concepts of substantial form and monad, and the eighteenth- and nineteenth-century type-concept. They include also the idea of a scale of nature, which presupposes increasing complexity. Evolution must indeed be regarded as the gradual unfoldment of possibilities, and the manifestation of potentialities.

The growth of the deep structure underlying organic evolution (the increase of the amount of information) started with the origination of primordial life, and progressed when living substances began to exist as definite bodies, and when reliable methods of self-replication and bisexual reproduction arose. The first important ascent in the scale of increasing complexity consisted in the origination of multicellular organisms, whilst the origin of many metazoan phyla is probably closely connected with the subsequent origin of segmentation. In the introduction, I have already mentioned the importance of a structuralist approach in the study of segmentation and the recognition of two levels: a level of similarity and a superimposed level of divergency. The origination and subsequent evolution of segmentation is an event of which a hypothetical explanation in terms of genetic control is of paramount importance; a similar explanation of Lankester's so-called laws of metamerism (see Lankester, 1902, 1904) would also be of great interest.

My structuralist approach in the study of evolution, i.e. my search for laws underlying the manifestation of evolution, is demonstrated here with the help of four completely different subjects: numerical changes in patterns of setae and setiform organis, evolutionary changes in the life-cycle, the evolution of the appendages, and transformation of form.

LAWS UNDERLYING NUMERICAL CHANGES IN PATTERNS OF SETAE AND SETIFORM ORGANS

Many details with reference to a hierarchy of systems of transformation are now known in the case of numerical changes in patterns of setae and setiform organs in Actinotrichid mites (a superorder of Chelicerata). Data pertaining to these changes have recently been summarised by me (see Van der Hammen, 1981b, 1985c, 394-397; 1988a, 23-63, 148-51).

A detailed study of these numerical variations (also in clones) has revealed that evolutionary changes of this kind are based on an evolutionary potentiality, and have a certain probability of manifestation. They are not immediately hereditary, because the offspring inherits again a certain probability of manifestation (which kind of manifestation is similar in the cases of parthenogenetic and bisexual reproduction). Manifestation is originally unilateral (although it can be bilateral in cases of a high probability of manifestation), and a mathematical analysis reveals that manifestation and distribution of similar changes in a pattern are due to a number of elementary processes (the influence of individual strength and priority, a complicated balance within the pattern as a whole). Probability of manifestation can increase or decrease in the course of evolution, and manifestation of changes is apparently based on changes in systems of genotypic interactions (which generally manifest themselves in the course of postembryonic development). It appears that structural genes for setae and setiform organs are similar in all species of Actinotrichid mites, and that a great variety of different patterns arose by differences in regulatory programmes (different mechanisms can, however, influence the same element: similar changes in the same element are not always homologous). Evolutionary changes in numbers of individual setae (in the course of evolution, the level of postembryonic manifestation can be subject to change) can be associated with translocations in the pattern as a whole; it has appeared that the changes can be co-ordinated with changes in the environment. Numerical evolution is greatly influenced by the unequal resistance of the elements to regression and multiplication, as a result of which certain numbers and patterns are more common than others. It appears that, in the course of evolution, regular patterns and fixed numbers gradually arose from chaotic patterns and numbers; fixed numbers can subsequently be subject to regression as well as multiplication (Figure 1). One of the deepest layers of the structure underlying the evolution of setae and seta-like organs appears to pertain to segmentation.

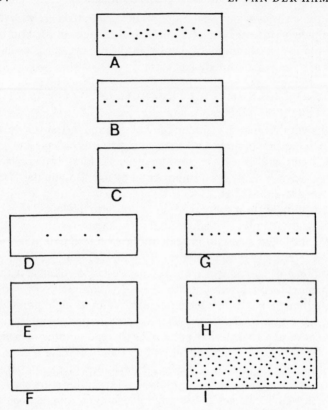

Figure 1. Schematic representation (a rectangle representing a segment) of the various stages in the evolution of chaetotaxy in Actinotrichida; A, primordiotrichy (ancestral chaotic chaetotoaxy); B, hypertrichy (presence of setae in regular numbers surpassing that of normal holotrichy); C, holotrichy (chaetotaxy characterised by the presence, in regular numbers, of all the setae normally present in a natural group); D, E, meiotrichy (chaetotaxies characterised by the presence of setae in regular, but reduced numbers); F, atrichosy (absence of a setae as a result of regression); G-I, neotrichy (secondary formation of setae by multiplication); G, cosmiotrichy (neotrichy with simple recognisable disposition of setae); H, oligotrichy (weakly developed neotrichy); I, plethotrichy (neotrichy with numerous, chaotically arranged, setae). Primordiotrichy and hypertrichy are not (or not yet, or not always) distinguishable from neotrichy.

LAWS UNDERLYING CHANGES IN THE CHELICERATE LIFE-CYCLE

Evolutionary changes in the chelicerate life-cycle pertain to the number of successive forms as well as to the morphology of the forms and the types of moulting (types of moulting are not discussed in the present paper). Three types of forms can be distinguished: (1) forms which are the result of growing moults or repetition moults which bring no change, except in size (isophena); (2) and (3) forms which are the result of moults that are associated with morphological changes (instars). In a life-cycle, instars can occur in variable

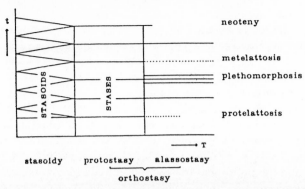

Figure 2. Model of the evolution of the chelicerate life-cycle (ontophylogenetic diagram; t = ontogentic time, T = phylogentic time). The hypothesis is that the evolution of the life-cycle has started with stasoids (instars which are morphologically different from the preceding and following instars by discontinuous characters, but which occur in variable number, so that they cannot be homologised with instars in other specimens and taxa of the same group) and presented only one immature phase (consisting of nymphoids). It is supposed that a life-cycle with stases (instars which are, as in the case of stasoids, morphologically different from the preceding and following instars, but which occur in fixed numbers, by which they can be homologised with instars in other specimens and taxa of the same group) arose from a life-cycle with stasoids, by which two evolutionary periods can be distinguished: stasoidy and orthostasy. It is further supposed that the ancestral number of stases has, in all cases, been six (protostasy; as still found in several groups). By divergent phylogeny of the levels, different phases can have arisen (prelarval, larval, nymphal and adult). In the course of evolution, various levels of the ancestral protostasic life-cycle can have been subject to changes (alassostasy), including regressive evolution (protelattosis and metelattosis), the attainment of maturity at previously immature levels (neoteny), and the formation of isophena, i.e., forms which are the result of growing or repetition moults (plethomorphosis). It is evident that, at a certain stage of evolution, stasoids and stases can occur in one and the same life-cycle. The possibility cannot be excluded that, as to phylogeny, the model could be read in both directions, and that a third period (neostasoidy) should be recognised, which is still indistinguishable from stasoidy.

numbers, by which condition they cannot be homologised with similar instars in other life-cycles (stasoids); or they occur in fixed numbers, by which condition they can be homologised with similar instars in other life-cycles (stases). It is supposed that the evolution of the chelicerate life-cycle started from a life-cycle with one immature phase comprising an irregular number of stasoids. Several groups of Chelicerata are characterised by the occurrence of a so-called protostasic life-cycle with a fundamental number of six stases. At a certain stage of evolution, stasoids and stases can occur in one and the same life-cycle. By divergent phylogenies of the levels of postembryonic development, different phases can have arisen (prelarval, larval, nymphal, adult). In the course of evolution, various levels of the protostasic life-cycle can be subject to changes, including regressive evolution (protelattosis and metelattosis), the attainment of maturity at previously immature levels (neoteny) and the formation of isophena at certain levels of development (plethomorphosis). A model of the evolution of the chelicerate life-cycle is represented in Figure 2.

The fundamental number of six stases has arisen several times in different groups, by parallel evolution; the potentiality for a manifestation of this number is apparently a general character of the Chelicerata (it is part of the chelicerate evolutionary programme). The general laws of the numerical evolution of instars (chaotic number — fixed number — decrease or increase in number) are apparently similar to those of the numerical evolution of setae. The regressive evolution of the first instar(s) (protelattosis; it can extend to more than one level), is a general character of all Chelicerata (it is part of the chelicerate evolutionary programme). In Actinotrichid mites, other instars can also have been subject to regression (metelattosis), viz. the deutonymph in Acaridida, and the proto- and tritonymph in Trombidina; in these cases the evolutionary phenomena are manifestations of the evolutionary programmes of groups of lower taxonomic rank.

LAWS UNDERLYING THE EVOLUTION OF THE CHELICERATE APPENDAGES

Chelicerata (with the exception of Xiphosura) differ from other Arthropods by the fact that the main promotor-remotor movement is at the coxa-trochanter or body-trochanter joint, and not at the body-coxa joint. In the case of Xiphosura, it is supposed that coxae were first associated with ingestion only (adduction and abduction), as in Opilionida and Scorpionida, and subsequently became also associated with locomotion (see Van der Hammen, 1988b). It has now become evident that coxae have evolved, relatively late, from epimera (the sternites of the prosoma) by a gradual separation of these from the sternal exoskeleton, a gradual increase in movability, and a subsequent extension in antiaxial direction (associated with the inclusion of pleural regions). Epimera are present in Palpigradi, Actinotrichida, Solifugae and Pseudoscorpionida. The coxae of Arachnida s. str. (Uropygi, Amblypygi, Araneida) demonstrate the gradual transition from coxae with ventral position and slight movability to coxae with lateral position and increased movability. The problem of the homologisation of leg segments (podomeres) is now definitely solved: the main promotor-remotor movement is (with the exception of Xiphosura) at the base of the trochanter; a levator-depressor movement is at the pivot join between trochanter and femur (in case this joint is repeated, there is a second trochanter); a knee with a hinge joint is present between femur and patella (genu) or tibia (in the case of a second femur, an extra hinge joint is present between the trochanter-femur and the knee joint); patella, tibia and tarsus can easily be recognised because of the number of true (eudesmatic) articulations in the descending part of the leg (the articulation between basi- and telotarsus, if present, is adesmatic). This original pattern can be changed by secondary transformations (the origination of rocking joints from privot joints, the origination of extensor muscles in hinge joints, etc.), but generally remains recognisable. The following model of the evolution of the chelicerate appendages has now been prepared by me (see Van der Hammen, 1985a, 50-1; 1985c, 400-3, figs. 4-5; 1988b; see also figure 3).

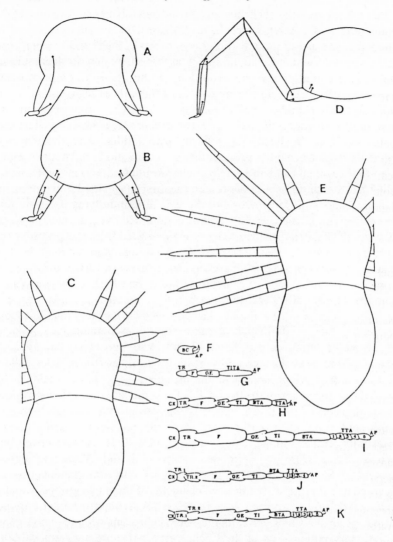

Figure 3. Stages in the evolution of the chelicerate appendages; A, B, single body-segment, with pair of limbs, of hypothetical Anthropod in transverse section; A, with lobopodia; B, with archepodia; C, dorsal view of hypothetical Arthropod with archepodia; D, single body-segment with left limb, in transverse section, of hypothetical Chelicerate with protopodia; E, dorsal view of hypothetical Chelicerate with three-segmented limb 1, and five-segmented protopodia (limbs 2-6); F-K, appendages of the adult of a group of extant Chelicerata (Ricinulei) in dorsal view; F, chelicera; G, palp; H, leg I; leg II; J, leg III; K, leg IV. Notations: AP, apotele; BC, body of the chelicera; BTA, basitarsus; CX, coxa; F, femur; GE, genu; TI, tibia; TITA, tibiotarsus; TR, trochanter; TR.1, trochanter 1; TR.2, trochanter 2; TTA, telotarsus; TTA.1-5, telotarsus 1-5.

Because the six pairs of chelicerate appendages (chelicera, palp and legs) are homonomous structures which have developed by parallel evolution from lobopodia, the ancestral number of the segments of the chelicera (three) could be the original number for all the appendages (archepodia; the deepest level of the structure underlying the evolution of the chelicerate appendages is apparently common to all the appendages); these three segments are usually called trochanter, body (of the chelicera) and apotele (or claw-segment). This number of segments could have occurred in short-legged species which stood up on their legs. In chelicerate embryos, palp and legs first divide into four segments: prototrochanter, protofemur, prototibia and prototarsus. A leg with these four segments and an apotele or claw-segment (i.e. five segments: a so-called protopodium) could represent the first stage in the evolution of a hanging stance (this second level of the structure underlying the evolution of the chelicerate appendages is apparently common to five pairs of appendages). All types of chelicerate palps and legs can be derived from this primitive type. As mentioned above, free coxae arose from epimera, and can include pleural regions. Protopodia arose from archepodia, either by a further subdivision of segments, or by the addition of projecting parts of the body (see Van der Hammen, 1985a: 50). Because trochanter 2, in Anactinotrichida, disappears by suppression, it must originally have evolved by repeated manifestation of the same genotypic information. Because femur 2, in Actinotrichida, disappears by fusion of femur 1 and femur 2 (see Van der Hammen, 1982: 38), fusion takes place by the regression and disappearance of the muscles, followed by the gradual disappearance of the articulation), it must originally have evolved by subdivision of the femur. Patella (genu) and tibia originally evolved by subdivision of the prototibia; it is interesting that this subdivision has manifested itself in two different ways: the patella-tibia articulation is, ancestrally, either a hinge joint or a pivot joint. It is also interesting that a second femur arose in Epimerata (Palpigradi and Actinotrichida) and Apatellata (Solifugae and Pseudoscorpionida) only; its presence must be regarded as a unique shared derived character of these two groups (which are now regarded as constituting a separate class). A second trochanter is found in various groups of Chelicerata; its presence is apparently founded on a general evolutionary potentialiity of the Chelicerata. It is quite understandable that repetition of information, in the case of trochanter 2, is a shared evolutionary potentiality of all Chelicerata, but that division of the femur (the development of new characters) is a shared derived character of some groups only.

The data mentioned in this subsection demonstrate that it has been possible to reconstruct the general laws underlying the evolution of the chelicerate appendages, as well as the hierarchy of evolutionary programmes. It may, finally, be remarked here that, from a certain moment in evolution (probably coinciding with the beginning of terrestrial life), there apparently arose a tendency towards a decrease in the number of segments in the ascending part of the legs, and a tendency towards an increase in the descending part.

LAWS UNDERLYING TRANSFORMATION OF FORM

Three-dimensional changes of form are more difficult to analyse than simple numerical changes. These can, however, also be understood as the result of changes in systems of genotypic interactions and the changes of growth-rates involved in it. When Darwin was still alive, Von Baer (see Von Baer, 1876: 49-105, 170-480; Stölzle, 1897: 195-289) gave already as his view that transmutation is a process of change manifesting itself in the course of ontogeny, and resulting in important (i.e. discontinuous) modifications. (Modifications are, generally, more important as they manifest themselves earlier in embryonic development.) Since D'Arcy Thompson (1917) we know that, in a taxon, differences in form (even important ones) can be explained in terms of relative growth (he analysed transformation of form by the method of co-ordinates). Needham (1936) remarked that nobody had applied D'Arcy Thompson's method to embryology and morphogenesis, whilst growth-rate and differentiation-rate yet seem to be aligned with one another.

Considerable progress could already be made when differences in form were analysed in great detail in a single taxon, e.g. in all representatives of a genus, so that all transformations could be understood as resulting from changing growth rates. (An analysis of this kind was carried out by Gould (1984) for the case of shells of the Gastropod genus *Cerion*.) This type of research will certainly be time consuming, but the results will probably be of great value: laws underlying transformation of form could, in this way, be disclosed.

EVOLUTIONARY CONCLUSION

Although the structuralist approach in the study of evolution has been demonstrated with the help of four groups of phenomena only, it is evident that, in this way, general laws underlying the manifestation of evolution can be disclosed, and that these laws pertain to hierarchic systems of interactions and the gradual manifestation of evolutionary potentialities. Each level of the hierarchic system of interactions represents the realisation of potentialities and includes new potentialities. Taxa are apparently characterised by evolutionary programmes of which generally, at a certain moment of evolution, not all parts have become manifest (manifestation is supposed here to be regulated cybernatically). It has also been demonstrated that evolutionary changes can be represented schematically by diagrams, etc. Evidently, it is possible to represent all the evolutionary potentialities of a taxon by a series of similar diagrams. A complete series of these diagrams, hierarchically arranged, will represent what I have called the archetype of a group (Van der Hammen, 1981a): the complete representation of its evolutionary potentialities and their modes of manifestation. The construction of such an archetype (a model of the deep structure) is within our reach, although it presupposes a wide field of research. Realisation of this project will again be time consuming, but I am convinced that, after the construction of a model of the deep structure of a group, and after the mathematical analysis of the complicated correlations, etc., something of the process of evolution will at last be understood.

CLASSIFICATION

From a structuralist point of view, data supplied by the study of the overall similarity of representatives of a taxon, constitute a surface structure which is a reflection of relations at the levels of deeper structures. Whilst a phenetic classification is evidently based on a surface structure, evolutionary and phylogenetic classifications should be based on the deep structure (a hierarchy of synchronic systems). A model of this hierarchy is constituted by the archetype as defined in the previous section. It will be evident that, once the archetype has been constructed, classifications based on it will easily be comparable and even more or less similar. Brooks and Wiley (1985) recently argued that the deep structure of systematic techniques is constituted by systematic theory. This is not a very fruitful idea, because theory is a man-made structure which has no direct relationship to the naturalness of a classification (evolutionary or phylogenetic).

In the previous section, it was pointed out that the hierarchy of deep structure is characterised by the presence of evolutionary potentialities which can manifest themselves separately (and discontinuously) by parallel evolution. I repeat here that parallel evolution (see Van der Hammen, 1986a) should be regarded as the separate manifestation, at the level of the surface structure, of identities at the level of the deep structure. The important difference between the evolutionary potentialities of the deep structure and their manifestation at the surface, is generally not taken into account in current work in the field of phylogenetic systematics. It is now evident that branching points in a scheme underlying phylogenetic classification should correspond with the separation of systems of transformation and evolutionary programmes, and not with the manifestation of their evolutionary potentiali-ties at the level of the surface structure (the distinction between the development of new potentialities, on the one hand, and changes in systems of interactions, on the other, should constitute one of the foundations of taxonomy). It is also evident that the hierarchy of the natural classification should correspond with the hierarchy of deep structures. In the previous section, it has been demonstrated that evolutionary changes in chaetotaxy, life-cycle and segmentation of the appendages, can be attributed to definite levels in the hierarchy of systems of transformation and, as a consequence of this, to definite levels in the hierarchy of the natural system. The structuralist approach (it could be characterised as structuralist taxonomy) is particularly important in the case of higher classification, and it decisively influenced my final view of the higher classification of Chelicerata (see Van der Hammen, 1986c, 224-8, fig. 3; 1988b). Particularly at the supraordinal levels, current taxonomic methods tend to develop atomistic views in which the organism as a functional whole has virtually no place, and in which the hierarchic value of characters is not sufficiently analysed and discussed. It is evident that, pre-eminently in this field, the structuralist approach will advance the naturalness of a classification.

REFERENCES

Baer, K. E. von (1876) Reden gehalten in wissenschaftlichen Versammlungen und kleinere Aufsätze vermischten Inhalts, 2. Studien auf dem Gebiete der Naturwissenschaften. St Petersburg. xxvi. 408pp. 22 Figs.

Brooks, D. R. and Wiley, E. O. (1985) Theories and methods in different approaches to phylogenetic systematics. *Cladistics*. 1. 1-11.

Gould, S. J. (1984) Morphological channelling by structural constraint: convergence in styles of dwarfing and gigantism in Cerion, with a description of two new fossil species and a report on the discovery of the largest Cerion. *Paleobiology*. 10. 172-94. Figs. 1-14. Tab. 1-8.

Hammen, L. van der (1978) The evolution of the chelicerate life-cycle. *Acta Biotheoretica*. 27. 44-60. Figs. 1-6.

——(1979) Comparative studies in Chelicerata I. The Cryptognomae (Ricinulei, Architarbi and Anactinotrichida). *Zool. Verh. Leiden*. 174. 1-62. Figs. 1-31.

——(1981a) Type-concept, higher classification and evolution. *Acta Biotheoretica*. 30. 3-48. Figs. 1-7.

——(1981b) Numerical changes and evolution in Actinotrichid mites (Chelicerata). *Zool. Verh. Leiden*. 182. 1-48. Figs. 1-13.

——(1982) Comparative studies in Chelicerata II. Epimerata (Palpigradi and Actinotrichida). *Zool. Verh. Leiden*. 196. 1-70. Figs. 1-31.

——(1983) Unfoldment and manifestation. The natural philosophy of evolution. *Acta Biotheoretica*. 32. 179-93.

——(1985a) Comparative studies in Chelicerata III. Opilionida. *Zool. Verh. Leiden*. 220. 1-60. Figs. 1-34.

——(1985b) Functional morphology and affinities of extant Chelicerata in evolutionary perspective. *Trans. Roy. Soc. Edinburgh. Earth Sciences*. 76. 137-46. Figs. 1-8.

——(1985c) A structuralist approach in the study of evolution and classification. *Zool. Med. Leiden*. 59. 391-409. Figs. 1-5.

——(1986a) On some aspects of parallel evolution in Chelicerata. *Acta Biotheoretica*. 35. 15-37. Figs. 1-9.

——(1986b) Comparative studies in Chelicerata IV. Apatellata, Arachnida, Scorpionida, Xiphosura. *Zool. Verh. Leiden*. 226. 1-52. Figs. 1-23.

——(1986c) Acarological and arachnological notes. *Zool. Med. Leiden*. 60. 217-30. Figs. 1-3.

——(1986d) Some notes on taxonomic methodology. *Zool. Med. Leiden*. 60. 231-56.

——(1988a) *Unfoldment and manifestation. Seven essays on evolution and classification*. SPB Academic Publishing, The Hague. xii. 181 pp. 33 Figs.

——(1988b) *An introduction to comparative arachnology*. SPB Academic Publishing, The Hague. x. 576 pp. 302 Figs.

Lankester, E. R. (1902) Arthropoda. *Encyclopaedia Britannica* (10th edition). 25. 689-701. 11 Figs.

——(1904) The structure and classification of the Arthropoda. *Quart. Journ. Micr. Sci.* (N.S.) 47. 523-82. Pl. 42.

Needham, J. (1936) *Order and Life*. Yale University Press. [I have used the paperback edition, Cambridge, Mass. & London (The M I T Press) 1968. xxii. 175 pp.] 45 Figs.

Stölzle, R. (1897) *Karl Ernst von Baer und seine Weltanschauung*. Regensburg. xii. 688 pp.

Teichmüller, G. (1877) *Darwinismus und Philosophie*. Dorpat. viii. 90 pp.

Thompson, D'Arcy W. (1917) *On growth and form*. Cambridge University Press. [I have used the 1977 reprint of the abridged paperback edition, edited by J. T. Bonner (Cambridge University Press). In this edition, the chapter On the Theory of Transformation, or the Comparison of Related Forms is found on pp. 268-325.]

12. Sexual Differentiation and Mate Recognition: the Dynamics of Structure

A. J. Hughes and D. M. Lambert

In a series of lectures about gender, sex and society delivered at Berkeley in 1982, Ivan Illich remarked that never before had so many colleagues and friends attempted to dissuade him from a task on which he had embarked. He said: 'Most felt that I should turn my attention to something less trivial, less ambiguous, or less scabrous; others insisted that, in the present crisis of feminism, talk about women was not for men. Listening carefully, I came to see that most of my interlocutors felt uneasy because my reasoning interfered with their dreams.' What Illich intended to convey, we think, is that almost everyone has strong ideas of one sort or another about 'sex'. There is nothing at all surprising about that. It is also to be expected that the majority will not be sure where many of their attitudes have come from. This occurs in part because much of our cultural perspective on 'sex' lies in the realm of the 'tacit component' (Polanyi, 1958) and is therefore not easily explicated. In other words, hidden social attitudes have to a large extent determined our collective 'way of seeing' sexual phenomena (Hughes and Lambert, 1984). For biologists this presents an especially serious difficulty, and we will argue that therein lies the primary reason why biology has failed so far to address the complexity of 'sex' and 'sexuality' in an adequate manner.

A structuralist analysis of recent developmental and neuroendocrine data suggests that a new theoretical approach may now be possible. Clearly it is first necessary to understand how sexual differentiation and mate recognition operate in the lifetime of individual organisms before broad models can be developed. Of fundamental importance is the realisation that sexual differentiation and mate recognition have common developmental origins. Because it is impossible to consider them independently of each other, many of the assumptions that now parameterise these fields must be discarded. The central challenge remains to formulate a new 'way of seeing' that does not derive directly from cultural attitudes, the keyword field of functionalist biology (Lambert and Hughes, 1986), or concepts of what is 'normal' and what is 'abnormal'.

Sexual differentiation and mate recognition are dynamic phenomena and their correct frame of reference is the whole organism as it develops through

143

time. Jantsch (1980) is explicit on this point: 'What is meant here is not merely a spatial structure. In connection with dynamic systems, the notion of a space-time structure is in the focus, in other words, the arrangement of processes in space and time.' Similarly, Bohm (1965) talks of space-time as a discrete 'structural process'. He says: 'By "structural process" we refer to a set of "space-like" elements as they move and unfold in the "process" of development.' So the 'space-time structure' of Jantsch (1980), the 'structural process' of Bohm (1965), the 'structuring' of Ho (1986) and the 'dynamic structure' referred to in this paper can, we think, be understood as broadly equivalent propositions. Using this perspective we will investigate some of the complex interrelationships between sexual differentiation and mate recognition in an attempt to unify these processes.

It has been appreciated for many years that complex sex determining mechanisms operate in insects (Bull, 1983), and these have been investigated using a number of different mutations which alter the 'normal' pathways of sexual differentiation (Hall, 1981; Cline, 1985). Such studies clearly indicate that there is no straightforward relationship between sex chromosomes and body form. For example, Sturtevant (1945) discovered a genetic mutant in *Drosophila melanogaster* called transformer located on chromosome 3 which, when in the homozygous condition in chromosomally female (xx) individuals, results in adults with male morphology. These flies court and mate with typical females but are always sterile. We are now aware of a range of mutations with similar effects, including a transformer-2 allele (tra-2) in which homozygous individuals develop male body form irrespective of their genetic sex (Cline, 1985).

In an important contribution Belote and Baker (1982) investigated the differentiation of sexual morphology in *Drosophila melanogaster* using a special tra-2 mutant (tra-2^m) which is inactivated at higher temperatures. Their experiments showed that the wild type (tra-2^+) gene-product triggers binary decisions involving the physically distinct male and female genital primordia. The tra-2^+ gene product apparently does not act early to establish a sexually determined cellular state, but rather is required throughout development to mediate all the steps necessary for 'normal' sexual differentiation. Belote and Baker (1982) found clear evidence that tra-2^+ prevents male development and stimulates the female genital primordium to differentiate into female structures. If it is not present, the cells of the male genital primordium differentiate in the male direction and all female development is suppressed.

Of course, sexual differentiation in *Drosophila* is not limited to external morphology alone. Direct evidence for this comes from the work of Hotta and Benzer (1976) who used mosaic fate mapping in conjunction with behavioural observation to locate the position within the body of discrete neurological structures which are sensitive to species-specific signals. Such centres are called foci and are known to be important in mate recognition (Hall, 1979). By the use of an unstable ring X chromosome Hotta and Benzer (1976) produced a range of sex mosaics in which some cells were chromosomally male (XY) and others were chromosomally female. Their experiments were possible because, unlike the situation in humans, XO cells in *Drosophila* are male. By studying such sex mosaics Tompkins and Hall (1983) confirmed that 'male' and 'female' foci in the anterior cortex of the brain differ significantly in morphology. They also showed that 'male differentiated' foci are required for the performance of courtship behaviours, and 'female differentiated' foci are essential for receptivity to copulation (Tompkins and Hall, 1983).

This conclusion is supported by comments in Benzer (1973) about a remarkable mutant of *Drosophila melanogaster* called 'fruity' which has subsequently been renamed 'gay'. Chromosomally male individuals homozygous for this mutation behave like females in that they stimulate other males to court them. 'Gay' male flies exhibit the same three stage mate recognition sequence seen in all 'normal' females. They do not reject courting males, and they show the 'female' acceptance response to mounting which involves spreading the wings and lowering the tip of the abdomen. They are, however, morphologically male in almost every respect. We are currently investigating the hypothesis that 'gay' male flies have 'female differentiated' foci by examining the sp11 cells in the anterior cortex in conjunction with a detailed analysis of individual sexual behaviour patterns (Lambert *et al.*, 1985).

The plurality of sex determining mechanisms in insects (Bull, 1983) challenges the simple and attractive notion that XY means 'male' and XX means 'female'. In fact male birds are homogametic and no discrete sex chromosomes at all are to be found in turtles or a wide variety of other organisms (Bull, 1983). It is essential to break out of constrained modes of thinking if such systems of sexual development are to be properly understood.

In *Homo sapiens*, the bifurcation of sexual morphology is more directly dependent on the action of hormones than it is upon chromosomal make-up. At two months of age the human foetus is neither 'male' nor 'female'. As the type and quantity of sex hormone varies, so too does body form (Siiteri and Wilson, 1974). The external genitalia differentiate under the influence of androgens in months three and four after fertilisation (Feder, 1981), and sexual morphology also changes again drastically at puberty. Secondary sexual characteristics — in the male, beard growth, body hair, muscularity and deepening of the voice — normally appear at that time. However, the human foetus does not inevitably develop into distinctly 'male' or 'female' forms and a surprising range of intermediate sexual morphs are possible. Such 'intersexes' are called hermaphrodites.

Individuals exhibiting hermaphroditism have been traditionally classified according to their gonadal morphology into true hermaphrodites, male pseudohermaphrodites and female pseudohermaphrodites:

(a)   True hermaphrodites possess ovarian and testicular tissue in the same or opposite gonads of a single individual (Hall *et al.*, 1979). The differentiation of the genital tract is variable and the external genitalia are usually ambiguous.

(b)　Male pseudohermaphrodites possess testes exclusively but their genital ducts, external genitalia or both exhibit female morphological character-istics or those of an incompletely differentiated male.

(c)　Female pseudohermaphrodites possess ovaries exclusively but their external genitalia exhibit some masculine morphological characteristics.

Wilson and Foster (1985) have modified and expanded this general scheme to include a minimum of twenty-seven basic categories of 'anomalous' sexual development. It is clear from their classification that having 'male' sex chromosomes does not necessarily make the human body male. Consider, for example, the testicular feminisation syndrome in which chromosomally male foetuses with 'normal' testosterone production do not develop external male genitalia. Such individuals have testicular gonads but the tissues of the body are insensitive to androgens, so the appearance of the external genitalia is female. However, there is no uterus and only a short, blind-ending vagina and menstruation and fertility are missing (Madden *et al.*, 1975; Ehrhardt and Meyer-Bahlburg, 1981).

Similarly, having female sex chromosomes does not necessarily make the human body female. In the absence of testes there is an inherent tendency for the external genitalia to feminise, however a female foetus will masculinise if subjected to androgens from some extragonadal source. The degree of foetal masculinisation is determined by the stage of differentiation at the time of exposure (Wilson and Foster, 1985). For example, in the condition congenital adrenal hyperplasia (CAH) the cortex releases an excess of adrenal androgens from foetal life onward (Lee *et al.*, 1977) and as a result the external genitalia are masculinised. Because the internal genitalia develop well before the external genitalia, clear-cut dissociations of sexual morphology are possible (Ehrhardt and Meyer-Bahlburg, 1981; Dörner, 1985b). In fact six major subtypes of CAH alone have now been described and each has distinctive clinical and biochemical features (Wilson and Foster, 1985). Individuals with several different enzyme 'deficiencies' can even present the same outward appearance, which highlights the inadequacy of categorisations that are based exclusively on body form.

Just as external sexual morphology changes over time in a complex manner so too does the structure of the brain. The same hormones that control the former also influence the latter as the brain is an inseparable part of the developing foetus (Goy and McEwen, 1980; Arnold and Gorski, 1984). However, in the brain, sex hormones operate later in development and their effects are considerably more complex. Human male and female brains are broadly similar up to four months after fertilisation. Between months four and five sexual differentiation begins to occur, and it has recently been shown that several loci in the human brain are structurally quite different in adult males and females (Swaab and Fliers, 1985). Similar findings were previously reported in monkeys (Ayoub *et al.*, 1983) and rats (Döhler *et al.*, 1982). By selectively destroying these specific brain sites and noting the major effects on sexual behaviour (Arendash and Gorski, 1983), it can be inferred that these areas are directly involved in mate recognition (Vom Saal *et al.*, 1983; Baum, 1983).

It is also clear that sex hormone levels early in development exert a powerful influence on sexual behaviour after maturity (Clemens and Gladue, 1978; Payne, 1979; Meyer-Bahlburg and Ehrhardt, 1986). In addition, a number of specific hormonal effects — such as the conversion of 'male' sex hormones or androgens into 'female' sex hormones or oestrogens — appear to occur primarily in the brain (Feder, 1981; MacLusky and Naftolin, 1981). Of course this labelling is itself a major category mistake because sex hormones are not intrinsically either 'male' or 'female' (Breuer, 1980; Rose *et al.*, 1984). Both types are produced in the ovary, the testis and also in the adrenal cortex. It is now well established that differences in sexual morphology and sexual behaviour actually arise as a result of temporal fluctuations in the ratios of various androgens and oestrogens in target organs (Bardin and Catterall, 1981; Döhler *et al.*, 1986).

Because sexual differentiation of the brain occurs after that of the body, it is possible for a 'female mating centre' to develop in a 'male' body if sex hormone metabolism changes over time (Dörner and Kawakami, 1978). Dörner (1976) showed that it is possible to alter the sexual behaviour of a morphologically male rat by changing sex hormone levels immediately before the 'mating centre' develops. Thus a chromosomally and morphologically male rat can be induced to exhibit so-called 'female' sexual behaviour, including the distinctive lordosis response to mounting. It appears that this occurs at least in part because its sensory foci have been rendered structurally similar to those of morphological females. Such an animal is entirely receptive to male copulation — unlike typical males — and illustrates that the absolute independence of sex-specific brain differentiation from genetic sex is possible (Dörner, 1976). Similar results have recently been obtained in other mammals. For example, in pigs it has been known for some time that sexual differentiation of the brain occurs postnatally rather than *in utero*. So Ford (1983) castrated chromosomally and morphologically male pigs within forty-eight hours of birth and treated them thereafter with oestrogens. His experiments show clearly that attraction to mature males is a sexually dimorphic behavioural trait mediated by sex hormones.

The two studies discussed above by Dörner (1976) and Ford (1983) are especially significant because an overt attempt has been made to evaluate both sexual differentiation and mate recognition within a single coherent experimental protocol. In both cases the 'body sex' of the animal has been made to differ from its 'brain sex' by hormonal manipulation during critical periods of sex specific brain differentiation. This highlights the extraordinary category mistake involved in assigning 'sex' solely on the basis of external sexual morphology.

As we have already established, the human foetus is bipotential. In chromosomal males, testes develop from the undifferentiated gonads in about the seventh week of gestation. In contrast, ovarian development in chromosomal females does not begin until around the thirteenth week (Wilson and Foster, 1985). Testicular differentiation is controlled by the short arm of the Y chromosome and, once established, the testes secrete testosterone which sets the foetus on the 'male' as opposed to the 'female' developmental path. The external genitalia, like the gonads, develop from common primordia. In the female, the urogenital tubercle becomes the clitoris, the urogenital swellings the labia majora and the urogenital folds the labia minora. In the male, the urogenital tubercle becomes the glans penis, the urogenital folds the shaft of the penis, and the urogenital swellings the scrotum (Imperato-McGinley and Peterson, 1976).

It is now clear that, in males, not all events in the differentiation of the external genitalia are mediated by testosterone alone. Dihydrotestosterone (DHT), a 5 alpha-reduced enzyme metabolite, does not appear to be secreted by the foetal testes in appreciable quantities but is instead formed in the genital tissues themselves (Saenger et al., 1978). DHT acts in utero to induce the development of the male urethra and prostate, and in the urogenital tubercle, swellings and folds, to cause midline fusion, elongation and enlargment, thus leading to 'normal' male external genitalia. So in absence of the enzyme 5 alpha-reductase — which is responsible for the conversion of testosterone to DHT — 'anomalous' male sexual differentiation may be expected to occur. As it happens this phenomenon provides the best 'natural experiment' reported so far to investigate the relationship between sexual differentiation and mate recognition in humans.

Male pseudohermaphroditism caused by 5 alpha-reductase deficiency was first described by Imperato-McGinley et al. (1974) in thirty-eight affected subjects from twenty-three families located in the Dominican Republic. This was the first significant study of individuals who passed through childhood, adolescence and adulthood without medical intervention, and, consequently, without alteration of the natural history of the phenomenon (Imperato-McGinley et al., 1980). In all the Dominican families, males with 5 alpha-reductase deficiency were born with marked feminisation of the external genitalia and as a result were raised unambiguously as girls. At birth they had bilateral undescended testes, a labial-like scrotum, a urogenital sinus with a blind vaginal pouch and a clitoral-like phallus (Imperato-McGinley et al., 1974). Affected individuals first began to notice that they were different between seven and twelve years of age (Imperato-McGinley et al., 1979a). At puberty, the voice deepened and typical male body form developed with a striking increase in muscle mass. Breast enlargement was completely absent. The penis grew to adult proportions and was capable of erection. The scrotum rugated and hyperpigmented, the testes descended from the inguinal canal, and ejaculation was possible but only from the urethral opening located on the perineum. However, the prostate remained small, beard growth was scanty, and there was no temporal recession of the hairline or male pattern body hair. These latter events appear to be mediated directly by DHT. In contrast it is significant that in all cases examined spermatogenesis was complete with a normal epididymis, vas deferens, seminal vesicles and ejaculatory duct. Because these subjects had testosterone levels in the high normal range, it can be inferred that sexual differentiation of almost all the internal male genitalia is controlled by testosterone. Indeed, the biosynthesis and peripheral action of testosterone was normal throughout development in affected individuals (Imperato-McGinley *et al.*, 1979b).

One major issue remains to be considered. What effect, if any, does 5 alpha-reductase deficiency have on the sexual differentiation of the brain? The question is particularly significant because it has been accepted by most authorities for the last twenty-five years that 'sex of rearing' — that is 'learning' over the first three or four years of life — determines both gender identity and sexual orientation in humans (Money and Ehrhardt, 1972; Money, 1984, 1985). ('Gender identity' is defined here as the belief that one is either male or female, while 'sexual orientation' is the direction of sexual attraction, for example, male to female or male to male.) In the Dominican study 'sex of rearing' and testosterone mediated biological sex were clearly discordant. Moreover, unlike many cases of pseudohermaphroditism, no apparent social stigma or medical intervention of any kind — such as castration and oestrogen supplementation — occurred that may have overriden or masked the 'normal' sexual differentiation of the brain. Families and neighbours accepted without difficulty the transition at puberty from 'female' to 'male' in affected individuals.

Imperato-McGinley *et al.* (1979b) present psychosexual data which indicates that at puberty seventeen out of eighteen subjects had changed to an unambiguous male gender identity. This gradually evolved over several years as individuals passed through stages of no longer feeling they were girls, to the feeling that they probably were men and finally to the conscious awareness that they were indeed men. Furthermore, fifteen of the eighteen subjects were married or living with a woman at the time of the study and so it appears that 'sex of rearing' has not determined eventual sexual orientation either. Instead, and not altogether surprisingly, high testosterone levels have resulted in parts of the brain differentiating in the 'male' direction (Imperato-McGinley *et al.*, 1979b). These data also strongly suggest that gender identity and sexual orientation in the human male are testosterone rather than DHT mediated phenomena.

Normally 'sex of rearing' and sexual differentiation of the brain occur in unison. However, if they are discordant, hormonal factors will prevail if the complete events of adolescence are permitted to occur. Most other cases of 5 alpha-reductase deficiency that have been reported were either castrated prepubertally or during puberty. Such procedures do not alter androgen induction in utero or neonatally, but do perturb or eliminate the androgen activation process that characterise male puberty.

Imperato-McGinley *et al.* (1980) present one further unmanipulated case of 5 alpha-reductase deficiency that supports all the conclusions of the Dominican studies. Their sixty-five-year-old male subject was born in southern Italy and raised as a girl. He emigrated to the United States at sixteen years of age, and retrospective psychosexual evaluation indicates that he gradually changed from a strong female to a strong male gender identity at puberty. He reported numerous sexual experiences with women, including two sexual relationships of greater than ten years duration. However, due to a strict and non-supportive family environment, he continued to present himself publicly as a woman, despite the fact his voice, muscle development and general body form were unmistakably 'masculine'. This example illustrates particularly clearly the extent to which social expectations can obscure the biology of sexual differentiation and mate recognition in humans. Imperato-McGinley *et al.* (1979b, 1980) have provided us with some good evidence that sexual orientation is not 'learned' but their work is often ignored or misinterpreted. They have also, as it happens, compiled a persuasive case for the elimination of the conceptual dichotomy between 'normal' and 'abnormal' in biology as a whole (Birke, 1982).

Recently Dörner (1985a, 1985b) has attempted to synthesise data from a broad range of experimental and clinical fields into a general theory of sex-specific brain development in humans. His model is based on three quasi-independent neurological centres which differentiate over distinct 'critical periods'. Dörner (1985a) hypothesizes that:

(a) The 'sex centre' controlling 'female-type' (cyclic) or 'male-type' (tonic) gonadotropin secretion is organised by oestrogens or by androgens which are metabolised in the brain to oestrogens, but not by non-convertible androgens.

(b) The 'mating centre' controlling sexual orientation differentiates as a result of the antagonistic effects of oestrogens and androgens which are both convertible and non-convertible to oestrogens.

(c) The 'gender identity centre' controlling 'female-type' or 'male-type' gender identity is organised mainly by androgens.

It is clear from this formulation (Dörner, 1985a, 1985b) that androgens and oestrogens are jointly involved in the sexual differentiation of every human brain. Some androgens can also be metabolised to oestrogens in neurological tissue and, as a result, the androgen to oestrogen ratio in the body is particularly important during brain differentiation (Dörner, 1985b). Moreover, it is now known that the 'critical periods' for sexual differentiation of the three neurological foci are not the same (Dörner *et al.*, 1983). Different sex hormones also appear to be responsible for organising the three centres over time (Dörner, 1985a). Several specific combinations and dissociations of gonadotropin secretion, sexual orientation and gender identity are therefore possible (Dörner, 1985b; Rohde *et al.*, 1986), and these discrete end states arise as a result of the operation of common generative mechanisms (Webster and Goodwin, 1982). It is apparent to us that a functionalist perspective does not add anything useful to this scheme. Neither does any teratological explanation which attempts to preserve artificial dichotomies by labelling all variants 'abnormal' (Birke, 1981; Hirst and Woolley, 1982) when it is the underlying laws that should be of primary interest (Bernard, 1957).

In conclusion, we reaffirm the comments of Blumstein and Schwartz (1977): 'By and large, investigators working with sexual data have accepted uncritically the pervasive cultural understandings of sexuality and have assumed there to be a simple and 'correct' conceptual scheme readily modifiable to the requirements of scientific rigour. Escaping scientists' borrowed notions of sexuality is difficult indeed, because they play an important part in shaping the actual data themselves.' Arguments asserting that biology has little to do with 'sexuality' rest on the incorrect premise that 'male' and 'female' are polar opposites (Hughes and Lambert, 1984). In fact the human foetus does not begin to develop morphological 'maleness' or 'femaleness' until about the third month after conception and a large number of intermediate forms do occur. Because the brain differentiates under the influence of the same sex hormones as the rest of the body it is clear that we cannot expect to understand mate recognition in animals — including humans (Bell *et al.*, 1981; Whitam, 1983; Whitam and Zent, 1984) — without reference to biology. Indeed some recent evidence suggests that biological factors play a major role in the development of human 'sexuality' (Pillard *et al.*, 1981, 1982; Eckert *et al.*, 1986; Pillard and Weinrich, 1986). This is not surprising because, in the real world, it is impossible to decouple sexual morphology from sexual behaviour. We have tried to show here that sense can be made of all the data that is now available if sexual differentiation and mate recognition are viewed as unified developmental phenomena. We think that this approach provides the logical starting point for a thorough structuralist reanalysis of 'sex' and 'sexuality' which promises significant new theoretical and experimental insights.

ACKNOWLEDGEMENTS

Many people have helped us to develop the ideas contained in this paper. We would especially like to thank Gerry Webster, Brian Goodwin, Jack Hailman, Søren Løvtrup, Hiro Sibatani and Miriam Saphira. We also thank Tony Walker for editing, Barbara Lockington for typing the manuscript and the Auckland University Research Committee for Grant No. 449.202 to D. M. Lambert.

REFERENCES

Arendash, G. W. and Gorski, R. A. (1983) Effects of Discrete Lesions of the Sexually Dimorphic Nucleus of the Preoptic Area or Other Medial Preoptic Regions on the Sexual Behaviour of Male Rats. *Brain Research Bulletin.* 10. 147-54.

Arnold, A. P. and Gorski, R. A. (1984) Gonadal Steroid Induction of Structural Sex Differences in the Central Nervous System. *Annual Review of Neurosciences.* 7. 413-42.

Ayoub, D. M., Greenough, W. T. and Juraska, J. M. (1983) Sex differences in Dendritic Structure in the Preoptic Area of the Juvenile Macaque Monkey Brain. *Science.* 219. 197-8.

Bardin, C. W. and Catterall, J. F. (1981) Testosterone: A Major Determinant of Extragenital Sexual Dimorphism. *Science.* 211. 1285-94.

Baum, M. J. (1983) Hormonal Modulation of Sexuality in Female Primates. *BioScience.* 33 (9). 578-82.

Bell, A. P., Weinberg, M. S. and Hammersmith, S. K. (1981) *Sexual Preference — Its Development in Men and Women.* Alfred C. Kinsey Institute for Sex Research. Indiana University Press, Bloomington.

Belote, J. M. and Baker, B. S. (1982) Sex determination in *Drosophila melanogaster*: Analysis of transformer-2, a sex-transforming locus. *Proceedings of the National Academy of Sciences, USA.* 79. 1568-72.

Benzer, S. (1973) Genetic dissection of behaviour. *Scientific American.* 229(6). 24-37.

Bernard, C. (1957) *Introduction to the Study of Experimental Medicine* [1865]. Dover Books, New York.

Birke, L. I. A. (1981) Is Homosexuality Hormonally Determined? *Journal of Homosexuality.* 6(4). 35-49.

——(1982) Cleaving the Mind: Speculations on Conceptual Dichotomies. In *Against Biological Determinism.* Allison and Busby, London.

Blumstein, P. W. and Schwartz, P. (1977) Bisexuality: Some social psychological issues. *Journal of Social Issues.* 33. 30-9.

Bohm, D. (1965) Space, Time and the Quantum Theory Understood in Terms of Discrete Structural Process. In *Proceedings of the International Conference on Elementary Particles* held in Kyoto, Japan. Oxford University Press, Oxford.

Breuer, H. (1980) Androgen production in the woman. In *Androgenisation in women.* Excerpta Medica, Amsterdam.

Bull, J. J. (1983) *Evolution of Sex Determining Mechanisms.* Benjamin/Cummings Publishing Company, London.

Clemens, L. G. and Gladue, B. A. (1978). Feminine sexual behaviour in rats enhanced by prenatal inhibition of androgen aromatisation. *Hormones and Behaviour.* 11. 190-201.

Cline, T. W. (1985) Primary Events in the Determination of Sex in *Drosophila melanogaster.* In *The Origin and Evolution of Sex.*. Alan R. Liss Inc., New York.

Döhler, K. D., Coquelin, A., Davis, F., Hines, M., Shryne, J. E. and Gorski, R. A. (1982) Differentiation of the Sexually dimorphic Nucleus in the Preoptic Area of the Rat Brain is Determined by the Perinatal Hormone Environment. *Neuroscience Letters.* 33. 295-8.

——Coquelin, A., Davis, F., Hines, M., Shryne, J. E. and Gorski, R. A. (1986) Aromatisation of Testicular Androgens in Physiological Concentrations does not Defeminise Sexual Brain Functions. In *Systemic Hormones, Neuro-transmitters and Brain Development.* Karger, Basel.

Dörner, G. (1976) *Hormones and Brain Differentiation.* Elsevier, Amsterdam.

——and Kawakami, M. (1978) Hormones and Brain Development. *Developments in Endocrinology.* 3. 1-158.

——Rohde, W., Schott, G. and Schnabl, C. H. (1983) On the L H response to oestrogen and L H - R H in transsexual men. *Experimental and Clinical Endocrinology.* 82. 257-67.

——(1985a) Systemic Hormones, Neurotransmitters and Sex-specific Brain Differentiation. Presented at the 4th International symposium on Psycho-neuroendocrinology in Reproduction, Riva del Garda, Italy, July, 1985.

——(1985b) Sex-specific gonadotropin secretion, sexual orientation and gender role behaviour. *Experimental and Clinical Endocrinology.* 86(1). 1-6.

Ehrhardt, A. A. and Meyer-Bahlburg, H. F. L. (1981) Effects of Prenatal Sex Hormones on Gender-Related Behaviour. *Science.* 211. 1312-18.

Eckert, E. D., Bochard, T. J., Bohlen, J. and Heston, L. L. (1986) Homosexuality in Monozygotic Twins Reared Apart. *British Journal of Psychiatry.* 148. 421-5.

Feder, H. H. (1981) Hormonal Actions on the Sexual Differentiation of the Genitalia and the Gonadotropin-Regulating Systems. In *Neuroendocrinology of Reproduction: Physiology and Behaviour.* Plenum Press, New York.

Ford, J. J. (1983) Postnatal Differentiation of Sexual Preference in Male Pigs. *Hormones and Behaviour.* 17. 152-62.

Goy, R. W. and McEwen, B. S. (1980) *Sexual Differentiation of the Brain.* M I T Press, Cambridge.

Hall, J. C. (1979) Control of male reproductive behaviour by the central nervous system of *Drosophila*: Dissection of a courtship pathway by genetic mosaics. *Genetics.* 92. 437-57.

——(1981) Sex Behaviour Mutants in *Drosophila. Bioscience.* 31. 125-30.

Hall, R., Evered, D. and Greene, R. (1979) *A Colour Atlas of Endocrinology.* Wolfe Medical Publications Ltd., London.

Hirst, P. and Woolley, P. (1982) Social Relations and Human Attributes. Tavistock Publications, London.

Ho, M-W. (1989) A Structuralism of Process: Towards a Post-Darwinian Rational Morphology. This volume, pp. 31-48.

Hotta, Y. and Benzer, S. (1976) Courtship in *Drosphila* mosaics: Sex-specific foci for sequential action patterns. *Proceedings of the National Academy of Sciences U S A.* 73. 4154-8.

Hughes, A. J. and Lambert, D. M. (1984) Functionalism, Structuralism and 'Ways of seeing'. *Journal of theoretical Biology.* 111. 787-800.

Illich, I. (1982) *Gender.* Pantheon Books, New York.

Imperato-McGinley, Guerrero, J. L., Gautier, T. and Peterson, R. E. (1974) Steroid 5 alpha-reductase Deficiency in Man: An Inherited Form of Male Pseudo-hermaphroditism. *Science.* 186. 1213-15.

——and Peterson, R. E. (1976) Male Pseudohermaphroditism: The Complexities of Male Phenotypic Development. *American Journal of Medicine.* 61. 251-72.

——Peterson, R. E., Gautier, T. and Sturla, E. (1979a) Male pseudohermaphroditism secondary to 5 alpha-reductase deficiency — a model for the role of androgens in both the development of the male phenotype and the evolution of a male gender identity. *Journal of Steroid Biochemistry.* 11. 637-45.

——Peterson, R. E., Gautier, T. and Sturla, E. (1979b) Androgens and the evolution of male-gender identity among male pseudohermaphrodites with 5 alpha-reductase deficiency. *New England Journal of Medicine.* 300(22). 1233-7.

——Peterson, R. E., Leshin, M., Griffin, J. E., Cooper, G., Draghi, S., Berenyi, M. and Wilson, J. D. (1980) Steroid 5 alpha-reductase Deficiency in a 65-year-old Male Pseudohermaphrodite: The Natural History, Ultrastructure of the Testes, and Evidence for Inherited Enzyme Heterogeneity. *Journal of Clinical Endocrinology and Metabolism.* 50(1). 15-22.

Jantsch, E. (1980) *The Self-Organising Universe.* Pergamon Press, Oxford.

Lambert, D. M. and Hughes, A. J. (1986) Keywords: The importance of language in structuralist biology. Presented at the International Workshop on Structuralism in Biology, Osaka, Japan. December 1986.

——and Millar, C. D. (1985) Mate recognition and sexual differentiation in *Drosophila melanogaster*. Presented at the Annual Conference of the N.Z. Entomological Society, Auckland, New Zealand. March 1985.

Lee, P. A., Plotnick, L. P., Kowarski, A. A. and Migeon, C. J. (1977) *Congenital Adrenal Hyperplasia*. University Park Press, Baltimore.

MacLusky, N. J. and Naftolin, F. (1981) Sexual Differentiation of the Central Nervous System. *Science*. 211. 1294-1303.

Madden, J. D., Walsh, P. C., MacDonald, P. C. and Wilson, J. D. (1975) Clinical and endocrinological characterisation of a patient with the syndrome of incomplete testicular feminisation. *Journal of Clinical Endocrinology and Metabolism*. 41. 751-60.

Meyer-Bahlburg, H. F. L. and Ehrhardt, A. A. (1986) Prenatal Diethylstilbestrol Exposure: Behavioural Consequences in Humans. In *Systemic Hormones, Neurotransmitters and Brain Development*. Karger, Basel.

Money, J. (1984) Gender-Transposition Theory and Homosexual Genesis. *Journal of Sex and Marital Therapy*. 10(2). 18-25.

——(1985) Gender: History, Theory and Usage of the term in Sexology and its Relationship to Nature/Nurture. *Journal of Sex and Marital Therapy*. 11(2). 71-9.

——and Ehrhardt, A. A. (1972) *Man and Woman, Boy and Girl: The Differentiation and Dimorphism of Gender Identity from Conception to Maturity*. John Hopkins University Press, Baltimore.

Payne, A. P. (1979) Neonatal androgen administration and sexual behaviour: Behavioural responses and hormonal responsiveness of female golden hamsters. *Animal Behaviour*. 27. 242-50.

Pillard, R. C., Poumadere, J. and Carretta, R. A. (1981) Is Homosexuality Familial? A Review, Some Data and a Suggestion. *Archives of Sexual Behaviour*. 10(5). 465-75.

——Poumadere, J. and Carretta, R. A. (1982) A Family Study of Sexual Orientation. *Archives of Sexual Behaviour*. 11(6). 511-20.

Pillard, R. C. and Weinrich, J. D. (1986) Evidence of Familial Nature of Male Homosexuality. *Archives of General Psychiatry*. 43. 808-12.

Polanyi, M. (1958) *Personal Knowledge — Towards a Post-Critical Philosophy*. Routledge and Kegan Paul, London.

Rohde, W., Uebelhack, R. and Dörner, G. (1986) Neuroendocrine Response to Oestrogen in Transsexual Men. In *Systemic Hormones, Neurotransmitters and Brain Development*. Karger, Basel.

Rose, S., Kamin, L. J. and Lewontin, R. C. (1984) *Not in Our Genes: Biology, Ideology and Human Nature*. Penguin Books, Harmondsworth.

Saenger, P., Goldman, A. S., Levine, L. S., Korthschutz, S., Muecke, E. C., Katsumata, M., Doberne, Y. and New, M. I. (1978) Prepubertal diagnosis of Steroid 5-alpha reductase Deficiency. *Journal of Clinical Endocrinology and Metabolism*. 46(4). 627-34.

Siiteri, P. K. and Wilson, J. D. (1974) Testosterone Formation and Metabolism during Male Sexual Differentiation in the Human Embryo. *Journal of Clinical Endocrinology and Metabolism*. 38. 113-25.

Sturtevant, A. H. (1945) A gene in *Drosophila melanogaster* that transforms females into males. *Genetics*. 30. 297-9.

Swaab, D. F. and Fliers, E. (1985) A Sexually Dimorphic Nucleus in the Human Brain. *Science*. 228. 1112-5.

Tompkins, L. and Hall, J. C. (1983) Identification of Brain Sites Controlling Female
Receptivity in Mosaics of *Drosophila melanogaster*. *Genetics*. 103. 179-95.

Vom Saal, F. S., Grant, W. M., McMullen, C. W. and Laves, K. S. (1983) High Fetal
Estrogen Concentrations: Correlation with Increased Adult Sexual Activity and
Decreased Aggression in Male Mice. *Science*. 220. 1306-8.

Webster, G. and Goodwin, B. C. (1982) The Origin of Species: A Structuralist
Approach. *Journal of Social and Biological Structures*. 5. 15-47.

Whitam, F. L. (1983) Culturally Invariable Properties of Male Homosexuality:
Tentative Conclusions from Cross-Cultural Research. *Archives of Sexual
Behaviour*. 12(3). 207-26.

——and Zent, M. (1984) A Cross-Cultural Assessment of Early Cross-Gender
Behaviour and Familial Factors in Male Homosexuality. *Archives of Sexual
Behaviour*. 13(5). 427-39.

Wilson, J. D. and Foster, D. W. (1985) *Williams Textbook of Endocrinology*.
W. B. Saunders Company, Philadelphia.

13. DNA Domains — Their Classification and Organisation

A. Lima-de-Faria

The term domain has mainly been used in protein chemistry. Three properties are associated with this concept. 1) The protein domain represents a specific structural component. It has been defined as 'a compact folded part of the structure that appears separate from the rest, as if it would be stable in solution on its own' (Watson *et al.*, 1987). 2) There is a co-linear correspondence between the structural domain and the amino acids of the protein, i.e. a single domain is formed by a continuous sequence of amino acids. 3) Each domain is associated with a specific function such as recognition and binding of molecules (Steitz *et al.*, 1982).

In nucleic acid chemistry and in the study of genes the term domain has only been used at times (e.g. Lewin, 1983; Watson *et al.*, 1987). Moreover, it has been applied without specifying the structural components involved and without defining its exact functional meaning.

In the present work we will attempt the following: 1) Define a nucleic acid domain. 2) Characterise its structural components. 3) Characterise its function. 4) Describe the types of DNA domains found in chromosomes. 5) Relate the structure and properties of these domains with the structure and properties of the chromosome as a whole, i.e. with its behaviour as a centromere-telomere field unit.

DEFINITION OF DNA DOMAIN

The term domain is here defined as a sequence of nucleotides making up a part of chromosomal DNA which is characterised by a specific molecular pattern and which displays a well-defined function at the chromosome level. The domain has sharply defined limits but is at the same time an integral part of a larger unit which conditions its behaviour in certain circumstances. This definition requires qualifications.

The nucleotide sequence may extend from a single base to millions of bases. This does not mean that the domain is a poorly defined entity but that both the pro- and eukaryotic chromosomes are divided into specific regions that show considerable difference in length.

The DNA domain is characterised by two main properties. 1) The molecular pattern which it displays usually contains elements of symmetry in the arrangement of its bases or has termini defined by specialised DNA sequences. 2) The function of the domain is a specific one, but its most important aspect is that this function is expressed at the *chromosome level* and not, for instance, at the organism level. The fact that the function is expressed at this level is what gives the domain its full genetic significance. A DNA sequence which is part of a given domain has to obey to its main function. Once it is moved to another domain, where another function dominates, it may be affected by the activity of the new domain and a new genetic situation may arise.

UNDERSTANDING OF DOMAIN INTERACTION MAY LEAD TO PREDICTION OF FUNCTION

At present it is hardly possible to predict what kind of changes occur in a DNA segment when it moves to another region because so little is known about the organisation of the chromosome as a whole and of its various compartments. The advantage of dividing the chromosome into domains lies in opening up the possibility of predicting the modifications that may arise in the properties of gene sequences when they change position along the pro- or eukaryotic chromosome. Moreover, it leads to a better understanding of the organisation of the chromosome by recognising the limits of its compartments.

TYPES OF DOMAINS AND THEIR MAIN FUNCTIONS

Chromosomes are biochemical edifices naturally divided into molecular regions which build a hierarchic system. The domains that can be well defined at present in molecular and functional terms are the following (Table 1).

Table 1. DNA domains present in chromosomes

Domain	Base Number	Function	Symmetry Elements or Special Features
1. Base	1	Unit of replication and transcription	—
2. Codon	3	Codes for an amino acid	—
3. Restriction Site	4 to 8 (usually)	Cleavage of specific sequence	Two-fold rotational symmetry = palindrome
4. Promoter	Circa 80	Sequence recognised by polymerase	Regions with symmetrical arrangement
5. Operator	About 24	Binding region of repressor protein	Symmetrical shape
6. Operon	Hundreds of bases	Genes with related functions transcribed into single messenger	Polarised transcription
7. Intron	251 to 1,600 (ovalbumin gene chicken)	Transcription into RNA not present in messenger	Begins with GT and finishes with AG

Domain	Base Number	Function	Symmetry Elements or Special Features
8. Exon	47 to 1,043 (oval-bumin gene chicken)	Transcription into RNA present in messenger	Exons are usually smaller than introns
9. Split Gene	21,000 and 16,000 (A1 and A2 vitel-logenin genes, Xenopus)	Unit of transcription and translation coding for protein or RNA	Order in splicing process
10. Transposon	750 to 40,000 (E. coli)	Moves genes to specific sites	Terminal sequences are symmetrical and target sites contain also elements of symmetry
11. Enhancer	Several hundred base pairs	Alters the transcription of RNA polymerase. Acts over great distances	Tandem repeats present
12. Position Effect Region	Depending on size of gene involved	Affected in its function by insertion of new segment	Range of action of segment extending to over one million base pairs
13. Gene Territory	Millions of base pairs	Segment in which a type of gene is preferentially located	Genes classified into centrons, medons and telons
14. Centromere	Millions of base pairs	Displays active mobility on spindle	Structure builds a reversed repeat in all eukaryotes studied
15. Telomere	Exact length not known	Characterised by unipolarity	Unipolar pattern
16. Nucleolar Organiser	8,000 (yeast) to 13,000 (mammals) Pre-ribosomal RNA regions	Building of nucleolus	Genes tandemly arranged separated by spacers
17. Chromosome Arm	Usually over 10^6	Delimited by telomere and centromere	Polarised DNA replication (Rye)
18. Chromosome	4.6×10^7 (Human No. 21, haploid)	Telomere at each end and centromere	Centromere as prime organiser of centromere-telomere field

1. The *base* which is part of a nucleotide and which is the basic component of all DNA sequences. Its function is characterised by being the unit of DNA replication and of DNA transcription.

2. The *codon* which is a group of three bases. Its function is expressed in its ability to code for an amino acid. The code is universal with the exception of mitochondrial DNA (Barrell *et al.*, 1979).

3. The *restriction site* is a DNA sequence usually composed of four to eight bases. The bases form a segment which shows two-fold rotational symmetry around a given point. This symmetrical arrangement of the bases in the two DNA strands forms what is called a palindrome (Smith, 1979). This domain has

a very well-defined function. Restriction enzymes of class II recognise and cleave these DNA sequences. The sequence of the bases within this type of domain has been established for over 100 enzymes and the specificity of interaction between the protein and the DNA is so accurate that a single change in the methylation of a base modifies the interaction of the enzyme with the DNA domain (Taylor, 1984).

4. The *promoter* is the DNA sequence recognised by a polymerase. The *lac* promoter of *E. coli* is formed by about 80 base pairs. It consists of two functionally distinct regions. One is the RNA polymerase interaction site, the other is the CAP (catabolite gene activator protein) site to which the cAMP-CAP complex binds. The binding of this complex facilitates the RNA polymerase attachment at its own site. The promoter partly overlaps with the operator and for this reason the binding of the repressor to the operator prevents RNA polymerase from binding to the *lac* promoter. Both the CAP site and the operator contain regions of symmetry. The CAP site contains 40 base pairs of which 16 build the symmetrical arrangement (Dickson *et al.*, 1975). This is a type of domain which functions as the site of attachment for three proteins: the CAP complex, RNA polymerase and the repressor (partly). Over 100 promoters have been compared. They possess two common sequences that consist of six nucleotides which occur about 10 base pairs and about 35 base pairs before the site where the RNA synthesis starts. These consensus sequences differ only slightly from promoter to promoter and represent the critical component of their function (Rodriguez and Chamberlin, 1982).

5. The *operator* is the sequence to which repressor proteins can bind thereby preventing RNA transcription. Most operators have a symmetrical shape that results from the presence of an inverted repeat. The lactose operator has about 24 base pairs, 16 of them are related by a two-fold axis of symmetry centred at the base pair in position 11 (Pabo and Lewis, 1982; Pabo and Sauer, 1984).

6. The *operon* is composed of the genes with related functions, which are closely grouped on the bacterial chromosome, and which are transcribed into a single messenger RNA. In the *E. coli* chromosome over 75 different operons are known (Bachman, 1983). Since an operon results from the association of several genes it consists of hundreds of base pairs. Operons like those of bacteria do not exist in yeast which is a eukaryote, but in this species each gene is terminated by activating and repressing sequences.

7. The *intron* is the DNA sequence that is transcribed into RNA but an RNA that is not represented in the mature messenger RNA. The discovery of the split gene disclosed that there existed intervening sequences or introns within most eukaryotic genes. Transfer RNA introns have lengths ranging from 14 to 60 base pairs (Guthrie and Abelson, 1982). In the ovalbumin gene of the chicken their length varies from about 251 to 1,600 base pairs. The number of introns per gene may be as high as 50 as is the case with the chick type 1 alpha 2 collagen gene. The exon-intron sequences have been conserved throughout evolution. The sequences of several hundred interrupted genes have disclosed

that introns always begin with G T and finish with A G. This result has led to the so-called G T - A G rule (Chambon, 1981).

8. The *exon* is the gene sequence that produces an R N A which is spliced in the formation of a mature messenger R N A. The exons are the protein coding sequences of a gene but also include the leader and trailer sequences present in messenger R N A. Exons are on the average smaller than introns. Over three-quarters of the 7 700 base pairs of the chicken ovalbumin gene are contained in introns. The length of the exons of this gene ranges from 47 to 1 043 base pairs.

9. The *split gene* is the type of gene found generally in eukaryotes. It consists of an assembly of exons and introns. This assembly results from an ordered process. The splicing of the R N A is a specific and ordered phenomenon under the control of enzymes and under the guidance of the termini of the introns. An example of the size of the split gene is given by the A1 and A2 vitellogenin genes of *Xenopus* which have 21 000 and 16 000 base pairs respectively (Wahli *et al.*, 1981). As pointed out by Spirin (1986) special attention should be paid to the non-coding messenger R N A sequences. Their function may be to create the specialised three-dimensional secondary and tertiary structures that control peptide elongation and the binding of the messenger to recognition proteins that affect translation.

10. The *transposon* is the D N A segment that moves genes to new sites in the same or other chromosomes. In bacteria such as *E. coli* their length varies from 750 to 40 000 base pairs (Kleckner, 1981). Bacterial transposons are of two types: simple and complex. The first carry only the insertion sequences necessary for their transposition. The second contain besides these sequences several genes, such as those that specify antibiotic resistance. The most significant features of transposons are as follows: 1) They encode the genes that direct and regulate their own transposition, i.e. they have their own genetic machinery that allows them to behave as partly independent structures in the organisation of the chromosome. 2) They modify chromosome organisation by interrupting genes as well as by altering gene expression. 3) No random events are involved in their transpositions. They move with high precision thanks to their terminal D N A sequences which consist of a symmetrical duplication of 3 to 12 bases at the site of insertion. 4) Their target sites are also non-random, they transpose to specific four- or six-base symmetrical sequences, like those recognised by restriction enzymes (Craigie and Mizuuchi, 1985). In *Drosophila* three classes of mobile elements have been detected. These are: 1) The *copia elements* that are about 5 000 base pairs long and which possess long terminal direct repeats (consisting of several hundred base pairs). Their termini are characterised by about ten base pairs inverted repeats. 2) The *fold-back elements* which form hairpin structures due to their long inverted repeats. 3) The *P elements* are 500 to 1 400 base pairs in length and are closed by perfect 31 base pairs inverted repeats (Finnegan, 1985). Maize is the organism in which transposons were first discovered and these turn out to be similar to *Drosophila*

P elements. One such transposon, in maize, is the *Ds element* which varies in size from 400 to 4 000 base pairs and is derived from the *Ac element* (4 500 base pairs). Maize transposons also have elements of symmetry. Their termini consist of perfect inverted repeats of 11 base pairs flanked by direct repeats of 6 to 8 base pairs (Sutton *et al.*, 1984; Pohlmann *et al.*, 1984).

11. The *enhancer* is a D N A sequence consisting of several hundred base pairs which drastically alters the efficiency of transcription by R N A polymerase I I. Moreover, they are tissue specific. However, their most significant property, for our understanding of chromosome organisation, lies in the fact that they act over great distances. In viruses, such as SV40 and polyoma, the enhancers consist primarily of a tandem repeat of 72 base pairs. The deletion of an enhancer reduces gene expression by a factor of 100 (Schaffner *et al.*, 1985). The action of an enhancer can extend over up to several thousand base pairs (Khoury and Gruss, 1983). This is a key result that allows now to understand the position effects, so well established several decades ago, and for which there was no obvious molecular explanation.

12. The *position effect region* is the segment of D N A which is affected in its function by the insertion of new segments in its vicinity. This is a very well-established phenomenon which has been extensively studied in eukaryotes from plants to mammals but especially in *Drosophila* (Lewis, 1950; Baker, 1968; Spofford, 1976). The position effect may extend from a few to over one million nucleotide pairs (Lima-de-Faria, 1983). The position effects affect nearly, if not all, classes of genes. They show that most D N A sequences found within the eukaryotic chromosome are not independent structures, but have a function which is determined, at least in part, by their position within the chromosome. Not only R N A transcription, but also D N A replication and the structural configuration of the chromosome are among the phenomena modified by the change in position within the chromosome unit (Ananiev and Gvozdev, 1974). The discovery of the enhancer elements is a first step in the understanding of this phenomenon at the molecular level. However, only the change in R N A transcription is explained by enhancers. The modifications in D N A replication and in chromosome phenotype have to await the discovery of other molecular mechanisms that may be responsible for such organisatory changes.

13. The *gene territory* is the segment of D N A in which a gene is preferentially located. Genes are not located at random in the chromsomes as is usally believed, but every type of D N A sequence tends to occupy a specific territory within the *chromosome field* defined by the centromere-telomere region. Millions of structural rearrangements have occurred during species evolution. Although the genes were shuffled by this process they are not found distributed at random within chromosomes or within karyotypes. An extensive analysis of the position of specific D N A sequences in a wide number of species has disclosed that their position within the chromosome arm is related to the location of two main regions: the centromere and the telomere.

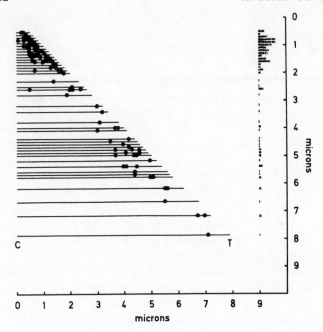

Figure 1. The 136 nucleolar chromosome arms from 92 species of plants belonging to
the family Ranunculaceae showing the location of the DNA sequences for ribosomal
RNA (black circles). All the arms are distributed according to their length with all
the centromeres building a vertical line (C). The telomeres are marked T and arms
of the same length occupy identical positions (dots on the right). The ribosomal
genes show a well-defined chromosome territory and are located near the telomere
irrespective of the variation in arm length. Of the 136 genes 125 are located within
one micron of the telomere and only 11 are outside this region. This means that
91.9% have a telon territory (from Lima-de-Faria and Mitelman, 1986).

This has made it possible to classify DNA sequences into *centrons, medons* and
telons, depending on whether they show a tendency to appear near the
centromere, in the middle of the arms or near the telomeres respectively. As an
example it may be mentioned that the genes for 28S and 18S ribosomal RNA
are telons. In 85.2 per cent of the cases studied (which include eukaryotes as
phylogenetically unrelated as algae and humans) they are located near the
telomere (Figures 1 and 2). Other sequences occur regularly near the
centromere and are classified as centrons. Examples are satellite DNAs
consisting of many repeated sequences. The optimal territory of each DNA
sequence is maintained irrespective of variation in arm length, of chromosome
type and of species (Lima-de-Faria, 1980). The discovery of transposons, with
their ability to move DNA sequences in an ordered way, furnishes a molecular
mechanism that allows to understand the primary events responsible for the
maintenance of gene territories. However, this is only one of the molecular

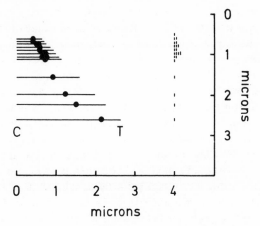

Figure 2. Location of the DNA sequences for 28S and 18S ribosomal RNA (black circles) in three species of mammals: human, gorilla and guinea pig. The arms of the nucleolar chromosomes which form the nucleolus (diploid number) are distributed according to their length, the centromeres (C) building a vertical line. The telomeres are marked T. The ribosomal RNA genes show the same telomere territory as those of plants and form a straight line parallel to that of the telomeres (from Lima-de-Faria and Mitelman, 1986).

mechanisms that may be involved, other processes dealing with the functional interactions with centromeres and telomeres are not yet understood.

14. The *centromere* is the region of the chromsome that displays active mobility on the spindle. Besides this function the centromere has another one which is still more important. It is the primary centre of organisation of most chromosome structures and functions appearing along the chromosome arms. In all species studied chromomere gradients originate only on both sides of the centromere. The phenomena of non-disjunction, the formation of chiasmata and crossing over as well as many other chromosome properties are all related to the position of the centromere (Lima-de-Faria, 1983). The structure of the centromere consists of fibrillae and chromomeres that are organised in the form of a reversed repeat. Hence it contains elements of symmetry like the other DNA domains (Lima-de-Faria, 1956). Yeast centromeres have been partly isolated and sequenced. Some of the functional sequences are contained within a 130-base-pairs long, very AT-rich region, flanked by two elements which are common to the centromeres of different chromosomes (Carbon, 1984). It must be kept in mind that yeast centromeres are about 100 times smaller than those of higher eukaryotes.

15. The *telomere* is the domain that is characterised by unipolarity. Like the centromere, it is a sequence of DNA without which chromosomes cannot survive. The basic function of the telomere domain is to seal the chromosome arms at their ends (Muller and Herskowitz, 1954). The type of base sequences

that may be present in telomeres have been discussed by Cavalier-Smith (1974). Significant from the point of view of chromosome organisation is that telomeres can substitute centromeres in their movement on the spindle and that centromeres can perform the function of telomeres. The first situation occurs when extra DNA sequences are introduced in the nucleus (Rhoades, 1978) and the second is evident in chromosomes that have only one arm, i.e. in which the centromere functions as telomere. Yeast telomeres have turned out to contain about 100 base pairs of irregularly repeated sequences with the general form poly(C_{1-3}A) (Walmsley *et al.* 1984). All other telomeres isolated from lower eukaryotes have a short, repeated sequence, with one DNA strand rich in guanine, the other in cytosine. The sequences thought to belong to the human telomeres seem to contain pure tandem repeats of six nucleotides, TTAGGG, repeated many times and without a single variation (Roberts, 1988).

16. The *nucleolar organiser* is the domain which has a function that is most evident since it results in the formation of a large organelle, the nucleolus. This domain consists of repeated genes for 28S and 18S ribosomal RNA which are tandemly arranged. They are separated by non-transcribed spacers. The regions that are transcribed into the large pre-ribosomal RNAs range in size from 8 000 bases (yeast, insects and lower vertebrates) to 13 000 bases (mammals) (Long and Dawid, 1980).

17. The *chromosome arm* is one of the best-defined domains. Its limits are established by two specialised regions: the centromere and the telomere. We usually tend to regard the chromosome as the main unit of the karyotype of a species. However, the chromosome arm may be an equally important if not more significant domain. The reasons are several. 1) In many species of animals the karyotype is formed by chromosomes that consist of a single arm, i.e. they have a telomere at one end and a centromere at the other. Examples are most lizard species (*Lacertidae*) in which all the chromosomes of the karyotype consist of a single arm (Gorman, 1973). In these chromosomes the functional unit is the single arm. 2) During karyotype evolution the fusion of one-armed chromosomes at the centromere has been a general phenomenon. This event has occurred so often in mammals that it is called the Robertsonian rule. During the evolution of these species the chromosome number has changed but the number of arms has remained constant. The changes in chromosome numbers have been due to a large extent to fusion of whole arms or to dissociation of chromosomes into whole arms. This mode of chromosome evolution is observed in a great number of mammalian families, an example being the Bovidae (Koulischer, 1973). 3) The DNA replication occurring in the chromosomes of plant species such as *Secale cereale* shows that each arm of every metacentric chromosome functions as a separate unit. The replication starts at the distal region of each arm and progresses along the whole arm toward the centromere but does not transverse it (Lima-de-Faria and Jaworska, 1972). Arm independence is also evident in the formation of chiasmata. In many species of animals the chiasma interference does not

extend over the centromere region in metacentric chromosomes (Callan and Montalenti, 1947). Hence, the chromosome arm appears as a domain with both a functional and an evolutionary significance.

18. The *chromosome* is the domain that is best known due to its universal occurrence in pro- and eukaryotes. In prokaryotes it is a clearly delimited structure. In bacteria the chromosome is a circular structure. The eukaryotic chromosome is a prisoner of the nucleus from which it can only escape during metaphase and anaphase when the cell divides into two daughter cells to be again locked in the nucleus at telophase. The DNA of this chromosome type is also a prisoner of the association with the histones which condition the assembly of the DNA into nucleosomes and direct the transformation of the chromosome into a metaphase structure. It is at this last stage that the chromosome appears as a very well-defined domain with a telomere at each end and having its centromere oriented in the spindle. It is from this stage that this domain is best known. What is, however, significant is that the eukaryotic chromosome is a functional unit as disclosed by the ordered distribution of its genes in the centromere-telomere field. Moreover, the change in position of these genes within the field alters their function (Lima-de-Faria, 1983). The centromere appears as the prime organiser of the field (Lima-de-Faria, 1980). So far no molecular mechanisms are available that elucidate this interaction. One of the reasons is that the DNA of the centromere has not yet been sequenced in higher eukaryotes.

THE MECHANISMS RESPONSIBLE FOR THE FORMATION OF
THE DNA DOMAINS

We seem to take for granted that the domains described above result from the physico-chemical properties inherent to the initial construction of DNA. This is undoubtedly one of the main factors shaping the natural regions of the chromosome. However, it cannot be the only one. Different types of RNAs and different types of proteins ought to have been involved in this process. For instance the domain *codon* is a direct product of the interaction of the messenger RNA, derived from the chromosomal DNA, with the anti-codon of transfer RNA. If the transfer RNA would not have three bases at its recognition site the code could not have been read in groups of three bases. The same is true for the *restriction enzyme*, the *promoter* and the *operator* domains. These are recognised by different types of proteins. The amino acids of the proteins bind specifically to the bases along these domains (Gursky *et al.*, 1977). Hence, the interaction protein-DNA is expected to have contributed to the initial formation of these domains.

TESTING THE VALIDITY OF THE MAINTENANCE OF GENE
TERRITORY IN THE CHROMOSOME FIELD

The question may then be asked: is there a way to test the validity of the concept of gene territory within the centromere-telomere field? What kind of experiments can be carried out and what chromosomal system can be chosen which may elucidate this situation?

To investigate this problem we chose the most extreme case of variation in chromosome number known to exist in any mammalian family. The Cervidae have chromosome complements ranging from $2n = 6$ (female, $2n = 7$ male) in *Muntiacus muntjak* to $2n = 70$ in *Rangifer tarandus* (reindeer). *Muntiacus reevesi* has an intermediate value $2n = 46$. The DNAs of five Cervidae species were cleaved with restriction enzymes, specific DNA fragments were isolated and hybridised by Southern blot. Homologies were found to be present between the highly repetitive sequences of the five species (Lima-de-Faria *et al.*, 1984). In a subsequent study eight species were included and a highly repetitive sequence, 770 base pairs long, was isolated from *Cervus elaphus* (red deer $2n = 68$). After cloning, it was hybridised in situ with metaphase chromosomes of *M. muntjak* ($2n = 7$) and red deer. The cloned DNA sequence was found to occupy the same position, in the proximal regions of the arms, in both red deer and the muntjac chromosomes despite the drastic chromosome reorganisation that led to extreme chromosome numbers (Lima-de-Faria *et al.*, 1986).

In a subsequent experiment we carried out the hybridisation in situ of the same sequence with the metaphase chromosomes of *Muntiacus reevesi*, which has $2n = 46$ chromosomes. Such an intermediate chromosome number allows a further test of the validity of the predictions based on the chromosome field theory. The same result was obtained with this species. The cloned sequence is not distributed at random but occurs in all the three species mainly in the proximal regions of the arms, very close to the centromere. This happens irrespective of the very large variation in number and in size between the chromosomes of the red deer and the two muntjac species. Despite the drastic changes which have occurred in chromosome number and morphology the territory of this DNA sequence has been strictly maintained (Figures 3-6).

An analysis of other DNA sequences in these same chromosomes discloses that the ribosomal genes and the centromeres themselves also have maintained their territory during the enormous chromosome reorganisation that has taken place in the deer species (Lima-de-Faria *et al.*, 1986; Scherthan *et al.*, 1987) (Figure 7 and Table 2)

Ce Cn Dd Cc Aa Rt Mr Mm C. O. B.

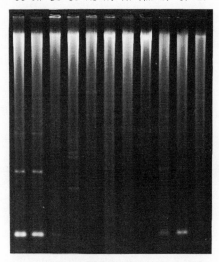

Ce Cn Dd Cc Aa Rt Mr Mm C. O. B.

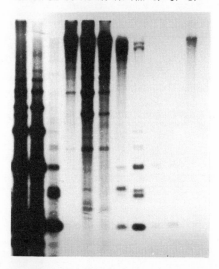

Figure 3. *Cleavage of total* DNA from eight species of Cervidae and three species of Bovidae with the restriction enzyme Bam H1. *Upper part* of the figure without hybridization. *Lower part* of figure after hybridization with the DNA of the red deer band 770 b.p. which was cloned in the plasmid vector pBR322, nick translated with ^{32}P and hybridized with all DNAs. Three groups of labelled band patterns are evident (*lower part* of figure): (1) red deer, sika deer and fallow deer (Ce, Cn, Dd); (2) roe deer, elk and reindeer (Cc, Aa, Rt); (3) Indian and Chinese muntjacs (*M. reevesi* and *M. muntjak*). The pattern of the muntjacs resembles more that of fallow deer (Dd) than that of the species of the second group. The Bovidae are goat, sheep and bull (C., O. and B.) (from Lima-de-Faria *et al.*, 1986).

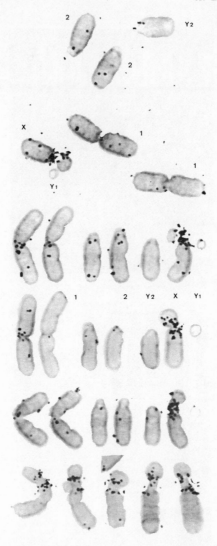

Figure 4. *Muntiacus muntjak* chromosomes (2n = 7, male) from tissue culture cells at metaphase of mitosis. The D N A of the 770 base pair band of red deer was cloned in plasmid pBR322, nick translated with ³H and hybridized in situ with the chromosomes. *Upper part:* Cell at metaphase showing distinct labelling in the proximal regions of the arms of the X chromosome. *Middle part:* Karyotypes from three cells showing considerable labelling in the proximal regions of the arms of the X chromosome and light labelling in the same regions of chromosome 1. *Lower part:* Five X chromosomes which show that the labelling is not located at the centromere but in the proximal regions of the arms on both sides of the centromere (from Lima-de-Faria *et al.*, 1986).

Figure 5. *Cervus elaphus* (red deer) chromosomes (2n = 68, male) from tissue culture cells at metaphase of mitosis. The same red deer probe labelled with ^{3}H (as in Figure 4) was used for in situ hybridization. The centromeres are terminal in 64 autosomes and in the X and Y, only two large autosomes have median centromeres. *Upper part:* A cell showing labelling in the proximal region of the arm of most chromosomes. *Lower part:* Karyotype from another cell. The 64 telocentric autosomes are aligned according to their length and all show labelling at the proximal region of the single arm. The two large metacentrics at the bottom show no labelling. The X chromosome is the largest of the complement and it is also unlabelled, the Y chromosome shows labelling at the proximal region of the arm (from Lima-de-Faria *et al.*, 1986).

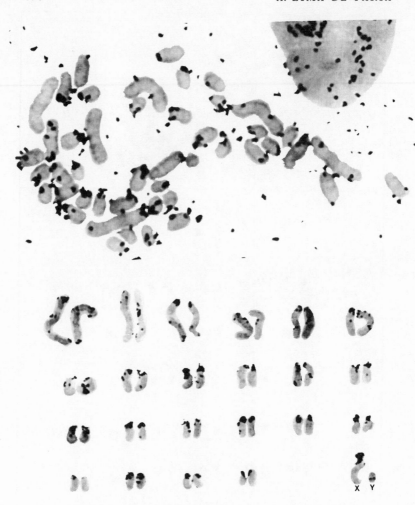

Figure 6. *Muntiacus reevesi* chromosomes (2n = 46) from tissue culture cells at metaphase of mitosis. The D N A of the 770 base pair band of red deer was cloned in plasmid pBR322, nick translated with ^{3}H and hybridized in situ with the chromosomes. *Upper part:* Cell at metaphase showing heavy labelling in the proximal regions of the arms of most chromosomes. All autosomes of *M. reevesi* are acrocentric or telocentric and the X is acrocentric. Only the Y is submetacentric. *Lower part:* Karyotype from another cell. The autosomes were aligned according to their length. The labelled regions appear in 44 of the 46 chromosomes on the proximal regions of the arms quite near the centromere (from Scherthan *et al.*, 1987).

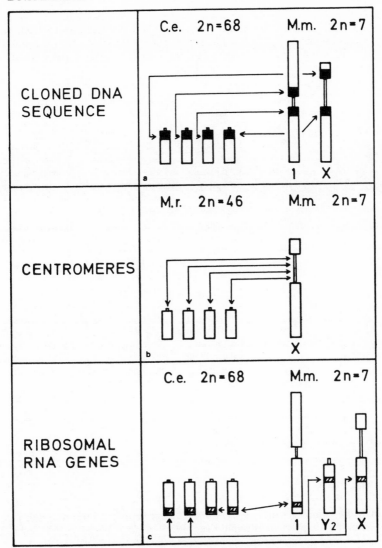

Figure 7. Diagram summarising the evidence in Deer species demonstrating the existence of rigid order in chromosome reorganisation. Repetitive DNA sequences, centromeres and ribosomal RNA genes maintain their main chromosome territory, despite drastic chromosome rearrangements, as was predicted by the chromosome field theory. For the sake of simplicity only four chromosomes are represented out of 68 and 46. For the same reason only some of the chromosomes of *M. muntjak* are represented. For explanation, see Table 2. The arrows indicate that the rearrangements may occur in both directions, since they may take place from a high to a low chromosome number but also in the reverse direction (from Lima-de-Faria *et al.*, 1986).

Table 2. Experimental evidence in Deer species demonstrating the existence of rigid order in chromosome reorganisation. Cloned DNA sequences, centromeres and ribosomal RNA genes maintain their main chromosome territory, despite drastic chromosome rearrangements, as was predicted by the chromosome field theory (from Lima-de-Faria *et al.*, 1986).

DNA sequences	Location in high chromosome number	Technique	Location in low chromosome number	Type of distribution
Cloned DNA sequence of 770 base pairs	*Cervus elaphus* $2n = 68$ Located in proximal regions of arms of 65 chromosomes	Southern blot hybridization and in situ hybridization (This paper)	*Muntiacus muntjak* $2n = 7$, male Located in proximal regions of arms of chromosomes X and 1	Non-random distribution. Territory maintained in proximal regions of arms
Centromeres	*Muntiacus reevesi* $2n = 46$ Located at one end of all the 46 chromosomes	Centromere-specific antiserum Immunofluorescent probe (Brinkley *et al.*, 1984)	*Muntiacus muntjak* $2n = 7$, male Located together with other centromeres building linear bead-like arrays which form giant cetromeres in all chromosomes	Non-random distribution Centromeres not eliminated but maintain territory
Ribosomal RNA genes	*Cervus elaphus* $2n = 68$ Nucleolar organisers located near telomeres in four large chromosomes	Hybridization in situ with ribosomal RNA and silver staining (Pardue and Hsu, 1975; Goldoni *et al.*, 1984)	*Muntiacus muntjak* $2n = 7$, male Nucleolar organisers located near telomere in chromosome 1 and in median region of arms in chromosomes Y_2 and X	Non-random distribution. One group of ribosomal genes maintains telomere territory, the other occupies median position of arms

REFERENCES

Ananiev, E. V. and Gvozdev, V. A. (1974) Changed pattern of transcription and replication in polytene chromosomes of *Drosophila melanogaster* resulting from eu-heterochromatin rearrangement. *Chromosoma.* 45. 173-91.
Bachman, B. J. (1983) Linkage map of *E. coli* K-12, ed. 7. *Microbiol. Revs.* 47. 180-230.
Baker, W. K. (1968) Position-effect variegation. In *Advances in Genetics,* Vol. 14 (ed. M. Demerec). Academic Press, New York. pp.133-69.
Barrell, B. G., Bankier, A. T. and Drouin, J. (1979) A different genetic code in human mitochondria. *Nature.* 282. 189-94.
Brinkley, M. M. Valdivia, A., Tousson, A. and Brenner, S. L. (1984) Compound kinetochores of the Indian muntjac. *Chromosoma.* 91. 1-11.
Callan, H. G. and Montalenti, G. (1947) Chiasma interference in mosquitoes. *J. Genet.* 48. 119-34.
Cavalier-Smith, T. (1974) Palindromic base sequences and replication of eukaryote chromosome ends. *Nature.* 250. 467-70.

Carbon, J. (1984) Yeast centromeres: Structure and function. *Cell* 37. 251-3.

Chambon, P. (1981) Split genes. *Sci. Am.* 244(5). 48-59.

Craigie, R. and Mizuuchi, K. (1985) Mechanism of transposition of bacteriophage Mu: Structure of a transposition intermediate. *Cell.* 41. 867-76.

Dickson, R. C., Abelson, J., Barnes, W. M. and Reznikoff, W. S. (1975) Genetic regulation: The lac control region. *Science.* 187. 27-35.

Finnegan, D. J. (1985) Transposable elements in eukaryotes. *Int. Rev. Cytol.* 93. 281-326.

Goldoni, D., Rubini, M. and Fontana, F. (1984) Cytogenetic studies on Cervus elaphus L. constitutive heterochromatin and nucleolus organiser regions. *Caryologia.* 37. 439-43.

Gorman, G. C. (1973) The chromosomes of the reptilia, a cytotaxonomic interpretation. In *Cytotaxonomy and Vertebrate Evolution.* (Eds. A. B. Chiarelli and E. Capanna). Academic Press, London and New York. pp.349-424.

Gursky, G. V., Tumanyan, V. G., Zasedatelev, A. S., Zhuze, A. L., Grokhovsky, S. L. and Gottikh, B. P. (1977) A code controlling specific binding of proteins to double-helical DNA and RNA. In *Nucleic Acid-Protein Recognition.* (Ed. H. J. Vogel). Academic Press, New York. pp.189-217.

Guthrie, C. and Abelson, J. (1982) Organisation and expression of tRNA genes in Saccharomyces cerevisiae. In *The Molecular Biology of the Yeast Saccharomyces: Metabolism and Gene Expression.* (Eds. J. N. Strathan, E. W. Jones and J. R. Broach.) Cold Spring Harbor, N.Y., Cold Spring Harbor Laboratory. pp.487-528.

Khoury, G. and Gruss, P. (1983) Enhancer Elements. *Cell.* 33. 313-14.

Kleckner, N. (1981) Transposable elements in prokaryotes. *Ann. Rev. Genetics.* 15. 341-404.

Koulischer, L. (1973) Common patterns of chromosome evolution in mammalian cell cultures or malignant tumours and mammalian speciation. In *Cytotaxonomy and Vertebrate Evolution* (Eds. A. B. Chiarelli and E. Capanna). Academic Press, London and New York. pp.129-64.

Lewin, B. (1983) *Genes.* John Wiley & Sons, New York. pp.1-715.

Lewis, E. B. (1950) The phenomenon of position effect. In *Advances in Genetics* (Ed. M. Demerec). Academic Press, New York. Vol. III. pp. 73-115.

Lima-de-Faria, A. (1956) The role of the kinetochore in chromosome organisation. *Hereditas.* 42. 85-160.

——(1980) Classification of genes, rearrangements and chromosomes according to the chromosome field. *Hereditas.* 93. 1-46.

——(1983) *Molecular Evolution and Organisation of the Chromosome.* Elsevier, Amsterdam, New York, Oxford. pp.1-1186.

——Arnason, U., Widegren, B., Essen-Möller, J., Isaksson, M., Olsson, E. and Jaworska, H. (1984) Conservation of repetitive DNA sequences in Deer species studied by Southern blot transfer. *J. Mol. Evol.* 20. 17-24.

——Arnason, U., Widegren, B., Isaksson, M., Essen-Möller, J. and Jaworska, H. (1986) DNA cloning and hybridisation in Deer species supporting the chromosome field theory. *BioSystems.* 19. 185-212.

——and Jaworska, H. (1972) The relation between the chromomere size gradient and the sequence of DNA replication in rye. *Hereditas.* 70. 39-58.

——and Mitelman, F. (1986) The chromosome territory of human oncogenes. *Bioscience Reports.* 6(4). 349-54.

Long, E. O. and Dawid, I. B. (1980) Repeated genes in eukaryotes. *Ann. Rev. Biochem.* 49. 727-64.

Muller, H. J. and Herskowitz, I. H. (1954) Concerning the healing of chromosome ends produced by breakage in *Drosophila melanogaster. Am. Nat.* 88. 177-208.

Pabo, C. and Lewis, M. (1982) The operator-binding domain of lambda repressor: Structure and DNA recognition. *Nature*. 298. 443-7.

——and Sauer, R. (1984) Protein-DNA recognition. *Ann. Rev. Biochem*. 58. 293-321.

Pardue, M. L. and Hsu, T. C. (1975) Locations of 18S and 28S ribosomal genes on the chromosomes of the Indian muntjac. *J. Cell Biol*. 64. 251-4.

Pohlmann, R. F., Fedoroff, N. V. and Messing, J. (1984) The nucleotide sequence of the maize controlling element Activator. *Cell*. 37. 635-43.

Rhoades, M. M. (1978) Genetic effects of heterochromatin in maize. In *Maize Breeding and Genetics* (Ed. D. B. Walden). John Wiley, New York. pp.641-71.

Roberts, L. (1988) Chromosomes: The ends in view. *Science* 240. 982-3.

Rodriguez, R. and Chamberlin, M. (1982) *Promoters: Structure and Function*. Praeger, New York.

Schaffner, W., Serfling, E. and Jasin, M. (1985) Enhancers and eukaryotic gene transcription. *Trends in Genetics*. 1. 224-30.

Scherthan, H., Arnason, U. and Lima-de-Faria, A. (1987) The chromosome field theory tested in muntjac species by DNA cloning and hybridization. *Hereditas*. 107. 175-84.

Smith, H. O. (1979) Nucleotide sequence specificity of restriction endonucleases. *Science*. 205. 455-62.

Spirin, A. S. (1986) *Ribosome Structure and Protein Biosynthesis*. The Benjamin/Cummings Publishing Company, Inc., Advanced Book Program, Menlo Park, California, USA. pp.1-414.

Spofford, J. B. (1976) Position-effect variegation in *Drosophila*. In *The Genetics and Biology of Drosophila* (Eds. M. Ashburner and E. Novitski). Academic Press, New York. Vol. 1c. pp.955-1018.

Steitz, T. A., Weber, I. T., and Matthew, J. B. (1982) Catabolite gene activator protein: Structure, homology with other proteins, and cyclic AMP and DNA binding. *Cold Spring Harbor Symp. Quant. Biol*. 47. 419-26.

Sutton, W. D., Gerlach, W. L., Schwartz, D. and Peacock, W. J. (1984) Molecular analysis of Ds controlling mutations at the Adhl locus of maize. *Science*. 223. 1265-8.

Taylor, J. H. (1984) DNA methylation and cellular differentiation. *Cell Biology Monographs*. Springer-Verlag, Wien, New York. Vol. 11. pp.1-135.

Wahli, W., Dawid, I. B., Ryffel, G. U. and Weber, R. (1981) Vitellogenesis and the vitellogenin gene family. *Science*. 212. 298-304.

Walmsley, W., Chan, S. M., Tye, B.-K. and Petes, T. D. (1984) Unusual DNA sequences associated with the ends of yeast chromosomes. *Nature*. 310. 157-60.

Watson, J. D., Hopkins, N. H., Roberts, J. W., Steitz, J. A. and Weiner, A. M. (1987) *Molecular Biology of the Gene*. The Benjamin/Cummings Publishing Company, Inc., Menlo Park, California. Vol 1, 4th edn. pp. 1-744.

14. Genetics and the Inheritance of Biological Structures

G. Sermonti

My chapter aims to oppose the current view that the structure and function of DNA are the progressive outcome of the engagement of the organisms in their living process. There is no important increase in the structural genetic information from prokaryotic microbes up to higher eukaryotes. Biochemical complexity is by no means a late outcome of evolution. We meet it at the assumed origin, in the smallest microorganisms, and it stays essentially constant in all living forms. Enzymes are the key to life: there is no evidence that there are more enzymes in a mammal or in a plant than in a microbe. As Francois Jacob (1977) puts it, 'Biochemical changes do not seem to be a main driving force in the diversification of living organisms. The really creative part in biochemistry must have occurred very early. . . . It is not biochemical novelties that generated diversification of organisms.'

Whenever complexity is to be found at the origin, we have to abandon a historical perspective. Such complexity is not the result of the vicissitudes of history. We must approach inheritance as a structure not as a legacy. The structure of the inheritance is not what stays constant from generation to generation, but the set of laws of transformation which ensure its constancy. There is no such process as self-reproduction. DNA does not self-reproduce. Each component strand organises along itself a complementary strand, according to the rather mysterious rules of stereomeric complementation, not those of copying. Reproduction of DNA also involves coiling and uncoiling, polymerization, ligation, etc. An indispensable part of the self-regulation of DNA is its repair process, which is strictly connected with the process of single or double strand exchange, namely with crossing-over. Crossing-over is a general occurrence in all living beings, not necessarily related to sexuality and chromosome pairing. I will consider it in parallel with another process, also involving DNA unfolding, namely gene activation. I will limit my comments to my laboratory experience, first as a botanist and then as a microbial geneticist. Even within these limits I will trespass on lands that I have never practised in before.

THE SUPPOSED EVOLUTION OF DNA

When DNA structure was discovered and its code deciphered, it immediately became commonplace to relate the information encoded into the DNA double helix to a long discourse recorded on a magnetic ribbon or typed in one or more pages. The discourse of a virus was regarded as a booklet of a few pages, that of a bacterium as a small volume, that of man as an enormous encyclopaedia. Never before had evolution been apparent in such an unequivocally quantitative way! The instructions for a virus were expectedly much less than those required to make a man. I remember that when I was a student I was taught that a bacterium could have a few thousand genes and a man a few millions. When more and more data on the amount of DNA per cell in various organisms became available, attempts were made to construct a sigmoid curve representing the increase in DNA with the increasing complexity of living beings, as if the organisms were derived in series through a kind of expansion of their DNA content. DNA provided the best Aristotelian ladder of life. One step was a virus, another a bacterium, a third a protozoan, the last a man. The amount of DNA has indeed nothing to do with an ascending evolutionary ladder. The DNA contents of the extant species are clustered around two quite distinct averages: a few millions of nucleotide pairs for prokaryotes and a few billions of nucleotide pairs for eukaryotes. There are some extreme deviations (no overlaps) but they have no relation with structural complexity or with geological antiquity (Lima-de-Faria, 1983).

Notwithstanding the enormous diversity in the DNA content in prokaryotes and eukaryotes, the amount of genetic information, as expressed in number of structural genes, or gene families, is essentially the same throughout the whole living kingdom (Table 1). This means that roughly only one part per thousand of the eukaryotic DNA is involved in transcription. The rest is parasite, junk, or has possibly some regulatory function.

Table 1. DNA per gene (or gene family) in various organisms

	Total DNA (nucelotide pairs)	Gene Number	DNA per Gene (nucleotide pairs)
E. coli	$4 \cdot 10^6$	5,000	800
Drosophila	$1.6 \cdot 10^8$	5,000*	32,000†
Triturus	$2.2 \cdot 10^{10}$	5,000‡	44,000,000
Xenopus	$2.2 \cdot 10^9$	5,000‡	4,000,000

* based on the n. of bands (Judd *et al.*, 1972); also on the frequency of lethals per generation (M) divided by the mutation rate per gene (u): $M/u = 0.05/10^{-5} = 5,000$
† a value of 35,000 is obtained from the average size of five genes (mal, ry, w, N, lz) based on intragenic recombination
‡ based on the n. of loops in lampbrush chromosomes (Bostock and Summer, 1978)

How many genes are required for present life? The most recent estimates range from 5,000 to 10,000. I personally prefer the lower estimate, but this is of minor relevance if one considers the previous gigantic evaluations of gene numbers in higher organisms, of the order of millions.

There is indeed a general trend in evolutionary thought, whenever two species, one primitive and another evolved, are related, be they amoeba and elephant or ape and man or a prokaryote and a eukaryote. The assumed relationship between two species passes through three or four phases:

First: one species is considered as ancestor, the other as derived;

Second: they become cousins, both deriving from a common extinct ancestor;

Third: their phylogenetic connection is disregarded. They are considered as different transformations of the same basic structure;

Fourth: 'derivation' is considered in a different context, as the extent of structural transformation in respect to an ideal model.

Prokaryotes and eukaryotes were long considered as ancestors and derived, respectively, as their names imply. In fact their nuclei appear now as two essentially distinct transformations of the basic structure of DNA (Doolittle, 1978), their phylogenetic connection is disregarded, and it is actually hard to state which of the two organisations is more 'derived' even in a structuralist context.

MEIOSIS, A PRIMITIVE CONDITION

Before the last war, bacteria were thought to reproduce asexually (even with no genes, according to J. Huxley's New Synthesis) and higher organisms to have invented sex and its various performances. The result of sex was increasing genetic variability, therefore sex must have been provided with an effective device for gene reassortment. This device was the well-known chromatid crossing-over, with its apparent manifestation in meiotic chiasmata.

When viral and bacterial recombination were first discovered, in the '40s and '50s, it immediately became evident that the reassortative ability of bacteria was outstanding. *Escherichia coli* K12 had a chromosome map as long as that of mouse, but one thousandth less DNA. The latter was therefore much more finely reassorted in a bacterium than in a mammal. A virus-like bacteriophage T4 had an even more reassorted DNA, having 10,000 cross-overs, for the same length of DNA, than a mouse! If one looks at the absolute and relative crossing-over rates in various species, the former, namely the total number of cross-overs per nucleus per meiotic (or meiotic-like) division, varies within one order of magnitude and it is essentially the same in the bacterium and in the mouse (20 cross-overs, corresponding to a map of 2,000 units). The resolving power of crossing-over is instead much higher in prokaryotes, up to three orders of magnitude higher (Table 2). It is hard to attribute to prokaryote crossing-over a genetic object, as that of producing

Table 2. Cross-over rates in various organisms

	Total DNA (nucleotide pairs)	Total Cross-overs (average per nucleus)	Cross-overs (per 10^8 n.p.)
Phage T4	$2 \cdot 10^5$	8.0	4,500
E. coli	$4 \cdot 10^6$	20.0	500
Streptomyces	$8 \cdot 10^6$	2.6	32
Aspergillus	$8 \cdot 10^7$	6.6	8
drosophila	$1.6 \cdot 10^8$	2.9	1.8
mouse	5.10^9	19.5	0.4
corn	7.10^9	13.5	0.2

Modified, from Pontecorvo, 1958.

gene rearrangements. Prokaryote chromosomes undergo pairing, crossing-over and reduction as soon as they have the opportunity of merging in the same cell forming a diploid condition. Usually this occurs after the migration of a small immigrant piece of a chromosome in a recipient cell (merodiploid). In most bacteria, however, cellular exchanges are but exceptional opportunities, possibly with no significance in nature.

Crossing-over is much reduced in eukaryotes, from yeasts to vertebrates. It takes place only in particular cells, the gametocytes or the sporocytes of animals or plants, and in those cells at a reduced rate. Other cells, the somatic or mitotic ones, virtually have no crossing-over. This might be due to their structural conformation, but they should possibly not be considered as lazy introverted, entangled DNAs, rather as sophisticated, dignified structures able to strictly modulate their performances.

MITOTIC CROSSING-OVER

Crossing-over is not fully absent in somatic cells. The first instances of mitotic crossing-over were described fifty years ago (1936) by Curt Stern in heterozygous drosophila as manifested by patches on somatic tissues. As an outcome of mitotic crossing-over the distal part of the involved chromosome may become homozygous and thus disclose the recessive phenotype in a somatic clone. Mitotic crossing-over was later carefully studied in heterozygous diploid molds by the Pontecorvo's school (Pontecorvo, 1958), to which I feel I belong. In green diploids, heterozygous for yellow or white colour markers, somatic crossing-over produces beautiful patches and sectors.

Crossing-over in mitotic chromosomes reveals the latent ability of DNA pairing and exchanging in somatic cells. Differentiation corresponds thus to the almost complete silence of the recombination apparatus. Suddenly, in the plant sporocytes or in the animal gametocytes a burst of crossing-over takes place, during the first meiotic prophase, to again fade away in the first post-meiotic division. It is, however, technically possible to induce pairing and mitotic crossing-over in somatic cells to a rate comparable to the meiotic performance. An effective induction of somatic crossing-over can be obtained by treating spores or hyphae of diploid moulds by various mutagens, oncogens or mitosis inhibitors (Fratello *et al.*, 1960).

Examples of so-called recombinagens are UV-rays, X-rays, nitrogen mustards, formalin, caffeine, fluorodeoxyuridine, mitomycin C. . . . Their action was interpreted within the picture of the precocity theory of meiosis of Darlington. According to that theory, in mitosis chromatids are already spiralized when they start their movements. In meiosis kinetics is precocious and unspiralized chromatids recognize their homologous partners. Since most, if not all, recombinagens retard the DNA synthesis, their effect might be that of presenting unspiralized chromatids at the mitotic prophase. This is surely the case with the prokaryotic transient diploids (or merodiploids), where a resident chromosome is visited by an immigrant DNA molecule, often at the stage of a single strand. Pairing is immediately established and a burst of crossing-overs takes place. Recombinagens also trigger the synthesis of a crowd of repair enzymes, which are required to perform both the DNA repair and the DNA exchange.

The two processes are for sure strictly related. Both require single strand breakage by endonucleases, single strand digestion by esonucleases, repair synthesis by polymerases, splicing by ligases. It is remarkable that the recombinagens are often known to be oncogens, namely inducers of an extensive protein synthesis. Their action reverts the DNA of the differentiated mitotic cell towards an actively repaired (or recombined), and extensively translated structure, be that referred to an oocyte or to an oncocyte. The burst of recombinant activity in mitotic cells after mutagen treatment is beautifully documented in chromosomes stained by fluorescent acridine dyes after treatment with Bromo-uridine-desoyxyribose (Budr). These exchanges have no genetic consequence, occurring between sister strands of the same chromosome.

CROSSING-OVER AS REPAIR MECHANISM

The outburst of crossing-over after mutagenic treatment qualifies it rather as a repair mechanism. Most of the occurring crossings-over, both spontaneous and induced, intragenic or long range, do not bear any genetic effect and do not reassort the genetic material. After recombinagen treatment of diploid molds, intragenic crossings-over are increased ten times more than long-range ones. Short-range crossings-over are detected whenever intragenic recombination is under study. When cross-over is selected within a gene, frequently the exchange does not affect the flanking genes, it is an affair within the gene or within the operon. Many intricate mechanisms have been suggested to explicate the process, which usually resort to a switchback close cross-over correcting the effect of the selected one. An alternative explanation of the non-involvement of the chromosome assumes the occurrence of discontinuities (or 'linkers') at one or both ends of the gene (Sermonti and Carere, 1968). These would break the node before it entangles the whole web. I personally favour the idea of that long-range crossing-over is only an extension of the more frequent short-range crossing-over, whenever a local strand exchange drags the whole chromosome with itself.

Short-range crossing-over is known to be a common repair process after mutagenic treatment. This phenomenon, called postreplicative repair, was detected after mutagenic treatment of bacterial cells. It requires the involvement of several enzymes, among which the RecA protein is of special interest (Little and Mount, 1982). The RecA protein is an enzyme required for the accomplishment of legitimate crossing-over in all organisms. As response to mutagenic damage, the so-called SOS response, a large amount of recombination proteins is produced. They are formed as long as single stranded DNA is available. The repair process requires the resynthesis of a segment of DNA and this is not as accurate as in normal synthesis. It is the *error-prone* character of the resynthesis process to cause the nucleotide replacements eventually to be fixed as mutations. Crossing-over is a repair mechanism. (It is remarkable that the major pattern of DNA repair are surprisingly similar in *Escherichia coli* and in mammalian cells.) Paradoxically, mutation is the result of a repair, an *error-prone* repair.

Short-range crossing-over is unquestionably a repair process. Post-replicative four-strand DNA proposes itself to the RecA protein with a damage in one strand and a gap in another and eventually emerges with four intact strands. The process does not involve the discarding of any genetic information, it operates without selective devices. All strands survive, the logic of the survival of the fittest does not operate.

In which sense can the long-range crossing-over be viewed as a repair process? I have remarked, at the beginning, that it is not the biochemical novelty which creates the new species and drives evolution. Why should we reward the reshuffling of a neutral, irrelevant variability? The best service selection can do is to eliminate the unserviceable mistakes. This is a repair process, at the level of the population, but it is an expensive process, first because it requires the phenotypic expression of the mistake, second because it asks for a sacrifice, third because it would drag into the elimination the whole genome or chromosome. Crossing-over, by breaking the continuity of the chromosome, allows the sacrifice of only that very region which is affected by the mistake.

Let me conclude by stating that fertilisation also is a repair mechanism, cross-fertilisation I mean. Without entering into details I would just dare to ask: what is the effect of preventing cross-fertilisation in a cross-bred species, as in cultivated corn? Is it that of reducing its genetic variability or rather than of condemning it to a rapid decline because of the emergence of no longer concealed negative mutations? Cross-fertilisation is a device for preventing or postponing the emergence of genetic load. Gametogenesis is a repair process in a more important sense. It is a process of rejuvenation of the indifferentiated senescent organism, a return to the cellular origin, to the primordial totipotentiality.

DNA STRUCTURE AND GENE TRANSCRIPTION

In summary, crossing-over activity is widespread in prokaryotic DNA, and restricted in eukaryotic DNA. In the latter it is virtually confined to sporocytes or gametocytes, negligible in somatic cells. By means of treatments affecting DNA, crossing-over can be restored in mitotic cells, to an almost meiotic level. A parallel can be surmised at this point with the transcriptional activity of the genes. This also is widespread in prokaryotic DNA, and restricted in eukaryotic DNA; in the latter it is relatively high in oocytes, much reduced in somatic cells. Treatments affecting DNA certainly activate at least those genes which are required for DNA replication, exchange and repair, about 50 genes. If an oncogenic activity is triggered, many more genes are activated.

The parallel might just be superficial. However, as far as we know, DNA transcription by RNA polimerase is dependent on local DNA denaturation and uncoiling, essentially the same configurational transformations established in crossing-over. Prokaryotic DNA is largely involved in elastic supercoiling known to play a prominent role in gene transcription. That supercoiling, or torsional stress, is mediated by enzymes called topoisomerases, namely producers of different topological isomers of DNA (Wang, 1985).

Until recently topoisomerase-induced torsional stress was thought not to occur in eukaryotic DNA (Gellert, 1981). Elastic supercoiled DNA is more accessible to nuclease and preferentially sensitive to digestion with DNAase I. By that digestion it was possible to show that some torsional stress is present in eukaryotic DNA (Villeponteau, *et al.*, 1984). The restricted regions sensitive to digestion by DNAase I are those comprising the active genes.

In chicken red blood cells (12-day-old embryos) producing adult β-globin, the entire β-globin domain is DNAase I sensitive. The same domain is virtually insensitive in chick brain DNA. The supercoiling is produced by topoisomerase II. If red blood cells are treated by novobiocin, an inhibitor of topoisomerase II, the preferential DNAase sensitivity of the β-globin genes is reversed (Figure 1).

An active gene is ten times more accessible to digestion than the quiescent DNA. The regulatory region of the gene is hypersensitive, being digestible up to 100 times as much as the inactive DNA.

Effective transcription of genes is only possible in the presence of superhelical tension. When the DNA supercoiling is released and DNA is returned to a DNAase insensitive ground state, gene translational activity ceases.

The site of action of the topoisomerase was referred to some short DNA sequences (20-100 nucleotides), present in eukaryotes and known as *enhancers*. These sequences are conditional for gene activation. The enhancers have some interesting properties. They work irrespective of their orientation. They can be put upstream, in the middle of or downstream of the activated gene. More interesting, they can be found (or be artificially located) at various distances from the gene promoter, from a few dozens nucleotides to some thousands of

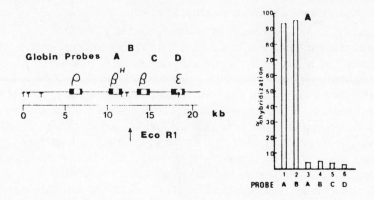

Figure 1. (Left) The ß-globin domain in embryonic chicken red blood cells (RBC). (Above) Cloned hybridization probes. (Right) DNAase I sensitivity in the globin gene domain: nuclei from embryonic brain (bars 1-2) and RBC (bars 3-6) were digested with DNAase I and the undigested DNAs were hybridized with globin probes. In brain, the ß-globin domain in DNAase I unsensitive (inactive); in RBC, is fully sensitive (active) (after Villeponteau *et al.*, 1984).

nucleotides, provided they are in the same closed topological domain as the affected gene (chromosome loop, virus or plasmid). A valid hypotheses is that the enhancer is a region involved in the organisation of the DNA topology. If a complete gene for immunoglobulin, containing the promoter and the enhancer is transfected in a competent cell, it becomes expressed and goes on being transcribed for along time. If the enhancer is missing the system remains silent. If, however, in already transcribing cells, the enhancer is lost, the cells remain active. Thus the enhancer appears to be necessary to the establishment of a new configuration of the genetic material which, once set, will remain stable. The enhancers work as modifiers of the DNA topology, able to operate from the distance and to induce stable alternative configurations of the genetic material, without altering the coded information (Ptashne, 1986).

An important problem at this point is to what extent chromosome topology is stable and inheritable. In higher organisms one deals with two kinds of supercoiling: a non-elastic one wound around nucleosome cores, and an elastic one giving rise to torsional strain in restricted chromatin domains. It is the latter which is related to transcriptional gene activity and whose inheritability interests us. It is known that the torsional stress is retained in specific genes present in differentiated tissues after they have ceased their translational activity (they remain DNAase I sensitive).

Is the elastic supercoiling transmittable from a mother cell to her sister cells? Self-reproduction of torsional stress is known in some viruses and could perhaps be of more general occurrence. I wish just to offer the possibility of the genetic transfer of DNA topology. This is a matter of the so-called gene 'ecology' and gene 'territories' (Naora, 1986). A proportional spacing of genes is required for their translational activity, and it seems reasonable to assume that it conditions the possibility of the DNA conformational changes needed to gene activation. Prolonged inactivity of a gene could result in a mutational alteration of its territory and in its irreversible silence. This I would call genetic assimilation, in Waddington's terminology.

CONCLUSION

The structure of DNA, clustered around two patterns of organisation, compact and disperse, does not lend itself to historical interpretation. Prokaryotes cannot be viewed as ancestors of eukaryotes. The prokaryotic nucleus is more active than the eukaryotic one, at least under two respects: 1) the prokaryotic DNA is much more amenable to reassortment by crossing-over; 2) the prokaryotic DNA is much more active in transcription. Both properties are related to DNA uncoiling and denaturation, required for crossing-over and transcription.

Active DNA tension is diffused and environmentally controlled in prokaryotes, and is severely restricted and specialized in eukaryotes, to particular tissues and to particular chromosome regions. Morphological differentiation, typical of eukaryotes, is to be connected to a generalized depression of DNA activity and to its differential local depression. To what extent is the latter clonally inheritable? To what extent is it species-specific and sexually transmittable? The general pattern of gene activation in the organism cannot be gene controlled. We assume that it is under the control of a morphogenetic field (Webster and Goodwin, 1982), which restricts its own potentialities during ontogenesis and resumes its total array in the egg cell.

REFERENCES

Bostok, C. J. and Summer, A. T. (1978) *The eukaryotic chromosome.* North Holland, Amsterdam.
Britten, R. J. and Davidson, E. H. (1969) Gene regulation for higher cells: a theory. *Science.* 165. 349.
Doolittle, W. F. (1978) Genes in pieces: were they ever together? *Nature.* London. 581-2.
Dressler, D. and Potter, H. (1982) Molecular mechanisms in genetic recombination. *Ann. Rev. Biochem.* 51. 727-61.
Fratello, B. Morpurgo, G. and Sermonti, G. (1960) Induced somatic segregation in Aspergillus nidulans. *Genetics.* 45. 785-800.
Jacob, F. (1977) Evolution and thinkering. *Science.* 196. 1161-6.
Judd, B. H., Schen, M. W. and Kaufmann, T. C. (1972) The anatomy and function of a segment of the chromosome of Drosophila melanogaster. *Genetics.* 71. 139.
Lima-de-Faria, A. (1983) *Molecular evolution and organisation of the chromosome.* Elsevier Science Pub., Amsterdam.
Lindhahl, T. (1982) DNA repair enzymes. *Ann. Rev. Biochem.* 51. 61-87.
Little, J. W. and Mount, D. W. (1982) The SOS regulatory system of Escherichia coli. *Cell.* 29. 11.

Naora, H. (1986) Gene ecology. *Riv. Biol./B. Fourm.* 79. 345-71.

Pontecorvo, G. (1958) *Trends in genetic analysis.* Columbia University Press, New York.

Ptashne, M. (1986) Gene regulation by proteins acting nearby and at distance. *Nature.* London. 322. 697-701.

Sermonti, G. and Carere, A. (1968) Mechanism for polarised recombination in Streptomyces. *Mol. Gen. Genetics.* 103. 141-49.

Villeponteau, B., Lundell, M. and Martinson, H. (1984) Torsional stress promotes the DNAase I sensitivity of active genes. *Cell.* 39. 469-78.

Wang, J. C. (1985) Topoisomerases. *Ann. Rev. Biochem.* 54. 665-97.

Webster, G. C. and Goodwin, B. C. (1982) The origin of species: a structuralist approach. *J. Soc. Biol. Struct.* 5. 15-47.

15. Gene-Ecological Aspects of Non-coding DNA Sequences and Genome Evolution

Hiroto Naora

AN ATTEMPT TO FIND AN INTRINSIC PRINCIPLE

In recent years, one of the major thrusts of molecular biology has been to elucidate the fine mechanisms by which gene expression is regulated. For example, attempts have been and will be intensively made to characterise factors and DNA elements of genes which control gene expression during development or in response to external and internal stimuli. However, I believe that the expression of a gene is not solely inherent in its own nucleotide sequences including flanking regulatory elements, but is a function of relations which can be assigned to the structure of a biological system (Webster and Goodwin, 1984; Naora, 1986). Therefore, a central question concerns the structure underlying the regulation of cell function. This further leads to the search for an intrinsic principle that holds gene expression in order.

To attempt the search for such a principle, here I shall focus onto the hitherto unappreciated concept of gene-to-gene interaction in the intracellular gene expression network. Various biological activities, such as reproduction or even the behaviour of living organisms have been shown to be complex functions that result from a response to population density and the spatial structure of the overall environment (Deevey, 1971; English and Mayfield, 1972; Naora, 1986). This provides us with a question as to whether the structure deeply underlying the biological function is formed on the basis of a density dependence. It is for this reason that I wish to examine whether there exists at the level of genes on chromosomes, a complex relationship between a gene's activity and the spatial structure of its environment, and to raise the question as to whether the principle of a (population) density dependence can be seen at the gene level, even at the dawn of genome evolution.

GENE ARRANGEMENT ON CHROMOSOMES AND GENE TERRITORIES

It has been postulated that gene clusters were formed mainly by gene duplication, followed by subsequent alteration (e.g. base alterations, block deletions and insertions) and correction of gene sequences (Ohno, 1970; Jeffreys, 1982). The resulting gene copies have often remained in close proximity within a certain region and thus formed a gene cluster. In some

185

cases, however, duplicated copies have been transpositioned to different regions and even translocated onto different chromosomes. For example, the human insulin-like growth factor I (IGF - I) gene is separated from other family members and lies on chromosome 12, whereas the insulin-like growth factor II (IGF - II) gene remains on chromosome 11 and is closely linked with the insulin gene, from which the former two genes arose (Bell *et al.*, 1985). However, gene duplication is not the sole event contributing to the formation of a gene cluster, because there are some clusters composed of entirely different genes.

A number of gene clusters has been characterised showing that there is a wide variety of gene sizes and intergenic distances, thus erroneously giving us an impression that there exists no uniformity in spatial arrangement of genes on chromosomes. However, the comparative analysis of the various cases of spatial arrangement has shown that the intergenic distance of a chosen pair of genes is not chaotically variable, but is a function of the total size of the paired genes (with special exceptions which will be described later) (Naora and Deacon, 1982a; Naora, 1986). It is of particular importance to mention here that the spatial arrangement of genes, in particular a gene-population-density, actually determines the potential activity of the gene in a cluster (Naora, 1986). Thus, this really concerns the question as to whether a gene-population-density dependence of gene expression represents one of the features of an intrinsic principle.

The results obtained in the comparative analyses of the spatial arrangement of chromosomal genes in eukaryotes have already been described in detail (Naora and Deacon, 1982a; Naora, 1986). A summary of the observations is as follows:

(i) The clustered genes on the chromosomes of eukaryotes (mainly higher eukaryotes) are each surrounded by extragenic DNA sequences; these extragenic DNA sequences both at 5'- and 3'-regions are called 'gene territories'. These must be of a certain size for active function.

(ii) The intergenic distance between two genes in a cluster is defined by the size of the genes. (An example will be described later). It increases as the genes become longer, but it reaches a plateau at 13.5 kb when the total length of a pair of genes become 5 kb or longer. A minimum intergenic distance is approximately 0.3 kb long.

(iii) The above relationship can only be seen when two genes lie on the same DNA strand, not when they lie on different strands.

(iv) A most striking observation is that when two genes lie on the same DNA strand and have an intergenic distance shorter than a defined length, the transcriptional activities of one or both genes are, in most cases, absent or greatly reduced; these we called 'territorial effects' (Naora and Deacon, 1982a and b; Naora, 1986). Both genes are incapable of being expressed at the same time (Emerman and Temin, 1984, 1986a and b; Naora, 1986). For example, a pair of 1 kb long genes which lie on the same DNA strand and possess a <4 kb long intergenic distance should show mutual interference by territorial effects.

However, no suppression or interference by territorial effects is seen at all if two genes lie on the different DNA strand even with a very short intergenic distance (Naora and Deacon, 1982a; Naora, 1986; Jaenish and Soriano, 1986.

(v) Territorial DNA sequences may contribute in part to the formation of a specific higher-order chromatin structure which may be necessary for efficient transcription. Evidence has been accumulated that transcription on eukaryote chromosomes is a function of higher-order chromatin structures. In fact, recent observations show that when a pair of genes has a short intergenic distance, the chromatin at the 5'-neighbouring region of transcriptionally active gene is more DNAase I-sensitive than that of transcriptionally inactive gene in a cluster (Emerman and Temin, 1986b). This suggests that a short intergenic DNA sequence in a gene cluster does not allow both genes to form the chromatin structure necessary for efficient transcription at the same time.

After gene duplication, the duplicated gene copies had often altered their sequences. Such alterations have occurred not only in coding sequences but also in intron sequences by base alteration, block insertion or deletion. The overall sizes of many duplicated copies, however, have not changed significantly over long evolutionary periods (Naora *et al.*, 1988). For example, despite the fact that the human δ and β-like globin genes diverged about 40 to 70 million years ago (Jeffreys, 1982), the difference in their size amounts to only 2 per cent (Lawn *et al.*, 1980; Spritz *et al.*, 1980). In some cases, however, marked alteration of the duplicated copies have occurred in their sizes. A good example is the cluster composed of the human insulin (1.4 kb long) and IGF-II genes (15 kb long) (Bell *et al.*, 1985). The IGF-II gene is more than ten times longer than the original gene. In spite of such a drastic alteration of the gene size during its evolutionary period, both genes lie on the same DNA strand with an intergenic distance of 12.6 kb, which is close enough to the required defined length (13.5 kb) (see Naora, 1986; Naora *et al.*, 1988). Similar observations have been made with other pairs of genes, e.g. *Drosophila melanogaster Antennapedia* complex (Kuroiwa *et al.*, 1985; see also Table 1). Since the intergenic distance is defined by the total size of a pair of genes, the above observation implies that extragenic territorial DNA sequences which are involved in the spatial arrangement of genes have evolved in concert with an alteration of the gene size (Naora *et al.*, 1988).

It seems possible that after or during gene duplication the following three possible mechanisms might, singly or together, have operated to adjust the spatial arrangement of duplicated copies on chromosomes.

(i) Suitable gene pairs which possess the defined intergenic distance between genes have been selected and have been maintained as a result of natural selection.

(ii) The mechanism involved in gene duplication intrinsically required a certain size of extragenic DNA sequences, corresponding to the defined length of an intergenic distance between duplicated copies. Alternatively, a 'distance defining' mechanism was built in the gene duplication machinery.

Table 1. Some examples of pairs of unequally sized genes

Gene clusters	Genes, intergenic distances (kb)	Ratios of genes	Total gene sizes (kb)
Newt histone (Stephenson *et al.*, 1981)	← ← -H3-H1- 1.11 0.54 0.76	1.41	1.30
Drosophila melanogaster histone (Kedes, 1979)	← ← -H1-H3- 1.35 0.95 0.52	1.83	1.47
Xenopus laevis globin (Patient *et al.*, *1980*)	→ → -α1-β1- 7.7 1.2 1.8	1.50	3.0
Human apolipoprotein (Karathanasis, 1985)	→ ← → -Apo AI-Apo CIII-Apo AIV 1.7 12 2.4	1.41	4.1
Human insulin (Bell *et al.*, 1985)	→ → -Insulin-Insulin like-growth Factor III- 12.6 1.4 15	10.7	16.4
Drosophila melanogaster bithorax complex (Beachy *et al.*,1985)	← ← -Ubx-bxd- 10 ~75 20	~3.8	~95
Drosophila melanogaster Antennapedia complex (Kuroiwa *et al.*, 1985)	← ← –X-Antp– ~16 ~0.4 <100	<250	<100.4

Arrows show the directions of genes. The numbers shown below the genes and intergenic regions of pairs of genes present on the same D N A strand represent the lengths of respective genes and intergenic distances. The relative gene sizes are compared by the ratios of (large gene)/(small gene) within a cluster.

(iii) In a normal situation, gene duplication is inevitably followed by the spatial rearrangement of genes on chromosomes in a correction mechanism. This mechanism was probably to adjust the distortion, resulting from gene duplication, of higher-order chromatin structures by block insertions or deletions of D N A sequences.

The selection mechanism listed in (i) seems most unlikely to operate within a cell. If the gene pairs with the defined length of an intergenic distance remained as a result of natural selection, these pairs should appear very rarely. Furthermore, the fact that genes have often changed in size after duplication should significantly reduce the probability of their appearance. In spite of this expectation, varieties of many genes have been found to be clustered in an appropriate form of spatial arrangement (see Table 1), suggesting that the first mechanism seems unlikely.

Regarding the second mechanism, unless subsequent alteration of gene sizes took place after gene duplication, this mechanism can account for some cases. However, when a gene changed in size, a correction mechanism such as that listed in iii) must have been operational.

In contrast to the previous two possibilities, it seems most likely that after gene duplication, the spatial arrangement of the copies were inevitably adjusted by a correction mechanism and thus the copies probably did not have any alternative choices in such a situation.

However, it appears that the correction mechanism was not rigidly operated. Some gene pairs escaped from the correction or failed to be adjusted. This would in part result in the formation of the pairs of genes with very short intergenic distances, e.g. presumably rat cardiac myosin heavy chain α and β genes (Mahdavi *et al.*, 1984). The failure might include excess deletions or insufficient insertions of DNA sequences. Accordingly, when the duplicated copy lay incidentally or inevitably in the near vicinity of the original gene or previously duplicated gene copies on the same DNA strand, transcriptional activity of one or both genes was severely curtailed and restricted by territorial effects (Naora, 1986). This would eventually result in one of the following two events. Obviously, it would cause the permanent cessation of the transcriptional activity of one or both genes, followed by the random alterations of nucleotide sequences. Then, the impaired genes would become pseudogenes. In fact, approximately 50 per cent of pseudogenes discovered so far lie in close proximity to a currently active gene in cluster (Naora, 1986). On the other hand, the pairs of gene copies which escaped from correction have been adopted to a secure regulatory mechanism for alternative expression of gene copies. Since both genes were incapable of being expressed at the same time, in such a situation, either genes might act as a suppressor to its neighbour simply by being active. Such a situation has probably continued up to the present. For example, an alternative expression of rat myosin heavy chain α and β genes is rigidly regulated under various physiological and pathological conditions (Lompré *et al.*, 1984). Similarly, β^H and adult β globin genes of chick (Dolan *et al.*, 1971; Landes *et al.*, 1982; Villeponteau *et al.*, 1982) are constitutionally regulated during development. In all of these cases the duplicated gene copies possess very short intergenic distances between copies and never express at the same time.

The next question naturally raised is which copy has become a pseudogene and which pair of genes has been adopted to a regulatory mechanism. There have been no data consistent with a view that some genes were especially selected for functional requirements. On the other hand, it seems possible that it was just a matter of arbitrariness and as a result, the surviving pairs of genes have become involved in a gene expression network, simply because these specialised pairs existed on chromosomes. This is my view of the origin of a secure regulatory mechanism for differential expression. Needless to say here, such a secure mechanism is based on the principle of a gene-population-density dependence.

INTRINSIC GENE TERRITORIES AND CONCERTED EVOLUTION WITH A GENE

As described in the previous chapter, the sizes of extragenic territorial DNA sequences are a key factor which determines the potential activity of clustered genes on eukaryote chromosomes. For a better understanding of this regulatory system, information on the molecular nature of extragenic territorial DNA sequences is required. At present this information is limited.

There are two concepts regarding gene territories; the first is concerned with territorial DNA sequences present in the actual intergenic region between two genes, and the second with intrinsic territories. The intergenic region referred to in this paper is composed of at least two extragenic territorial DNA sequences; those flanking the 3'-end of one gene and those flanking the 5'-end of the other. We do not know, at present, the actual sizes of the two individual extragenic territorial DNA sequences of a given pair of genes (Naora, 1986). However, the model analyses that were carried out to examine the basic properties of a gene territory have shown that the actual territories of a given gene change in size, depending upon the size of the neighbouring gene on the same DNA strand (Naora et al., 1988). In contrast to the variable nature of actual territories, an intrinsic territory can be considered as a specific invariable feature of a gene of a given size.

The size of the intrinsic territory can be estimated under a particular condition. Since a number of cases have been reported, in which a gene lies with a much smaller gene at the 5'- or 3'-regions on the same DNA strand (see Table 1), it is assumed that the gene adjacent to a gene of any given size becomes infinitely small. Then it would be possible to estimate the size of the intrinsic 5'- and 3'-territories of a given gene from the curve of the relationship between total gene size and defined intergenic distance (Naora, 1986). For example, it can be deduced that a 1 kb long gene possesses 0.8 kb long intrinsic territories at both 5'- and 3'-regions of equal size (Naora et al., 1988). What is striking is that the intrinsic territories are actually demarcated at the borders by specific conformations, i.e. altered secondary DNA structures. A good example is the *Drosophila melanogaster* alcohol dehydrogenase (ADH) gene, which possesses dual (adult and larval) initiation sites. The adult and larval genes are 1.8 and 1.1 kb long, respectively and are expressed differentially during the development of a fly (Benyajati et al., 1983). When the ADH genes are under negative torsional stress (see later description) they exhibit at least four S1 nuclease-sensitive sites at 2.7 kb and 1.4 kb upstream of the adult and larval initiation sites respectively and 0.8 kb and 3.0 kb downstream from the poly (A) addition site. As some of these sites are also sensitive to other single-stranded specific endonucleases, these observations suggest that the ADH gene possesses specific conformational features at these sites (Miyahara and Naora, manuscript in preparation). Assuming that the *D. melanogaster* ADH genes lie with the presumptive genes at the 5'- and 3'-regions on the same DNA strands and that these presumptive neighbouring genes become infinitely small in size, the adult and larval ADH genes are estimated to possess 2.9 kb and 0.9 kb long intrinsic territories (Naora *et al.*, 1988). The observed S1 nuclease sensitive sites exist just around or near the borders of these intrinsic territories. As similar observations were made with several other genes (see Table 2), the specific conformations found at the specific sites around the *D. melanogaster* ADH genes are not special cases, but seem to represent a general feature of various genes.

These observations provide several interesting insights into aspects of the gene territories involved in the regulation of gene expression. For example, the demarcated landmarks specific to individual genes appear to be involved in the formation of the higher-order chromatin structures required for efficient transcription within a nucleus.

Eukaryotic DNA in chromatin is under negative torsional stress which can lead to the formation of altered DNA (non-B form) conformation at certain sites (Villeponteau *et al.*, 1984; see also Naora *et al.*, 1988). Therefore, when the DNA molecule is under torsional stress, the landmarks at the borders of intrinsic territories become visible by conformational changes. This then would be followed by alteration to higher-order chromatin structures which are required for efficient transcription of the gene involved. Indeed, this has been shown in some cases. For example, it is known that torsionally strained chromatin corresponds to the transcriptionally active region which is DNase I hypersensitive. In particular, the altered secondary DNA structure formed by torsional stress at the demarcation site of the intrinsic territory of the chicken β-globin gene is seen at the site where the DNAase I hypersensitive structure is detected when the gene is actively expressed (Larsen and Weintraub, 1982; Weintraub, 1983). Another example is the molecular event observed around the *D. melanogaster* heat shock protein genes (proximal and distal *hsp* 70 genes) (Holmgren *et al.*, 1979). These genes possess specialised chromatin structures sensitive to S1 and *Neurospora crassa* nucleases at the sites corresponding to the landmarks of the intrinsic territories on the proximal and distal sides of the locus (Udvardy *et al.*, 1985; see also Noara *et al.*, 1988). It is of particular interest to mention that activation of the *hsp* 70 genes by heat shock is accompanied by specific alterations of the structures at the landmark sites. All these observations suggest that the landmarks of a given gene are deeply involved in the formation of specific higher-order chromatin structures required for the gene's expression.

Table 2. Sizes of intrinsic territories (referred from Naora *et al.*, 1988)

Genes	Gene sizes	Theoretical estimation of 5'- and 3'- intrinsic territories	Experimental estimation of sites sensitive to single strand-specific nucleases* (Distance in kb from termini of the gene)		References
	(kb)	(kb)	5'	3'	
Sea urchin histone					
H1	~0.6	~0.4	0.6	~0.4	Hentschel (1982)
Drosophila melanogaster					
Alcohol dehydrogenase					
Adult	1.8	2.9	2.7	3.0	Miyahara *et al.* §
Larval	1.1	0.9	1.4	0.8	Miyahara *et al.* §
Heat shock protein					
hsp 70	2.3	5.4	~5.0	~5.8	Udvardy *et al.*, (1984)
(proximal)					
hsp 28	1.1	0.9	0.8†	0.3	Selleck *et al.*, (1984)
hsp 23	0.8	0.5	0.2	0.2 or 0.5†	Selleck *et al.*, (1984)
Chicken globin					
ρ	1.2	1.1	1.4	none‡	Larsen *et al.*, (1982)
β^H	~1.5	~1.9	none‡	2.2	Larsen *et al.*, (1982)
β^A	1.5	1.9	none‡	1.3	Larsen *et al.*, (1982)
ε	1.6	2.2	1.7	N.D.	Larsen *et al.*, (1982)
Human sn RNA					
U1	~0.17	0.3	0.3	none‡	Htun *et al.* (1984)

* S1 nuclease (in some cases, Bal 31 or *Neurospora crassa* nucleases)-sensitive sites were examined in supercoiled plasmids except for the hsp 70 gene.
† The site is shared by the paired genes.
‡ No sites have been reported which correspond to those predicted. This does not necessarily imply the absolute absence at these regions.
§ Manuscript in preparation.
N.D. Not determined.

The landmarks are also likely to play another, but related role in organisation of chromosomes; that is involvement in the correction mechanism(s) for spatial arrangement of genes in clusters. It has been shown that the actual intergenic distance of a given pair of genes in a cluster is neither equal to the simple sum of their intrinsic territories nor simply proportional to the gene size (Naora *et al.*, 1988). The correction mechanism(s) for spatial arrangement described in the previous chapter is at present unknown. It is possible, however, that the specific conformations induced by torsional stress at the landmark sites of two genes in a cluster interacted with each other during the course of spatial rearrangement and, as a result of multiple interaction, the actual intergenic distance was determined.

The existence of the landmarks specific to individual genes raises a question as to how individual landmarks have evolved together with the gene. When the extragenic DNA sequences (including landmarks) were duplicated together with a gene and the gene size remained unchanged, as, presumably, for interferon IF-α for example (Ullrich *et al.*, 1981), the duplicated copy of the gene should be equipped with its own landmarks. However, the mechanism(s) for concerted evolution of landmarks might not be simple when a gene changed its size after duplication (Naora *et al.*, 1988). This is because the locations of landmarks are defined by gene sizes.

There are a few possible mechanisms by which the concerted evolution of landmarks may have taken place with the genes. For example, it is possible that many potential landmarks exist, scattered around at various places on the chromosomes. Genes newly evolved (e.g. by gene duplication, followed by alteration of sizes) or translocated, and even genes that were introduced by transfection experiments might utilise pre-existing landmarks at their new locations for active function (see Naora *et al.*, 1988). However, it seems more likely that the correction mechanism, in which landmarks themselves perhaps participate to adjust the spatial arrangement of genes in cluster, also operated to insert a landmark at a defined site. For example, it seems possible that the size change of an existing gene or introduction of an exotic gene resulted in a distortion of higher-order chromatin structure. This would inevitably lead to the correction of the distorted structure through inserting altered secondary DNA structures at the defined sites which correspond to the locations of landmarks. Therefore, a whole series of events, e.g. gene duplication, alteration of gene sizes, distortion of higher-order chromatin structures, correction of spatial arrangement of copies in a cluster and/or acquisition of new landmarks would be predetermined for a structure which is based on the principle of a density dependence.

Whatever the case, if genes failed to acquire their specific landmarks at the defined sites, it would be expected that these genes never become transcriptionally active and eventually become pseudogenes (Naora *et al.*, 1988). In fact, a number of 'intron' containing pseudogenes have been found, which were not truncated and completely separated from neighbouring genes (Naora, 1986). I propose that some of these pseudogenes might have resulted from a failure of acquisition of new landmarks after transposition of duplicated gene copies.

Once again concerted evolution of landmarks with genes is an example to suggest that the structure underlying the regulation of gene expression is formed on the basis of the principle of a (gene-population) density dependence. It is my view that such a structure has intrinsically determined a series of events which took place during a long evolutionary period, e.g. acquisition of landmarks.

EVOLUTION OF NON-CODING DNA SEQUENCES

Non-coding DNA sequences play an important role in spatial arrangement of genes on chromosomes (Zuckerlandl, 1986). However, most eukaryote cells still possess a further excess of non-coding sequences (Naora *et al.*, 1987).

In the hope of better understanding spatial arrangement of genes, I shall briefly discuss a possible origin of non-coding DNA sequences.

It is a reasonable assumption that a primordial polynucleotide was formed by random addition of mononucleotides without any specific template and thus the products were single-stranded molecules (Naora *et al.*, 1987). The view of RNA as primordial polynucleotides has been supported by some observations (Darnell and Doolittle, 1986), but still remains unsettled. Therefore, I will not deal with this issue here. As non-coding DNA sequences appear to be formed and evolved together with genes, I would first ask a question as to the origin of a primordial gene in the context of the formation of non-coding DNA sequences.

Definition of a primordial gene is ambiguous. However, I tentatively define the primordial gene to be an open reading frame which coded for a protein possessing biological functions, not necessarily efficient, e.g. protein-protein or protein-nucleic acid binding abilities and catalytic functions. There are other types of genes in contemporary organisms. For example, genes that are transcribed but not translated, are known. However, these genes form a relatively minor fraction of the total DNA of chromosomes and their origin is at present unknown. It is for this reason that only protein-coding genes will be dealt with in this discussion.

It is assumed that a protein-coding gene was transcribed and translated in a primordial soup/cell using primordial protein-synthesising machinery. I also assume that only stop and non-stop codons were involved in such a primordial system and that an initiation codon was not involved early in evolution (Naora *et al.*, 1987). Under these assumptions, I now consider the probability that a primordial gene would be generated in a primordial polynucleotide molecule at a reasonable frequency. To examine this probability, some basic information regarding the sizes of a primordial gene and genome are required. Various observations, though circumstantial, support the view that an ~0.55 kb long open reading frame was the original form of a functional primordial gene (Naora *et al.*, 1987). These observations include the critical size (~0.55 kb) of mosaic gene structures (Naora and Deacon, 1982c), the molecular mass (~18,000 Da) of proteinoids displaying some catalytic activities (Dose and Zaki, 1971), the smallest sizes (e.g. 198 amino acid residues) of serine proteases (Olson *et al.*, 1970), the domain sizes (approximately 100-200 amino acid residues) of contemporary proteins (Richardson, 1981; Blake, 1985) and the unit size (19,000 Da) of eukaryote protein molecules (Savageau, 1986). The next estimate required is that of the length of the single-stranded polynucleotide molecules which might be formed and maintained with a certain degree of stability in the primordial soup/cell. Although there are technical difficulties in detecting minute quantities of long single-stranded RNA and DNA molecules, no single-stranded contemporary polynucleotides markedly exceeding 20 kb in length have been found to date (see Naora *et al.*, 1987 for details). These include the single-stranded form of viral DNA and RNA and cellular single-stranded RNA. Furthermore, monomer proteins longer than 700,000 Da that require <20 kb long mRNA are extremely rare (Naora *et al.*, 1987). There is no reason to believe that the microenvironment surrounding primordial single-stranded polynucleotides was significantly different from the contemporary microenvironment in terms of biochemical, chemical and physical factors limiting the size of single-stranded polynucleotides (Naora *et al.*, 1987). Therefore, the length of the longest contemporary single-stranded RNA and DNA would provide us with a limit regarding that of primordial single-stranded polynucleotides. Taking all these observations into consideration, it is proposed that a 20-kb-long single-stranded polynucleotides was the longest molecule formed and maintained in the primordial soup/cell and thus may be considered as the progenitor genome form (Naora *et al.*, 1987). With all this information, the distribution of stop codons in a primordial polynucleotide molecule may be examined under the assumption that stop and non-stop codons were randomly and independently distributed over the primordial polynucleotide molecules formed in the primordial soup/cells. If there are n non-stop codons in a run of L codons, the number of opportunities for runs of non-stop codon is $(L-n + 1)$. Therefore, the probability that at least one of the $(L-n + 1)$ runs is at least r codons long is

$$1 - [1 - (\frac{n}{L})^r]^{L-n+1}$$

For large L and r this probability may be approximated by

$$P = 1 - \exp{[-(L-n + 1)(\frac{n}{L})^r]}$$

(see Naora *et al.*, 1987 for details).

The probabilities calculated using the above equation show that a run of at least 0.55-kb-long open reading frame would appear in the 20-kb-long primordial genome ($L = 1/3 \times 20,000$) at a frequency of 4.6 per cent when three stop codons were used from the total 64 codons (see Table 3). Such an event seems to be neither very rare nor very frequent, whereas, with two stop codons, surprisingly it would occur at a frequency of 46 per cent. This is a very high value. It seems highly likely that with two codons, primordial genes were densely distributed in a single polynucleotide molecule, resulting in a marked alteration of the gene-duplication pattern. Furthermore, it has been noticed that many contemporary genes are equipped with more than one stop codon, either consecutively or close by each other, in phase or in different phases at the end of a given reading frame, e.g. the human interleukin 2 gene (Fujita *et al.*, 1983). With only two stop codons, such a multiple stop codon system would have been less likely to evolve (Naora *et al.*, 1987).

With four stop codons, on the other hand, a 0.55 kb long primordial gene would have appeared very rarely, that is, at a frequency of 0.3 per cent. Under this condition, most of the open reading frame generated would have been too short to be functional (Naora *et al.*, 1987). Consequently, functional genomes

Table 3. Distribution of longest run, *r*, of non-stop codons when
$L = 1/3 \times 20\ 000$ codons (referred from Naora *et al.*, 1987)

Probability longest run ≥*r*	Size of *r*, expressed in kb		
	Stop codons, no.		
P	2	3	4
0.003	1.053	0.722	0.550
0.01	0.939	0.647	0.494
0.046	0.793	0.550	0.422
0.25	0.622	0.437	0.338
0.46	0.550	0.389	0.303
0.75	0.474	0.339	0.265
0.95	0.401	0.290	0.229

would not have been accumulated in sufficient quantity with four stop codons in a primordial soup/cell. All these observations suggest that if two or four stop codons rather than three stop codons were chosen in a primordial soup/cell, life on earth would not have evolved — at least not life in the present form (Naora *et al.*, 1987). This implies that the use of three stop codons at the dawn of evolution was a crucial event in the origin of the present forms of life on Earth.

No information is at present available as to how three stop codons were chosen in a primordial soup/cell. A common view is that three stop codons might have resulted from selection pressure. It is equally conceivable, however, that it was simply an arbitrary matter or the obligatory consequence of a series of events.

The next question concerns the excess quantity of non-coding DNA sequences present on eukaryote chromosomes. Examination of the distribution of three stop codons in a primordial polynucleotide molecule shows that most of the primordial genomes would have contained only one primordial gene, and this gene would most often be no longer than ~0.55 kb. Assuming that the prototype structure of such genomes, that is a 0.55 kb-long primordial gene associated with (20-0.55) kb-long non-coding sequences, was maintained despite a serial random duplication of DNA sequences through evolution, the total size, *m* kb, of nuclear non-coding DNA sequences of various species of eukaryotes and prokaryotes may be estimated by $m = N \times (20\text{-}0.55)$, where *N* is the number of genes in a given species of organisms (Naora *et al.*, 1987). Calculation of *m* values with reasonable estimates of *N* values (Cavalier-Smith, 1985a) in various eukaryotes and prokaryotes shows that the calculated amounts of non-coding DNA sequences do not differ significantly from those reported for these specific organisms with few exceptions (Naora *et al.*, 1987). These exceptional species include all prokaryotes and most lower eukaryotes of small genomic size and also special eukaryotes, e.g. *Protopteus aethiopicus*, that possess enormously amplified special sequences of non-coding regions (Cavalier-Smith, 1985a). The above observations imply that the genomes of the majority of higher eukaryotes retained the prototype genome structure during a long period of evolution and did not lose any obligatory by-products formed early in evolution (Naora *et al.*, 1987). It is a conventional view that these non-coding DNA sequences have been particularly retained on chromosomes by natural selection. However, there are no specific reasons to believe that such natural selection has actually taken place. On the other hand, it is equally conceivable that the by-products formed with genes were arbitrarily adopted to the complex organisation of genomes to the principle of a density dependence, simply because these by-products just co-existed with genes. Therefore, the presence of an excess of non-coding DNA sequences in contemporary species may not solely be a consequence of natural selection, but rather due to arbitrary events at the dawn of evolution.

THE UTILISATION OF NON-CODING DNA SEQUENCES AND CONTEMPORARY GENE STRUCTURES

The utilisation of non-coding DNA sequences probably represents one of the major events of the more recent stages of evolution. Needless to say, this event included block insertion of non-coding DNA sequences into intergenic regions to adjust the spatial arrangement of genes and also into coding regions of the gene. The latter, called intron insertion, has been a controversial issue in the context of the origin of a gene (Lonberg and Gilbert, 1985; Cavalier-Smith, 1985b; Rogers, 1985 and 1986; Marchronni and Gilbert, 1986; Gilbert *et al.*, 1986). As opposed to the view of the pre-existence of introns (Blake, 1978; Lonberg and Gilbert, 1985; Darnell and Doolittle, 1986), however, evidence has recently accumulated that strongly supports the idea of intron insertion into some genes, e.g. serine protease genes (Rogers, 1985; Irwin *et al.*, 1988) although an actual mechanism of intron insertion is currently unknown. Intron insertion seems to have been completed at least 450 million years ago (Irwin *et al.*, 1988). As some introns may have pre-existed, it seems possible that introns have not solely arisen by insertion of non-coding DNA sequences, but the utilisation of small reading frame separated by non-coding DNA sequences was also attributed to the origin of introns (Naora *et al.*, 1987).

An earlier study of the size distribution of exons has shown that many exons are around 140 bp long and 500 to 600 bp long exons are only exceptionally seen in the contemporary genes (Naora and Deacon, 1982c). When this survey was carried out in 1981, the types and numbers of genes available for examinations were strictly limited; for example, information on some globin genes, but less for other types of genes, were available. However, recent surveys carried out with much more data of a variety of gene types (Blake, 1985; Traut, 1988; Smith, 1988) have shown that the above earlier conclusion does not markedly differ from those of recent surveys and thus that around 140 bp represents the length of most introns of a gene. Since a primordial gene is considered to be ~550 bp long (Naora *et al.*, 1987), the primordial gene must have been split into smaller exons, in most cases around 140 bp long, by intron insertion.

The serine protease gene family probably evolved about one billion years ago (Doolittle, 1984) and is considered to retain its evolutionary history in the contemporary gene structure (Irwin *et al.*, 1988). In fact, a structural analysis of the serine protease gene family shows that the positions of introns are different in different family members, suggesting that intron insertion and deletion have often taken place (Rogers, 1985 and 1986; Irwin *et al.*, 1988). Therefore, the structural modification of a serine protease gene is a good case for utilisation of non-coding DNA sequences in evolution.

A serine protease requires specific histidine, aspartic acid and serine residues at its active sites (Hess, 1971; Keil, 1971). The amino acid sequences around the catalytically active site of the histidine residue in the N-terminal region of the enzymes have been well conserved. However, this region is immediately followed by non-conserved or block-deleted amino acid sequences among various species of organisms, thus showing length variation (Olson *et al.*, 1970; Kurosky *et al.*, 1980; Davis *et al.*, 1985). It has been proposed that the intron was probably present at this position before the vertebrate lineage split (Davis *et al.*, 1985). This implies that the major portion of serine protease genes was probably separated from a domain which coded for catalytically active histidine residue. Since the histidine residue is absolutely required for the catalytic activity, a proposal may be tentatively made that the primordial form of a 'serine protease' gene coded only for the protein exhibiting no catalytic functions, but probably the function of protein-protein contact. This function was probably analogous to that of haptoglobin, one of the family members of serine protease (Kurosky *et al.*, 1980; Greer, 1980). Haptoglobin displays no enzymatic function, but possesses a unique ability to bind hemoglobin (Nagel and Gibson, 1971). Unlike other family members, the protein does not possess a key histidine residue (actually replaced by lysine) in the N-terminal region (Maeda *et al.*, 1984; Maeda and Smithies, 1986). It seems conceivable therefore that the primordial gene was around 500 ~600 bp long, as the major domains for the strong protein-protein contact of the contemporary serine proteases are coded by the 500 ~600 bp DNA sequences. At a certain stage in evolution, a short and originally abortive reading frame which contained the DNA sequence coding for a key histidine residue was likely to be added as an exon to the primordial form of a 'serine protease' gene and thus become a real serine protease gene, of which the product was enzymatically active. Then, this newly formed serine protease gene was probably split into exons by insertion of non-coding DNA sequences, i.e. introns, followed by further intron insertions, deletions and moves. It is noted that the amino acid sequence around the histidine residue present at the catalytically active site in the N-terminal region of various contemporary serine proteases, i.e. chymotrypsinogen (Bell *et al.*, 1984), proelastase (Swift *et al.*, 1984), trypsinogen (Craik *et al.*, 1984), urokinase (Nagamine *et al.*, 1985), tissue-type plasminogen activator (Ny *et al.*, 1984), α- and γ-nerve growth factors (Evans and Richards, 1984), and kallikrein (Masson *et al.*, 1983), is actually coded by a short exon. This exon ends after the second nucleotide of the codon and contains the stop codon *in phase* at the end of the sequences. A possibility that the existence of the stop codon in phase in this short exon represents a molecular relic is attractive, but remains to be further elucidated together with the tentative proposal of the primordial form of a 'serine protease' gene.

Modification of a primordial gene structure by intron insertion may also be seen in the fibronectin gene (Rogers, 1986). The fibronectin proteins, involving in cell adhesion to extracellular materials, consist of well-defined different domains and contain multiple homologous but non-identical repeats of three types (Odermatt *et al.*, 1985). These three types of different repeats are basically coded by approximately 140 bp, 180 bp and 270 bp long DNA sequences (Petersen *et al.*, 1983). It seems possible that a primordial fibronectin gene was approximately 590 bp (= 140 bp + 180 bp + 270 bp) in length and subsequently was divided into three exons by intron insertion, followed by internal duplication and further intron insertion or movement. Once again, this is consistent to the view that a ~550 bp long primordial gene was modified by the utilisation of non-coding DNA sequences.

CONCLUSION

It was postulated that non-coding DNA sequences represent the molecular relics of obligatory by-products formed early in evolution. It seems conceivable that these DNA sequences were simply adopted to the organisation of genomes at a more recent stage in evolution. In fact, such relics play a key role in maintaining gene structures and regulating the gene expression in a present-day organism. In this chapter, I presented a few examples suggesting that the structure deeply underlying the regulation of gene expression is based on the principle of a (gene-population) density dependence. These examples include spatial arrangement of genes and the acquisition of landmarks of a gene's territories. It is my view that a density dependence represents one of the features of an intrinsic principle that holds not only gene expression but also other biological activities in order.

ACKNOWLEDGEMENTS

I thank Profs. R. N. Curnow, K. Murachi and A. Sibatani and Drs E. H. Creaser and K. Miyahara for fruitful discussions and comments, Mr D. W. Buckle and Mrs H. R. Liszczynsky for improving the manuscript and Mrs E. Robertson for her assistance in preparing this manuscript. This work was supported by grant No. 85-111-001 from the Toyota Foundation.

REFERENCES

Beachy, P. A., Helfand, S. L. and Hogness, D. S. (1985) Segmental distribution of bithorax complex proteins during Drosophila development. *Nature*. 313. 545-51.

Bell, G. I., Quinto, C., Quiroga, M., Valenzuela, P., Craik, C. S. and Rutter, W. J. (1984) Isolation and sequence of rat chymotrypsin B gene. *J. Biol. Chem.* 259. 14265-14270.

Bell, G. I., Gerhard, D. S., Fong, N. M., Sanchez-Pescador, R. and Ball, L. B. (1985) Isolation of the human insulin-like growth factor gene; Insulin-like growth factor II and insulin genes are contiguous. *Proc. Natl. Acad. Sci. USA*. 82. 6450-4.

Benyajati, C., Spoerel, N. Haymerle, H. and Ashburner, M. (1983) The messenger RNA for alcohol dehydrogenase in Drosophila melanogaster differs in its 5' end in different developmental stages. *Cell*. 33. 125-33.

Blake, C. C. F. (1978) Do genes-in-pieces imply proteins-in-pieces? *Nature*. 273. 267.

——(1985) Exons and the evolution of proteins. *Internatl. Rev. Cytol.* 93. 149-85.

Cavalier-Smith, T. (1985a) In *The Evolution of Genome Size*. Cavalier-Smith, T. (ed.). Wiley, Chichester. pp.69-109.

——(1985b) Selfish DNA and the origin of introns. *Nature*. 315. 283-4.

Craik, C. S., Choo, Q.-L., Swift, G. H., Quinto, C., MacDonald, R. J. and Rutter, W. J. (1984) Structure of two related pat pancreatic trypsin genes. *J. Biol. Chem.* 259. 14255-64.

Darnell, J. E. and Doolittle, W. F. (1986) Speculations on the early course of evolution. *Proc. Natl. Acad. Sci. USA*. 83. 1271-5.

Davis, C. A., Riddell, D. C., Higgins, M. J., Holden, J. J. A. and White, B. N. (1985) A gene family in Drosophila melanogaster coding for trypsin-like enzymes. *Nucl. Acids Res.* 18. 6605-19.

Deevey, E. S. Jr. (1971) In *Man and the Ecosphere*. Ehrlich, P. R., Holdren, J. P. and Holms, R. N. (eds.). W. H. Freeman and Co., San Francisco. pp. 49-55.

Dolan, M., Sugarman, B. J., Dodgson, J. B. and Engel, J. D. (1981) Chromosomal arrangement of chicken β-type globin genes. *Cell*. 24. 669-77.

Doolittle, W. F. (1984) In *The Plasma Proteins*. Putnam, F. W. (ed.), 2nd edit. Academic Press, New York. Vol. 4. 317-60.

Dose, K. and Zaki, L. (1971) *Hämoproteinode mit peroxidatisher und katalatischer Aktivität Naturforsch*. 266. 144-8.

Emerman, M. and Temin, H. (1984) Genes with promoters in retrovirus vectors can be independently suppressed by an epigenetic mechanism. *Cell*. 39. 459-67.

——(1986a) Quantitative analysis of gene suppression in integrated retrovirus vectors. *Mol. Cell. Biol.* 6. 792-800.

——(1986b) Comparison of promoter suppression in avian and murine retrovirus vectors. *Nucl. Acids Res.* 14. 9381-96.

English, P. W. and Mayfield, R. C. (1972) *Man, Space and Environment*. Oxford University Press, New York.

Evans, B. A. and Richards, R. I. (1985) Genes for the α and γ subunits of mouse nerve growth factor are contiguous. *EMBO J.* 4. 133-8.

Fujita, T., Takaoka, C., Matsui, H. and Taniguchi, T. (1983) Structure of the human interlukin 2 gene. *Proc. Natl. Acad. Sci. USA*. 80. 7437-41.

Gilbert, W., Marchionni, M. and McKnight, G. (1986) On the antiguity of introns. *Cell*. 46. 151-4.

Greer, J. (1980) Model for haptoglobin heavy chain based upon structural homology. *Proc. Natl. Acad. Sci. USA*. 77. 3393-7.

Hentschel, C. C. (1982) Homocopolymer sequences in the spacer of a sea urchin histone gene repeat are sensitive to S1 nuclease. *Nature*. 295. 714-6.

Hess, G. P. (1971) Chymotrypsin — Chemical properties and catalysis. In *The Enzymes*. Boyer, P. D. (ed.). Academic Press, New York. Vol. 3. pp.213-48.

Holmgren, R., Livak, K., Morimoto, R. Freund, R. and Meselson, M. (1979) Studies of cloned sequences from four Drosophila heat shock loci. *Cell*. 18. 1359-70.

Htun, H., Lund, E. and Dahlberg, J. E. (1984) Human U1 RNA genes contain an unusually sensitive nuclease S1 cleavage site within the conserved 3'-flanking region. *Proc. Natl. Acad. Sci. USA*. 81. 7288-92.

Irwin, D. M., Robertson, K. A. and MacGillivray, R. T. A. (1988) Structure and evolution of the bovine prothrombin gene. *J. Mol. Biol.* 200. 31-45.

Jaenisch, R. and Soriano, P. (1986) Retro-viruses as a probes for mammalian development: Allocation of cells to somatic and germ cell lineages and virus induced insertional mutagenesis. *Proc. Aust. Biochem. Soc.* 18. S28.

Jeffreys, A. J. (1982) Evolution of globin genes. In *Genome Evolution*. Dover, G. A. and Flavell, R. B. (eds.). Academic Press, London. pp.157-76.

Karathanasis, S. (1985) Apolipoprotein multigene family: Tandem organisation of human apolipoprotein AI, CIII, and AIV genes. *Proc. Natl. Acad. Sci. USA*. 82. 6374-8.

Kedes, L. H. (1979) Histone genes and histone messengers. *Ann. Rev. Biochem.* 48. 837-70.

Keil, B. (1971) Trypsin. In *The Enzymes*. Boyer, P. D. (ed.). Academic Press, New York. Vol. 3. pp. 249-75.

Kuroiwa, A., Kloter, J. Baumgartner, P. and Gehring, W. J. (1985) Cloning of the homeotic Sex combs reduced gene in Drosophila and in situ localisation of its transcripts. *EMBO J*. 4. 3757-64.

Kurosky, A., Barnett, D. R., Lee, T.-H., Touchstone, B., Hay, R. E., Arnott, M. S., Bowman, B. H. and Fitch, W. M. (1980) Covalent structure of human haptoglobin: A serine protease homolog. *Proc. Natl. Acad. Sci. USA*. 77. 3388-92.

Landes, G. M., Villeponteau, B., Priby, T. M. and Martinson, H. G. (1982) Hemoglobin switching in chickens. Is the switch initiated post-transcriptionally? *J. Biol. Chem.* 257. 11008-14.

Larsen, A. and Weintraub, H. (1982) An altered DNA conformation detected by S1 nuclease occurs at specific regions in active chicken globin chromatin. *Cell*. 29. 609-22.

Lawn, R. M., Efstratiadis, A. O'Connell, C. and Maniatis, T. (1980) The nucleotide sequence of the human β-globin gene. *Cell*. 21. 647-51.

Lompré, A. M., Nadal-Ginard, B. and Mahdavi, V. (1984) Expression of the cardiac venticular α- and β-myosin heavy chain genes is developmentally and hormonally regulated. *J. Biol. Chem.* 259. 6437-46.

Lonberg, N. and Gilbert, W. (1985) Intron/exon structure of chicken pyruvate kinase gene. *Cell*. 40. 81-90.

Maeda, N., Yang, F. Barnett, D. R., Bowman, B. H. and Smithies, O. (1984) Duplication within the haptoglobin Hp^2 gene. *Nature*. 309. 131-5.

——and Smithies, O. (1986) The evolution of multigene families: Human haptoglobin genes. *Ann. Rev. Genet.* 20. 81-108.

Mahdavi, V. Chambers, A. P. and Nadal-Ginard, B. (1984) Cardiac α- and β-myosin heavy chain genes are organised in tandem. *Proc. Natl. Acad. Sci. USA*. 81. 2626-30.

Marchionni, M. and Gilbert, W. (1986) The triosephosphate isomerase from maize: Introns autodate the plant-animal divergence. *Cell*. 46. 133-41.

Mason, A. J., Evans, B. A., Cox, D. R., Shine, J. and Richards, R. I. (1983) Structure of mouse kallikrein gene family suggests a role in specific processing of biologically active peptides. *Nature*. 303. 300-07.

Nagamine, Y., Pearson, D., Altus, M. S. and Reich, E. (1984) cDNA and gene nucleotide sequence of porcine plasminogen activator. *Nucl. Acids Res.* 12. 9525-41.

Nagel, R. L. and Gibson, Q. H. (1971) The binding of hemoglobin to haptoglobin and its relation to subunit dissociation of hemoglobin. *J. Biol. Chem.* 246. 69-73.

Naora, H. (1986) Gene ecology. A novel regulatory system in the gene expression network. *Biol. Forum.* 79. 345-71.

——and Deacon, N. J. (1982a) Clustered genes require extragenic territorial DNA sequences. *Differentiation.* 21. 1-6.

——(1982b) Implication of the effect of extragenic territorial DNA sequences on a mechanism involving switch-on/off of neighbouring genes by transposable elements in eukaryotes. *J. Theor. Biol.* 95. 601-6.

—— (1982c) Relationship between the total size of exons and introns in protein coding genes of higher eukaryotes. *Proc. Natl. Acad. Sci. USA.* 79. 6196-200.

——Miyahara, K. and Curnow, R. N. (1987) Origin of noncoding DNA sequences: Molecular fossils of genome evolution. *Proc. Natl. Acad. Sci. USA.* 84. 6195-9.

——and Koishi, K. (1988) Concerted structure with extragenic sequences and a gene, *Biology Forum* (in press).

Ny, T., Elgh, F. and Lund, B. (1984) The structure of human tissue-type plasminogen activator gene: Correlation of intron and exon structure to functional and structural domains. *Proc. Natl. Acad. Sci. USA.* 81. 5355-9.

Odermatt, E. Tamkun, J. W. and Hynes, R. O. (1985) Repeating modular structure of the fibronectin gene: Relationship to protein structure and subunit variation. *Proc. Natl. Acad. Sci. USA.* 82. 6571-5.

Ohno, S. (1970) *Evolution by gene duplication.* Springer-Verlag, New York.

Olson, M. O., Nagabhushan, N. Dzwiniel, M., Smillie, L. B. and Whitaker, D. R. (1970) Primary structure of α-lytic protease: a bacterial homologue of the pancreatic serine proteases. *Nature.* 228. 438-42.

Patient, R. K., Elkington, J. A., Kay, R. M. and Williams, J. G. (1980) Internal organisation of the major adult α- and β-globin genes of X. laevis. *Cell.* 21. 565-73.

Petersen, T. E., Thøgersen, H. C., Skorstengaard, K., Vibe-Petersen, K., Sahl, P., Sottrup-Jensen, L. and Magnusson, S. (1983) Partial primary structure of bovine plasma fibronectin: Three types of internal homology. *Proc. Natl. Acad. Sci. USA.* 80. 137-41.

Richardson, J. S. (1981) The anatomy and taxonomy of protein structure. *Adv. Protein Chem.* 34. 167-339.

Rogers, J. (1985) Exon shuffling and intron insertion in serine protease genes. *Nature.* 315. 458-9.

——(1986) Introns between protein domains: selective insertion of frame shifting? *Tred. in Gen.* 1. 223.

Savageau, M. A. (1986) Protein of Escherichia coli comes in sizes that are multiples of 14kDa: Domain concepts and evolutionary implications. *Proc. Natl. Acad. Sci. USA.* 83. 1198-202.

Selleck, S. B., Elgin, S. C. R. and Cartwright, I. I. (1984) Supercoil-dependent features of DNA structures at Drosophila locus 67B1. *J. Mol. Biol.* 178. 17-33.

Smith, M. W. (1988) Structure of vertebrate genes: A statistical analysis implicating selection. *J. Mol. Evol.* 27. 45-55.

Spritz, R. A., DeRiel, J. K., Forget, B. G. and Weissman, S. M. (1980) Complete nucleotide sequence of the human δ-globin gene. *Cell.* 21. 639-46.

Stephenson, E. C., Erba, H. P. and Gall, J. G. (1981) Characterisation of a cloned histone gene cluster of the newt Notophthalmus viridescens. *Nucl. Acids Res.* 9. 2281-95.

Swift, G. H., Craik, C. S., Stary, S. J., Quinto, C., Lahaie, R. G., Rutter, W. J. and MacDonald, R. J. (1984) Structure of the two related elastase genes expressed in the rat pancreas. *J. Biol. Chem.* 259. 14271-8.

Traut, T. W. (1988) Do exons code for structural or functional units in proteins? *Proc. Natl. Acad. Sci. USA.* 85. 2944-8.

Udvardy, A., Maine, E. and Schedl, P. (1985) The 87A7 chromomere. Identification of novel chromatin structures flanking the heat shock locus that may define the boundaries of higher order domains. *J. Mol. Biol.* 185. 341-58.

Ullrich, A., Gray, A., Goeddel, D. V. and Dult, T. L. (1981) Nucleotide sequence of a portion of human chromosome 9 containing a leukocyte interferon gene cluster. *J. Mol. Biol.* 156. 467-86.

Villeponteau, B., Landes, G. M., Pankratz, M. J. and Martinson, H. G. (1982) The chicken β-globin gene region. Delineation of transcription units and developmental regulation of interspersed DNA repeats. *J. Biol. Chem.* 257. 11015-23.

——Lundell, B. and Martinson, H. (1984) Torsional stress promotes the DNAase I sensitivity of active genes. *Cell.* 39. 469-78.

Webster, G. and Goodwin, B. C. (1984) A structuralist approach to morphology. *Riv. Biol.* 77. 503-31.

Weintraub, H. (1983) A dominant role for DNA secondary structure in forming hypersensitive structures in chromatin. *Cell.* 32. 1191-203.

Zuckerkandl, E. (1986) Polite DNA: Functional density and functional compatibility in genomes. *J. Mol. Evol.* 24. 12-27.

16. A New Hypothesis on the Mechanism of Macroevolution: A Structuralist Approach

Kiyohiko Ikeda

For over the last decade, probably since the proposal of punctuated equilibrium by Eldredge and Gould (1972), neo-Darwinism has been under fire, and there has been a gradual increase in the number of people challenging gradualism, one of its central contentions. Needless to say, many neo-Darwinists (e.g. Maynard Smith, 1982; Stenseth, 1985) argue against stasis-plus-punctuation. They assert that this phenomenon does not conflict with gradualism and can be explained by Darwinian theory, providing that the rapid change of environment is followed by a directive gradual change of form by natural selection, or assuming that the immigration of similar species results in the extinction of the original species. Being dead set against that, some paleontologists (Gould, 1980; Stanley, 1979) argue in favour of stasis-plus-punctuation and propose the concept of species selection, but their argument seems to stay within phenomenology, thus still not offering an effective explanation for the mechanism of macroevolution superior to neo-Darwinism. Several biologists, on the other hand, have been trying to construct new paradigms against neo-Darwinism to date. Some of them are neo-Lamarckians, and some are biological structuralists. The former state that the most important cause of change in form is the inheritance of acquired characters or something else in an organism to force progressive evolution, but no effective argument seems to have been presented from the time of Koestler (1967) to the more recent Steele (1981).

Neo-Darwinism argues that random genetic change and the mechanism of its fixation into a population, i.e. natural selection or genetic drift, are necessary and efficient to explain micro- to macroevolution. On the contrary, structuralists claim there must be more complicated machinery in evolutionary processes, at least in trans-specific evolution. From the viewpoint of structuralism, neo-Darwinism appears to be extreme reductionism in which all the evolutionary phenomena are due to undirected mutation, natural selection, and genetic drift. Structuralists assume that there exist at a higher level than genes some structures dealing with evolution. 'Structure' in terms of structuralism implies the rule of transformation between the elements of at least two series. It is somewhat arbitrary and not necessarily derived from physico-chemical laws, though it obeys them (Sibatani, 1985; Elder, 1986; Ikeda, 1986). There seem to be two structuralist approaches to evolution. It is presumed, on the one hand, that structure exists at a level somewhere between genotype and phenotype, or that there are generative laws in ontogeny whose changes cause macroevolution (Webster and Goodwin, 1982). On the other hand, structure is regarded as the rule controlling the change or reshuffle of genome DNAs, which is the main theme I will attempt to discuss in this chapter.

INTERNAL SELECTION

Lancelot Law Whyte (1965) proposed the concept of internal selection and defined it as the restriction of the direction of evolutionary change by internal organisational factors. Whyte asserted that the mutated genotypes are almost certainly not random, having been already subjected to internal selection. This runs counter to the dogma of neo-Darwinism, which demands the randomness of the mutated genotypes. Internal selection is neither external selection submitting phenotypes, nor natural selection operating in the cell during ontogeny; in other words, it is not the changing process caused by a difference in fitness. Can the directive change in a genome arise without the participation of natural selection? The molecular drive proposed by Dover (1982) is undoubtedly a kind of internal selection at the genomic level. Eukaryotic genomes contain a large number of multiple-copy families of genes and non-coding sequences. Molecular· drive was proposed to explain the family homogeneity within and between individuals of a species. Dover insisted the family homogeneity is achieved by molecular drive, which ensures that the existing members of a family are replaced in turn with a single variant member. Molecular drive implies that this replacement is not only stochastic but also directional. This progressive increase of a variant through a family occurs more or less simultaneously in each individual of a sexual population. The idea of Dover, like that of Whyte, appears to be somewhat structuralist for assuming the existence of a law or mechanism to bring about the directional change in the genome.

A NEW HYPOTHESIS

My hypothesis on the mechanism of macroevolution also asserts that the changes in genomes are not always random. My original article (Ikeda, 1985) on this subject was previously published in Japanese. In this chapter I will describe my hypothesis in the context of structuralism in biology.

If stasis-plus-punctuation is correct, i.e. a species keeps its form the same for a long period, then the genome corresponding to it must be preserved in a stable state. There are some factors known to force changes on a genome, for example, chromosome mutations, genetic mutations, and several kinds of movable genetic elements. Nevertheless, a species maintains a constant form, which may imply that there is a 'structure' controlling changes in the genome.

This is the first structure I hypothesise. This structure may be actualised to be a relation between unique particular genes and the other genes, or DNA sequences controlled by them. These particular genes, which I named 'stabilising centre genes' (Ikeda, 1985), are assumed to control the change of sequences themselves, more valuable than regulatory genes controlling the transcription. Since it was reported that there is a gene inhibiting crossing over (Abdullah and Charlesworth, 1974), and that there is a transposase to allow the transcription of movable genetic elements (e.g. Temin and Engels, 1984), stabilising centre genes can be regarded as genes that inhibit crossing over in some areas of the genome, or genes that produce a repressor to inhibit the function of a transposase. As little is known about genome dynamics, of course, there may be other mechanisms yet to be discovered. Such types of control may not always proceed under mediating proteins, if we consider the analogy of micRNA in the transcription of osmoregulation (Mizuno, 1984). This structure underlies the mechanism of 'stasis' of species.

If it is true that, as described by paleontologists, a species experiences a period of rapid change followed by a long period of stasis, the questions I have to ask are the following three. 1) What is the mechanism which keeps stabilising centre genes themselves stable for long periods? 2) Why can stabilising centre genes change nevertheless? 3) How do stabilising centre genes find a new stable state? Now I will hypothesise the second structure. This structure would be actualised in a relation between 'maintenance genes', which I so named (Ikeda, 1985), and the stabilising centre genes, which are controlled by them. The maintenance genes are assumed to preserve the invariability of a stabilising centre gene, although I cannot here describe their mechanism. Also, maintenance genes are assumed to comprise a multiple-copy family, or reiterated DNA sequences. Though some mutations may occur in some copies of a family, the other copies will maintain the invariability of a stabilising centre gene. If all the copies change, the invariability will no longer exist, and a stabilising centre gene will become variable. If a single new variant member of the family replaces the other old members by molecular drive, individuals in a sexual population will, after a long time, simultaneously change all the copies of the family of maintenance genes, thus resulting in a stabilising centre gene's loss of invariability. In some cases, of course, all the maintenance genes may change by chance or genetic drift.

By the way, how does a stabilising centre gene which has lost its invariability find a new stable state? There might be many maintenance genes corresponding to the stabilising centre genes of ancestral species. They might exit as redundant non-coding sequences in spacer areas in the present species, and might have accumulated several mutations allowed by the stabilising centre genes of some ancestral species. These remainders of old maintenance genes will become active again when the corresponding stabilising centre gene appears. A stabilising centre gene which has lost its invariability will undergo many changes, and for some new variants the genome may already possess the corresponding maintenance genes. If so, a stabilising centre gene which has lost its invariability may proceed rapidly to some new stable state. A newly established stabilising centre gene brings about a reorganisation of the genome, resulting in the appearance of a biological novelty. In short, the second structure underlies the mechanism of 'punctuation' of species. From these standpoints, species can be defined as organisms having the same set of stabilising centre genes.

WHAT DOES THIS NEW HYPOTHESIS IMPLY?

When a stabilising centre gene in germline cells becomes unstable as a result of the change of all the maintenance genes, some gametes may acquire a new stabilising centre gene. If most individuals in a population simultaneously lose the invariability of a stabilising centre gene by molecular drive or genetic drift, gametes having the same new stabilising centre gene will produce a successful zygote, but a zygote produced by the conjunction of gametes having incompatible stabilising centre genes will not be successful because of the discrepancy in the reorganisation of genome DNAs, and its lineage will soon die. On the other hand, when only a few individuals by chance lose the invariability of a stabilising centre gene, gametes having the new stabilising centre gene will find it difficult to encounter the same kind of gametes, but fortunately, should such a thing happen, a new species, with only a small number of individuals, might appear in the midst of the ancestral species. Several kinds of new stabilising centre genes will be established as a result of the simultaneous loss of the invariability of an old stabilising centre gene in most individuals of a population due to molecular drive or genetic drift: thus the number of new species to appear will correspond to the number of kinds of newly established stabilising centre genes. An ancestral species, therefore, would be divided into several descendant species. This implies that speciation in general is polychotomous, and that the dichotomy asserted by cladism (e.g. Hennig, 1966) is only a special case of speciation. Furthermore, in some cases an ancestral species may change to only one descendant species when only one new stabilising centre gene is established in place of the old one. If only a few individuals in a population lose the invariability of their stabilising centre gene by chance, some new species (in most cases only one species considering its probability) might diverge on rare occasions from an ancestral species. In any of the above cases, the general and main mode of speciation is regarded as sympatric. Allopatric speciation may appear to occur phenomenally when an isolated peripatric population acquires only one new stabilising centre gene in place of the old one as a result of the change of all the maintenance genes by molecular drive or genetic drift. Allopatric speciation, however, is regarded as a minor mode, because this hypothesis does not demand genetic isolation for speciation.

The size of populations may influence the stability of stabilising centre genes. Small populations may require less time to change a stabilising centre gene, perhaps because of the higher probability of achieving a new family homogeneity in its maintenance genes with the new variant, which have been caused by molecular drive or genetic drift. This, however, does not imply that rapid speciation occurs in only small populations as inferred by some paleontologists who advocate stasis-plus-punctuation (Stanley, 1979); it implies that it can occur in any population.

Zygotes which have acquired a new stabilising centre gene would not always grow into hopeful monsters (Goldschmidt, 1940), but in general this new lineage would change the phenotype rapidly from generation to generation with the gradual reorganisation of the genome as controlled by the new stabilising centre gene. Sooner or later the new stabilising centre gene of these new lineages will lead the genome to a new stable state, resulting in the establishment of a biological novelty having a new stable form. Some lineages, of course, would generate mere hopeless monsters which would then become extinct.

New species generated by the process described above move into various suitable ecological niches, and in some cases, therefore, allopatry in habitat will occur secondarily. This argument runs counter to the mode of sympatric speciation proposed by neo-Darwinism (Maynard Smith, 1966; Bush, 1975), which demands that niche segregation in population precedes speciation. This new hypothesis acknowledges that some species produced by sympatric speciation may possibly have niches which are identical or nearly so, especially when they are phytophagous species not engaged in rigorous interspecific competition. In some small oceanic islands such as Saint Helena in the South Atlantic, Rapa in the South Pacific (White, 1978), and the Bonin Islands in the North Pacific, there are many endemic coleopteran genera including many sympatric species. When some species are found to have the same niche, the sympatric speciation implied by this new hypothesis can give a reasonable explanation. For example, five species belonging to the endemic *Genus Boninella* (Coleoptera, Cerambycidae) in the Bonin Islands seemed to have almost identical niches, this based upon my brief observations (unpublished). I would maintain that the adaptive radiation was rarely the result of natural selection, but usually due to rapid speciations or the transformation of stabilising centre genes.

The invariability of newly established stabilising centre genes is dependent upon the stability of the new maintenance genes. When there are many copies of maintenance genes, the new stabilising centre gene they support will be safe in its invariability, but when maintenance genes are few, the invariability will be unstable. In the former case a species would maintain a stable form for long periods, but in the latter case, a species would rediverge within a comparatively short time. This is, I believe, a reasonable explanation for species selection (Stanley, 1979), say, a tendency for a certain branch to diverge more frequently than the other branches do. At the early stage of the evolutionary history of eukaryotes, they must have had only a few remnants of old maintenance genes, because there must have been only a few ancestral species. If so, it seems that a stabilising centre gene which had lost its invariability was very changeable. In most of the above cases, a newly established stabilising centre gene would have been supported not by remnants of old maintenance genes but by one new maintenance gene which had been produced by mutation. As molecular drive or some other cases made duplicates of this new maintenance gene, a species must have been gradually gaining stability. An explosive diversification of species during the Cambrian would be understood as the process in which many complementary relations between stabilising centre genes and maintenance genes were established. It is worth considering that the species after the Cambrian might have merely utilised these complementary relations repeatedly.

A species under a set of stabilising centre genes may change gradually by natural selection, genetic drift, or molecular drive. These changes must be allowed by the stabilising centre genes and may be reversible in general. I would contend that this mode of change is microevolution. Allopatric speciation, which is caused by genetic isolation, and which does not involve a change in stabilising centre genes, is superficial and in some cases reversible.

I can derive two modes of extinction from this hypothesis. In one scenario a species would become extinct from failing to adapt to environmental changes by the time new stabilising centre genes become established, this because of the excessive invariability in the stabilising centre genes. This mode may correspond to the Red Queen hypothesis (Van Valen, 1973). In the other scenario, all the newly established stabilising centre genes which succeed an old one which had lost its invariability would produce mere hopeless monsters, and the species would therefore soon become extinct.

This new hypothesis seems to strike many as grandiose and ridiculous, but unless the existence of 'structure' is assumed at the genome level, a convincing explanation could not found for a unitary understanding of the evolutionary phenomenon, no matter how different from my hypothesis.

REFERENCES

Abdulluh, N. F. and Charlesworth, B. (1974) Selection for reduced crossing over in Drosophila melanogaster. *Genetics*. 76. 447-51.
Bush, G. L. (1975) Sympatric speciation in phytophagous parasitic insects. In *Evolutionary Strategies of Parasitic Insects* (ed. P. W. Price). Plenum Press, London. pp.187-206.
Dover, G. (1982) Molecular drive: a cohesive mode of species evolution. *Nature*. 299. 111-7.
Elder, D. (1986) Structuralism and reductionism. *Riv. Biol.* 79. 75-81.
Eldredge, N. and Gould, S. J. (1972) Punctuated equilibrium: an alternative to phyletic gradualism. In *Mode in Paleontology* (ed. T. J. M. Schoph). Freeman Cooper and Co., California. 82-115.

Goldschmidt, R. B. (1940) *The Material Basis of Evolution.* Yale University Press, New Haven.

Gould, S. J. (1980) Is a new and general theory of evolution emerging? *Paleobiology.* 6. 119-30.

Hennig, W. (1966) *Phylogenetic Systematics.* University of Illinois Press, Urbana.

Ikeda, K. (1985) Discussion on some evolutionary theories including the presentation of a new hypothesis relating to the mechanism of macroevolution. *Biological Science* (Tokyo). 37. 199-206 (in Japanese).

——(1986) Why is structuralist biology so called? *Artificial Intelligence Journal* 6. 106-110 and 7. 102-8 (in Japanese).

Koestler, A. (1967) *The Ghost in the Machine.* Hutchinson, London.

Maynard Smith, J. (1966) Sympatric speciation. *Amer. Nat.* 100. 637-50.

——(1982) Evolution — sudden or gradual? In *Evolution Now* (ed. J. Maynard Smith). Macmillan, London. pp.125-8.

Mizuno, T. (1984) Regulation of gene expression by a small RNA transcript (micRNA). *Protein, Nucleic Acid and Enzyme.* 29. 908-13 (in Japanese).

Sibatani, A. (1985) Molecular Biology: a structuralist revolution. *Riv. Biol.* 78. 373-97.

Stanley, S. M. (1979) *Macroevolution: Pattern and process.* Freeman, San Francisco.

Steele, E. J. (1981) *Somatic Selection and Adaptive Evolution: On the Inheritance of Acquired Characters.* 2nd Ed. University of Chicago Press, Chicago.

Stenseth, N. C. (1985) Darwinian evolution in ecosystems: the red queen view. In *Evolution: Essays in Honour of John Maynard Smith* (eds. P. T. Greenwood, P. H. Harvey, M. Slatkin). Cambridge University Press, Cambridge. pp.55-72.

Temin, H. M. and Engels, W. (1984) Movable genetic elements and evolution. In *Evolutionary Theory: Path into the Future* (ed. J. W. Pollard). John Willy and Sons, Chichester.

Van Valen, L. (1973) A new evolutionary law. *Evol. Theory.* 1. 1-30.

Webster, G. and Goodwin, B. C. (1982) The origin of species: a structuralist approach. *J. soc. biol. Struct.* 5. 15-47.

White, M. J. D. (1978) *Mode of Speciation.* Freeman, San Francisco.

Whyte, L. L. (1965) *Internal Factors in Evolution.* Tavistock Publications, London.

17 Systematics and Panbiogeography

Hideyuki Chiba

Systematics is the first and the last, the beginning and the end. It is not only a prerequisite which other branches of biology are dependent upon, but also its ultimate goal which is to lead toward understanding the system of nature. Despite its importance, it has been questioned whether systematics qualifies as a true science or whether it is just a relic of nineteenth-century natural history. The quality of systematical work was influenced subjectively by the individual's ability, experience and intuition. Recent developments of phylogenetic systematics or cladistics are due to the demand that systematics, as a science, should be objective and amenable to statistical or numerical tests. Historical biogeography, on the other hand, is usually treated as a subject outside systematics. However, it is indispensable to the construct of biological synthesis. In this chapter, some problems of systematics and biogeography are discussed; and a panbiogeographic synthesis in the context of structuralism is proposed.

SYSTEMATICS AND BIOGEOGRAPHY

Since Léon Croizat and his panbiogeography arrived on the biological scene, several 'schools' have had heated arguments over the theories and methodologies of historical biogeography. The schools involved are dispersal biogeography (Mayr, 1969, 1970; Simpson, 1965; Darlington, 1957), phylogenetic biogeography (Hennig, 1966b; Brundin, 1972), vicariance biogeography (Nelson and Platnick, 1981; Nelson and Rosen, 1981) and panbiogeography (Croizat, 1952, 1958, 1960, 1962-4; Craw, 1988a; Craw and Page, 1988). These arguments focused not only on the causes and course of animal and plant distribution, but also on the method of systematics because it directly contributes to biogeography. Each of the above schools have distinct methods of systematics which are applied to biogeography, namely evolutionary systematics (Mayr, 1942), phylogenetic systematics (Hennig, 1966a), and transformed cladistics (Eldredge and Cracraft, 1980; Wiley, 1981; Nelson and Platnick, 1981), respectively. A systematic method specific to panbiogeography has not yet been developed.

In this chapter I do not include numerical phenetics (Sokal and Sneath,

1963) because they do not consider evolutionary synthesis. For comments on these schools from a cladist's point of view, see Wiley (1981).

EVOLUTIONARY SYSTEMATICS/DISPERSAL BIOGEOGRAPHY

Dispersal biogeography, popularised by Darwin in *Origin of Species* (1859), has dominated the field of biogeography for more than a century. Proponents of the school worked out a compromise between Darwin's theory and Wallace's (1876) static 'zoogeographical regions' (Chiba, 1988; Grehan, 1988). After closer examination, Darwin's theory of the mechanism of evolution changed radically and resulted in Neo-Darwinism (Romanes, 1892-7) or the Modern Synthesis (Huxley, 1942) period. However, his chorology has been accepted without question by most biologists. Mechanism of evolution and distributions of animals and plants are inseparable in Darwin's evolutionary synthesis (Craw, 1988a). Although Darwin was a dispersalist, his approach to classification seems to follow phylogenetic systematics more closely than evolutionary systematics. Despite the fact that he noted and described the importance of vicariism, he relied solely on 'causal migration' from certain limited centres to explain disjunct geographical distributions. Darwin's dependence on dispersalism has been challenged, most notably by Croizat (1984). However, arguments such as Croizat's have been generally ignored by the orthodox school (Croizat, 1982).

Two influential dogmas of dispersal biogeography are Darwin's 'centre of origin' and 'means of dispersal'. Those theories for practical purposes have the following suppositions: 'a) the most derived recent members of a taxon will be found at the centre of origin, b) the area with the most species is probably the centre of origin' (Wiley, 1981; see also Cain, 1944). Immediately, we are confronted by the problem of not truly knowing the most derived species. However, the evolutionary systematic school has not presented formal objective methods to resolve this problem. From my point of view, it seems that there may be no such thing as a derived (or primitive) species. For the second supposition, the total number of species in a higher category in a defined geographical area needs to be counted. However, the outcome depends on the concept of species and the means of species determination. In other words, the result differs considerably when we rank a taxon as a distinct species or just a geographical race. Evolutionary systematics persists in population genetics and adheres closely to Mayr's (1942) imperfect biological definition. It focuses on population level and local differentiation. This situation results in much attention devoted to generally undiscoverable taxa like sibling or cryptic species, which are unsuitable for historical biogeographic purposes.

Also, we must keep in mind that not all the taxa on the earth have been discovered. This problem is not only one of evolutionary systematics but also of numerical phenetics and cladistics (phylogenetic systematics and transformed cladistics). Phenetic and cladistic methods originally were for data analyses. Hence, these methods 'cannot be used if some data are missing' (Crovello, 1981). Panbiogeographical synthesis may possibly overcome this problem.

PHYLOGENETIC SYSTEMATICS/PHYLOGENETIC BIOGEOGRAPHY

'Only a system expressing nature's hierarchy of sister groups can function adequately as a general biological reference system' (Brundin, 1972). Phylogenetic systematics and phylogenetic biogeography are strongly based upon an 'evolutionary paradigm' (Webster and Goodwin, 1984). Phylogenetic systematists, therefore, take nature's hierarchy for granted. Structuralists have been moving in the opposite direction (Sibatani, 1985a). Namely structuralists interpret hierarchy as a comprehensive relationship rather than a holistic regulation in which higher categories control lower ones. One of the problems of this method is that they have to believe in the historical existence of unseen ancestral species on every division point of their phylogenetic tree.

TRANSFORMED CLADISTICS/VICARIANCE BIOGEOGRAPHY

Vicariance biogeography was derived from panbiogeography, while transformed cladistics originated from phylogenetic systematics. Popper's philosophy of science or parsimony principle sits between the two (Nelson and Platnick, 1981). One advantage of these methods is that it does not depend on the 'evolutionary paradigm' and, as a result, cladists can avoid the problem of determining ancestral species. However, transformed cladistics still share some of the methodological problems of phylogenetic systematics. For example, cladists must decide which character, not species, is primitive and which is derived. They assume that the most common character is primitive and, conversely, the most uncommon character is derived. I consider character from a different point of view.

For further discussion on problems of transformed/vicariance cladistics, see Croizat (1982) and Craw (1983).

COMPROMISE SYSTEMATICS AND BIOGEOGRAPHY

'Evolutionary classification is an eclectic approach in that it combines the important elements from phenetics and cladistics' (Bock, 1974).

The recent trend in systematics and biogeography, at least in the United States, is an attempt to develop a compromise theory and method of all the above. It is a numerical method using statistical data analysis (numerical phenetics) in conformity with Hennigian's idea of characters (polygenetic) systematics) and the parsimony principle (transformed cladistics). Proponents do not hesitate to analyse genetic data within population level (evolutionary systematics). Recent developments in systematics and biogeography in this context tend to be theoretical. The controversies seem to continue as proponents deny their opponents' previous arguments within their group (Funk and Brooks, 1981; Platnick and Funk, 1983).

PANBIOGEOGRAPHY

Panbiogeography was proposed as an alternative to all other historical-biogeographical thoughts rather than to oppose them. Croizat continuously referred to other biogeogrpahical procedures as 'theories' and his panbiogeography as a 'method', because the former 'not only analyse(s) and synthethises . . . [the facts] for the purpose of abstracting general rules about the normal operation of nature' but 'run(s) ahead of the facts' (Croizat, 1981).

After its founder, Léon Croizat's, death, recent developments of panbiogeography tend to concentrate on the quantitative approach (Page, 1987), since opponents attack the lack of mathematical basis of this method. In systematics, proponents adopt phylogenetic systematics (Craw, 1988b). It is important to remember that Croizat acquired his thoughts not from a theoretical critique of modern biogeography, but through earlier works on systematic botany (for complete bibliography, see Heads and Craw, 1984). Therefore, as a panbiogeographer, one should not neglect the qualitative side of systematics.

Panbiogeography adopts a holistic approach which is characteristic of structuralism. It considers the cause of the distribution of present biota, explained as a whole. The Neo-Darwinism dispersal method needs an *ad hoc* 'means of dispersal' for every single species. It also allows nature's hierarchy to be ignored so that the distributions of subspecies, genera, etc., can be explained in the same manner as for species.

STRUCTURALISTIC IDEA OF CHARACTERS

'Systema etiam omissas indicat per se plantas, quod nunquam Catalogi enumeratio' (Linnaeus, 1751).

Concepts of primitive and derived characters are based on the 'evolutionary paradigm' (Webster and Goodwin, 1984). In other words, it is believed that every single character is built to the ancestral species character by means of 'genetic change' and 'natural selection'. Hence, more species share more primitive or early accumulated characters and only a few particular species have more derived or recently accumulated characters within a group. In Hennigian terminology, the former is symplesiomorphy and the latter is synapomorphy. Darwin (1859) called this 'descent with modification'. From my point of view, characters are given not in an accumulative manner but in a permutation.

For example, the wing patterns of butterflies can be explained as varieties of a single theme called the groundplan. A groundplan is not a historical entity, but the theme or logic which each species directly uses to express its own pattern. Each specific pattern can be explained as a combination of an arbitrary choice of elements. Natural selection may work in full details like coloration. Butterflies of two nymphalid genera, the Oriental *Kallima* and the tropical American *Anaea*, are phylogenetically separated, but both have camouflage pattern which resemble dead leaves when the butterflies fold their wings.

Furthermore, those patterns are constructed from different elements of the groundplan respectively (Sibatani, 1985b). Evolutionary systematics may explain this example by saying that 1) ancestors of *Kallima* and *Anaea* had totally different patterns because they were phylogenetically separated; 2) individuals which resemble dead leaves were selected independently in these two lines; 3) in the process, selecting forces were effected on different elements in two genera respectively; 4) therefore, those two camouflage patterns evolved independently, and the similar appearance of butterflies occurred incidentally. This explanation adopts two different *ad hoc* selection hypotheses, because internal regulation is avoided. Moreover, we have heard it many times that a half-camouflaged pattern is by no means better than non-camouflage pattern. I believe that the pattern occurred inevitably by internal regulation or following the groundplan, but the choice was arbitrary.

On the other hand, we recognise two kinds of morphological characters, i.e. a topological character or structure and a geometric character or form (Saunders, 1980). Structure includes all the possible forms *a priori*. Hence, an organism only can diversify within the limits which a structure provides. In the above example, the groundplan is a structure and each detailed marking is a form. This idea is in touch with Croizat's 'orthogeny' or Darwin's 'laws of growth' (Grehan, 1984; Grehan and Ainsworth, 1985). The structure here includes three characters of structure which Piaget (1971) noted, namely, wholeness, transformation and self-regulation. In this sense, none of the characters can be designated primitive or derived. Since each species has a combination of these characters, species cannot be called primitive or derived.

Quantitative methods can be applicable only if a) we can distinguish structures and forms, and b) we can consider all the possible combinations. This may only happen with the help of developmental biology. However, the result is still not the relationship of taxa, but the similarity of the combination of characters.

TOWARD A PANBIOGEOGRAPHICAL SYNTHESIS

'It is in the plan of this book (*Space, Time, Form*) — and all my work in general — to lay down the basis for the beginning at least of a constructive synthesis of the factors of space, time and form in evolution. *It is not important that the reader agrees with me, but it is essential to scientific progress that the problem of space + time + form be seen, at long last overdue, as a sequential whole' (Croizat, 1962-4, p.124).*

Croizat's notion that evolution = space + time + form certainly directed attention to both the analytical and synthetical studies of nature with panbiogeography as a tool. Unfortunately, the unintelligible and eccentric writings of Croizet made 'serious scientists' (Croizat, 1962-4) avoid him.

The first step in panbiogeographic method is the construction of tracks either '1) connecting collection localities of *monophyletic taxa* by minimal spanning tree or 2) connecting geographically the nearest sister group which is obtained by prior phylogenetic study' (Page, 1987). In both cases, putative monophyletic groups have to be provided to start the very first step of the method. However, determination of the monophyletic group in practice has not been discussed by cladists and theoretical systematists, for it is strictly an experiential technique. Most cladists use data and numbers which other systematists provided. They believe that the initial hypothetical relationship is not necessarily definitive and accurate, because they can refine it by means of 'reciprocal illumination' (Hennig, 1947). Hence, they rather spend their time on theoretical issues such as the definition of monophyly. This kind of reciprocal illumination may detect unsuitable odd taxa within a group, but it cannot save overlooked or undiscovered taxa. On the other hand, the morphological analysis I mentioned above and panbiogeography give mutual feedback, because panbiogeography has a sufficiently truthful foundation: evolution = space + time + form, which cladistic method lacks. Tsukiyama and Chiba (1987) showed that this principle is not an *a priori* dogma in finding a same kind of rule independently.

For the 'panbiogeographic synthesis' I focused my attention on the structures and the direction of change. Detailed characters are considered as caenogenetic, and are discarded as noise (Chiba and Tsukiyama, 1983). This focus provides practical units which can be applied to biogeography. Vicariism can then utilise the relationship of these units. In this method, biogeography can contribute to systematics as much as systematics supports biogeography. There is a mutual necessity between these two fields. This kind of thinking goes along with Croizat's idea that 'life and earth evolve together'. A combination of possible characters and vicariism may possibly overcome the missing-data problem.

The above mentioned panbiogeographic synthesis, to some extent, resembles the modern synthesis in which all the biological fields are gathered together in the understanding of organic evolution. However, the modern synthesis is a dialectic method used to sort out a better solution from a jumble of data and ideas. Panbiogeographic synthesis, on the other hand, is based on evolution = space + time + form.

Biological phenomena can be historic or non-historic. The orthodox and cladistic school has been searching for the former, namely, evolutionary pattern or vertical relationship, but we now need to find the latter, i.e. the existing state of organisms or the horizontal relationship. Structuralism will largely contribute to the field of biology with this kind of approach. Panbiogeographic synthesis, then, unifies these two approaches as the new biological synthesis.

REFERENCES

Bock, W. J. (1974) Philosophical foundations of classical evolutionary classification. *Syst. Zool.* 22. 375-92.

Brundin, L. (1972) Phylogenetics and biogeography. *Syst. Zool.* 21. 69-79.

Cain, S. A. (1944) *Foundation of Plant Geography.* Harper and Row.

Chiba, H. (1988) A lepidopterist's view of panbiogeography. *Rivista di Biologia* (in press).

——and Tsukiyama, H. (1983) Phylogenetic revision of the genus *Halpe* from the Philippines. Summary of a presentation to the 29th annual meeting of the Lepidopterological Society of Japan. *Tyo to Ga.* 33. 187-8.

Craw, R. C. (1983) Panbiogeography and vicariance cladistics: Are they truly different? *Syst. Zool.* 32. 431-7.

——(1988a) Panbiogeography: method and synthesis in biogeography. In (Myers and Giller, eds.) *Biogeographic Analysis: Method, Patterns and Processes* (in press).

——(1988b) Continuing the synthesis between panbiogeography, phylogenetic systematics and geology as illustrated by empirical studies on the biogeography of New Zealand and the Chatham Islands. *Syst. Zool.* (in press).

——and Page, R. (1988) Panbiogeography: method and metaphor in the new biogeography. In (Ho and Fox, eds.) *Process and Metaphors in the New Evolutionary Paradigm* (in press).

Croizat, L. (1952) *Manual of Phytogeography.* W. Junk.

——(1958) *Panbiogeography.* 3 vols. Published by the author.

——(1960) *Principia Botanica.* 2 vols. Published by the author.

——(1962-4) *Space, Time, Form: The Biological Synthesis.* Published by the author.

——(1981) Biogeography: Past, present and future. In (Nelson and Rosen, eds.) *Vicariance Biogeography: A Critique.* Columbia Univ. Press.

——(1982) Vicariance/vicariism, panbiogeography, 'vicariance biogeography', etc.: A clarification. *Syst. Zool.* 31. 291-304.

——(1984) Charles Darwin and his theories (translated by Michael Heads). *Tuatara.* 27. 21-5.

Crovello, T. J. (1981) Quantitative biogeography: An overview. *Taxon.* 30. 563-575.

Darlington, P. J. Jr. (1957) *Zoogeography: The Geographical Distribution of Animals.* R. E. Krieger.

Darwin, C. (1859) *On the Origin of Species by Means of Natural Selection or the Preservation of Favoured Races in the Struggle for Life.* John Murray.

Eldredge, N. and Cracraft, J. (1980) *Phylogenetic Patterns and the Evolutionary Process: Method and Theory in Comparative Biology.* Columbia Univ. Press.

Funk, V. A. and Brooks, D. R. (1981) *Advances in Cladistics: Proceedings of the First Meeting of the Willi Hennig Society.* New York Botanical Garden.

Grehan, J. R. (1984) Evolution by law: Croizat's 'orthogeny' and Darwin's 'laws of growth'. *Tuatara.* 27. 14-9.

——(1988) Panbiogeography: Evolution in space and time. *Rivista di Biologia* (in press).

——and Ainsworth, R. (1985) Orthogenesis and evolution. *Syst. Zool.* 34. 174-92.

Heads, M. and Craw, R. (1984) Bibliography of the scientific work of Leon Croizat, 1932-1982. *Tuatara.* 27. 65-75.

Hennig, W. (1947) Probleme der biologischen systematik. *Forsch. Forschr.* 21/23. 276-9.

——(1966a) *Phylogenetic Systematics.* Univ. Illinois Press.

——(1966b) The Diptera fauna of New Zealand as a problem in systematics and zoogeography. *Pac. Ins. Monogr.* 9. 1-81.

Holloway, J. D. (1969) A numerical investigation of the biogeography of the butterfly fauna of India, and its relation to continental drift. *Biol. J. Linn. Soc.* 1. 373-85.

Huxley, J. (1942) *Evolution, The Modern Synthesis.* Allen and Unwin.

Linnaeus, C. (1751) *Philosophia Botanica* (reprint 1966, J. Cramer).

Mayr, E. (1942) *Systematics and the Origin of Species.* Columbia Univ. Press.

——(1969) *Principles of Systematic Zoology*. McGraw-Hill.

——(1970) *Populations, Species and Evolution*. Belknap Press of Harvard Univ.

Nelson, G. and Platnick, N. (1981) *Systematics and Biogeography: Cladistics and Vicariance*. Columbia Univ. Press.

——and Rosen, D. E. (1981) *Vicariance Biogeography: A Critique*. Columbia Univ. Press.

Page, R. D. M. (1987) Graphs and generalised tracks: Quantifying Croizat's panbiogeography. *Syst. Zool.* 36. 1-17.

Piaget, J. (1971) *Structuralism*. Routledge and Kegan Paul.

Platnick, N. and Funk, V. A. (1983) *Advances in Cladistics, volume 2: Proceedings of the Second Meeting of the Willi Hennig Society*. Columbia Univ. Press.

Romanes, G. J. (1892-97) *Darwin and after Darwin: An Exposition of the Darwinian Theory and a Discussion of Post-Darwinian Questions*. 3 vols. Open Court Publishing Co.

Saunders, P. T. (1980) *An Introduction to Catastrophe Theory*. Cambridge Univ. Press.

Sibatani, A. (1985a) Molecular biology: A structuralist revolution. *Rivista di Biologia.* 78. 373-98.

——(1985b) *The Principles of Structuralism in Biology*. Asahi Shuppan (in Japanese).

Sokal, R. R. and Sneath, P. H. A. (1963) *Principles of Numerical Taxonomy*. W. H. Freeman.

Simpson, G. G. (1965) *The Geography of Evolution: Collected Essays*. Chiton Books.

Tsukiyama, H. and Chiba, H. (1987) Male genitalia of butterflies: Structure and function. *Rivista di Biologia.* 80. 235-8.

Wallace, A. R. (1876) *The Geographical Distribution of Animals*. 2 vols. Macmillan.

Webster, G. and Goodwin, B. C. (1984) A structuralist approach to morphology. *Rivista di Biologia.* 77. 503-31.

Wiley, E. O. (1981) *Phylogenetics: The Theory and Practice of Phylogenetic Systematics*. J. Wiley and Sons.

18. Molluscan pigment pattern generation by a dynamic structure with intrinisc time, illustrating subjective autonomy

Yukio Gunji

INTRODUCTION

What I find intriguing in living systems is their unpredictable behaviour, in which we often find a teleological aspect. Independently of whether we observe the actions or the patterns of organisms, we find 'punctuated change' in sequences of patterns in ontogeny and/or phylogeny. If we consider the dynamics of this novelty-generating or self-emergent property, structuralism (Webster and Goodwin, 1982) can be used to describe 'biological' structure as distinct from physico-chemical structure. Varela (1982) pointed out that the emergence of novelty is an essential feature of organisms as self-organising systems, and that true novelty is defined by the plasticity of its dynamics. Sibatani (1987) used the term 'arbitrariness' for this teleonomical aspect of organisms. However, we biologists have to describe the intrinsic properties underlying novelty-generation, unpredictable change, complexity and final cause in the sense of Aristotle.

In describing pattern formation and morphogenesis, we are faced with this problem. When we observe pattern formation in organisms (i.e. development), we may find a sequence of discrete events A_1, A_2, A_3. . . . One may describe a set of differential equations for each event, giving the sequence of structures or rules f_1 (the transitional rule from the event A_1 to A_2), f_2 (from A_2 to A_3), f_3, and so on.

The idea of transformation of the structure during development may then arise. This idea of structural change, however, results from our recognition of the structure (f_1) as a transitional rule from equilibrium to equilibrium, which I call static structure. As far as we stick to this kind of structure, we do not recognise 'time' in the structure itself, and so we cannot describe autonomous features of living systems without multi-levelled functions. In this case 'time' is introduced from outside, and we adopt a hierarchical perspective. In order to change the static structure and to introduce intrinsic time, we need a multi-levelled structure different from the logical system of a static structure. When we describe the system by a structure including 'time' (dynamical structure), it is not necessary for us to hold the concept of the sequence of structures or the transformation of the structure.

219

In the present chapter, I consider the specific case of pigment colour pattern formation in molluscs, in which static structures of patterns appear to change during ontogeny, and show that the patterns can be explained by a dynamical structure with intrinsic time. We may simulate some patterns of pigmentation of molluscs utilising the reaction-diffusion systems (Waddington and Cowe, 1969; Meinhardt and Klinger, 1987). However, adopting this mechanism (static structure), we also introduce other agents or mechanisms in order to explain structural change in time and space during ontogeny (i.e. unpredictable branching of solitary waves in patterns of gastropods), and have to describe a specific model for a specific pattern.

Pigmentation is a good example of biological complexity, because we find punctuated change in ontogenetic pigmentation and various pigment patterns which cannot be explained by a unique structure. In *Ruditapes phillipiana* (A. Adams and Reeve), for example, there may be polymorphism in colour patterns, in which one is a triangular self-similar pattern and the other is a pattern of wavy oblique lines. We can evaluate the significance of biological complexity when we describe this structural change not from the outside of the system (control) but from the inside (autonomy).

I will suggest that the intrinsic time proposed in the model for pigment colour patterns results from the way that we write the structure as a diagram of the relationship between the observer and the object. I can also say that the subject (observer) identifies the object with himself. In this sense, I say this kind of structure is described from a 'subjective stance'. I think that this is the scientific recognition of final cause, and that this perspective is similar to the position of Saunders and Ho (1984), Goodwin (1982) and Rosen (1985), and especially with Rashevsky's (1954) relational biology.

It should be noted that I am not using the words 'autonomous system' in the ordinary sense used in dynamical system theory but in a more restricted sense as the system of autonomy according to Varela (1979). Varela (1979, 1984) discussed this complexity connected with self-organisation as autopoiesis. He prescribed autopoiesis as a process that maintains itself by self-definition. However, it is noted that self-reference is not an observed feature of living systems but an attribute that results from their emerging properties. In the present chapter I will show that the notion of spatially heterogeneous intrinsic time proposed in the model for pigmentation is a natural extension from this perspective of subjective stance. Based on a relationship between the observer and the object, intrinsic time is generated and a 'switching function' can be introduced. The transformation of the static structure is derived from this dynamic structure. Based on this approach, the relationship between control and autonomy is discussed from the viewpoint of objective and subjective stances.

PIGMENT COLOUR PATTERNS OF MOLLUSCS AND MODULATED ASYNCHRONOUS AUTOMATA (MAA)

Initially, concrete biological patterns will be used to show that intrinsic time plays an important role in complex pattern formation. Pigment colour patterns of molluscs have been regarded as excellent examples of complex patterns for the observer, and many papers on this topic have appeared. Though the patterns look highly complex, they are formed by one-dimensional accretion along the mantle edge of the animal. Therefore it is possible to construct a one-dimensional model. They have been mainly explained by diffusion–reaction systems (e.g. Meinhardt and Klingler, 1987) and various patterns of pigmentation (oblique lines, branching and crossing, meshwork- and tent-like patterns, and rows of dots) can be simulated by the activator-inhibitor model.

However, I think that the regularity of the patterns is exaggerated by existing models. Natural pigment patterns are not described by unique deterministic rules because of their irregularity. This requires the addition of a stochastic component to deterministic models. Moreover, in patterns of *R. phillipiana*, another functional level is required which controls the transformation of basic function in ontogeny, because the patterns of this species consist of oscillatory dots, solitary waves, and triangular (kink) patterns which appear to be ontogenetic transformations in time and space (Figure 3 d-f, k-m).

Pigment patterns are generally expressed by combinations of oscillatory dots, solitary waves and kinks. Diversity of pattern is realised by different frequencies in the occurrence of each pattern, and this is an essential feature of biological complexity. In the activator–inhibitor model, oscillatory dots are expressed by two-components system, and branching (tent-like) patterns by three components. However, in *R. phillipiana*, these two types of pattern are found in a single individual. Is it realised by multiple functional levels?

I proposed an asynchronous updating automaton model for pigment patterns, and express the feature of complexity by unique deterministic rules. Finite cellular automata are generally defined as:

1. descrete time ($t = 0, 1, 2 ..$) and space ($i = 1, 2, .., N$)
2. descrete state ($a_i(t) \in \{1,0\}$)
3. temporally and spatially local deterministic rule
   (i.e. $a_i(t_i) = f(a_{i-k}(t_{i-k}), .., a_i(t_i), .., a_{i+k}(t_{i+k}))$
4. synchronous updating (in equation (3),
   $t_i = t + 1, t_{i-k} = .. = t_i = .. = t_{i+k} = t$).

I modify the definition of (4), from synchronous to asynchronous updating. This is a natural assumption for biological systems. Because large molecules as active agents propagate much more slowly than the velocity of light (Matsuno, 1984; Maturana and Varela, 1984), differential equations in the ordinary sense are not stable. The interaction delays result in the asynchronous updating of cellular automata in which time is implicit. This switch may be actualised by self-excited oscillations which provide an 'intrinsic time' for asynchronous updating. The living system consists of a network of cells, that is, self-exciting oscillators, in which interactions propagate slowly. Some stimulus may bring about entertainment into shorter period oscillation and some others may prolong the period. These kinds of self-excited oscillations have been reported in living systems. For example, oscillations of Ca^{2+}, pH, A T P and N A D H are thought to be related to self-excited oscillations arising during the activity of mitochondria.

I adopt the concept of a switching function by 'intrinsic time', and introduce asynchronous updating in cellular automata for pigment colour patterns of molluscs. As discussed in a later section, intrinsic time is related to the perspective of the subjective stance, where self-exciting oscillators are regarded as autonomous units operating with self-reference. In a unit (cell) which interacts with its neighbours in a multi-cellular system, each cell stays in an active or refractory period owing to its identity of self-exciting oscillation. Hence, if the i-th cell updates before the updating of the $(i-1)$-th cell, the $(i-1)$-th cell receives the state of the i-th cell after the updating as input value. The time step of the input is said to be dependent on the phase of the self-exciting oscillator and/or the order of updating. Using the notation of Brownian algebra (Spencer-Brown, 1969) for a binary system, such an asynchronous updating automaton is formulated as,

$$a_i(t+1) = \overline{\overline{f_1}\Big|\ \overline{\pi_1(b_i)}\ \Big|\ \pi_2(b_i)\ \ \pi_3(b_i)\Big|}$$

$$\overline{\overline{f_2}\ \Big|\ \pi_1(b_i)\ \ \overline{\pi_2(b_i)}\ \Big|\ \pi_3(b_i)\Big|}$$

$$\overline{\overline{f_3}\ \Big|\ \pi_1(b_i)\ \ \pi_2(b_i)\ \ \overline{\pi_3(b_i)}\Big|\Big|}$$

$$\overline{\overline{\overline{\pi_3(b_i)}\Big|\ \overline{\pi_2(b_i)}\Big|\Big|\ \overline{\pi_1(b_i)}\ \Big|\ \overline{\pi_2(b_i)}\Big|\Big|\ a_i(t)\Big|\Big|}$$

$$b_i(t+1) = g(\pi_1(b_i),\ \ \pi_2(b_i),\ \ \pi_3(b_i),\ \ a_i(t))$$

where,

$$f_1 = f(a_{i-1}(t), a_i(t), a_{i+1}(t))$$

$$f_2 = f(a_{i-1}(t+1), a_i(t), a_{i+1}(t))$$

$$f_3 = f(a_{i-1}(t), a_i(t), a_{i+1}(t+1))$$

$$\pi j(b_i) = \pi j(b_{i1}(t), b_{i2}(t), b_{i3}(t)) = b_{ij}(t) \qquad j = 1, 2, 3.$$

It is noted that the mark ($\overline{}|$) represents the negation of formal language, and expression ab represents $a \vee b$. All formulas of the language can be described by only two operators, negation and disjunction (Gunji, 1987a, b). This equation implies that only when one of the three switching variables $b_{ij}(t)$ is in the active state does $a_i(t)$ change according to the asynchronous updating rule f_i (Figure 1 a-c). Otherwise, $a_i(t+1) = a_i(t)$.

This system results in attractors with locally periodic or globally chaotic patterns. Especially in the latter case, despite the mode of interaction being

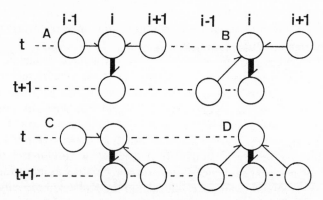

Figure 1. The schematic diagram illustrating the process of asynchronous updating. According to values of switching variable controlling the order of updating, various situations of updating can appear. Hence, time progresses hererogeneously in space. Structual change in the sense of static structure can be realised by this dynamical structure.

deterministic, the rule appears to the observer outside of the unit as if it was stochastically changed because the order of updating is changeable dependent on the switching variable b.

I propose a much simpler asynchronous automaton model for pigment colour patterns, because cells of the mantle can be regarded as autopoietic units. Because configurations of pigment are generated in one dimension (along the mantle edge) and a two-dimensional pattern is formed by their accretion, a one-dimensional cellular automaton model is sufficient to describe the process.

To simplify, we make the following assumption for simulations. The function of the operator b_i can be regarded as the ordering of updating of a_i. Then it is assumed that b_i is independent of a_i, and the period of b_i is assumed to be the same in each cell in the system, but the phase of sequences of b_i differ from one another among cells. Each cell interacts with neighbouring cells, dependent on b_i (Gunji, 1988a). In other words, this model simulates the situation in which each cell of the system has an internal clock whose time is variously set among the cells, and the interaction depends on the time of each cell. Now we can simulate a simple asynchronous automaton by giving the order of updating. If the system size n is given, and the order of updating is fixed, then only the parameter m (the number of updating cells in a single step) is changed and very long periods of the updating order can be realised. The condition that $m<n$ implies that not all cells (n) update simultaneously.

In the following simulations, the order of updating in spatial position i is set at random in the beginning. Then the updating order is deterministic to the end. An example of updating of cells according to this simple model is illustrated in Figure 1. It is noted that if $n=m$, cells update in the same order every time step, and thus the period of the switching operator is said to be n. In contrast, if $n>m$ or $n<m$, the period of the switching operators is said to be the least common multiple of integers n and m.

Figure 2 shows two patterns of this model with $n>m$. Rules 22 and 54 (Wolfram, 1984) were used in the simulation. (The relationship between dynamic behaviour and the algebraic property of the rules is analysed elsewhere by Brownian algebra (Gunji, 1988b)). The simulations by synchronous updating of the same rule is compared with those by asynchronous updating. The boundary condition is shown to be periodic. The asynchronous patterns are similar for particles (or solitons), kinks and breathers which appear as stable solutions of non-linear wave equations.

Particles or solitons are found as solutions of the K-dV equation, $u_t - 6uu_x + u_{xxx} = 0$ or modified K-dV equation, $u_t + 6u^2 u_x + u_{xxx} = 0$. Breathers are local oscillatory waves, another solution of modified K-dV equation. Kinks are found as solutions of the sine-Gordon equation, $\psi_{xx} - \psi_x = \sin \psi$, and they are called soliton-type waves. It is noted that in natural pigmentation patterns these three types of wave appear arbitrarily and that in asynchronous updating automata with nearest neighbour interactions all waves appear as solutions of a unique transitional rule.

Soliton-like behaviour is known to arise from the operation of most rules in synchronous cellular automata and filter automata (Park et al., 1986). It is considered that the present model generates obscure particles and kinks because the mode of asynchronous updating is not sequential in space as in filter automata.

Figure 3 shows that various patterns similar to pigment patterns can be simulated. In spite of the utilisation of only rule (50) for the interaction, various divergent patterns which appear to be generated by different models for observers can be developed, only by changing the order of updating and/or the parameter m. For all simulating studies we take the parameter $m = n \pm (0.6n)$ (Figure 3).

Various tent-like patterns of tropical gastropods (Olividae and Conidae) can be simulated by this model. Variations are actualised by changing the mode of asynchronous updating (Figure 3 a-c, g). Figure 3 d-f exhibits the corresponding natural patterns *Olivia prophilia* L., *Conus* sp. and *Darioconus* sp. The traits of natural tent-like patterns are recognised as solitary wavy lines, which sometimes branch. The tempo of the branching appears not to be deterministic, and local periodic patterns will arbitrarily appear. It is also noted that some wavy lines suddenly disappear, and that there are several different behaviour patterns of waves after collision. In the present model, changing only the value of the parameter m can bring about these various patterns. The angles of tents or the velocity of waves, the occurrence of local periodic patterns and so on are dependent on the value of the parameter m.

We can recognise most of the pigment colour patterns of *R. phillipinarum* when we see these simulated patterns, in spite of the same interaction rule (rule

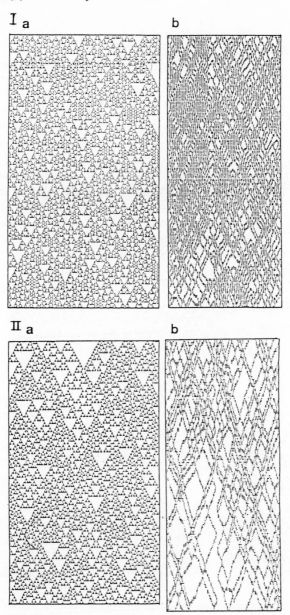

Figure 2. Patterns generated by the time evolution of the cellular automata with the nearest neighbour interaction. I. rule 22. II. rule 54. a) Patterns generated by synchronous updating, which is in the strict meaning of finite cellular automata. b) Patterns generated by MAA. Owing to the asynchronous order of updating, it is found that completely different pattern is generated in spite of adopting the same rule.

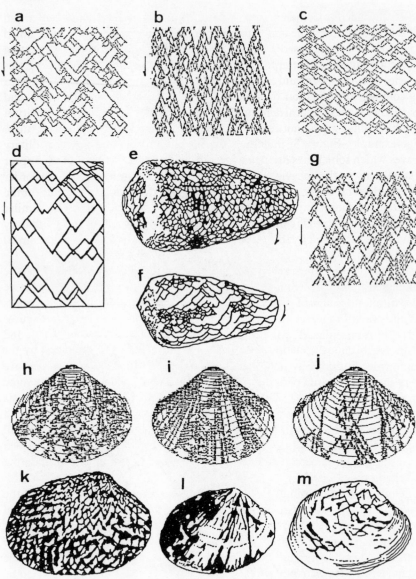

Figure 3. Comparison patterns generated by the simulation of the MAA with natural
pigmentation of patterns of molluscs. a-c, g-j) simulated patterns. Others are
sketches of natural patterns. d) *Olivia prophilia* L. e) *Conus* sp. f) *Darioconus* sp.
k-m) *Ruditapes phillipiana* (A. Adams and Reeve).

18) as the rule for Conidae. Typical patterns observed in *R. phillipinarum* can be demonstrated by the simulated patterns in Figures 3 h-j. It is to be noted that the same rule is used and only the value of *m* and the order of updating differ among these patterns. Fundamentally, both natural patterns of this species (Figure 3 k-m) and simulated patterns (Figure 3 h-j) can be interpreted as complex combination of kinks (triangular patterns), solitary waves and oscillatory waves (or local deterministic patterns). Because of the complexity of combinations, we cannot describe these living patterns by static structures. For example, Figure 3j illustrates the novelty of dots and obscure solitary waves which sometimes disappear after collision but sometimes do not appear like solitons, so the behaviour appears arbitrary. It is emphasised that the order of updating and/or the mode of re-entrant form of the switching variable for the function is more important than the mode of interaction itself. Similar variations of patterns (combinations of kinks, solitary waves and oscillatory waves) are generated by this model in the exchange of interaction rule from 50 to 18 (Gunji, 1988a).

Most mollusc patterns have the features mentioned above, and they can be simulated by the present model with rule 50 only. However, there seem to be also different groups of patterns. Figures 4b, c, f and g show simulation results by the present model with rule 182, compared with natural patterns (Figures 4d, e) of Acmaeidae. The pattern shown in Figure 4a is generated by rule 182 with synchronous updating, and those in Figure 4b, c are simulated by the same rule, but with asynchronous updating. Checker-flag-like patterns are very similar to natural patterns. This characteristic pattern is observed in some species of Haliotidae. The existence of this peculiar pattern-group suggests that rules of interaction may themselves also be important. However, although the present asynchronous updating mechanism is insufficient to generate all variations of patterns, I think that the diversity of patterns may be described by a unique dynamical structure with more varied asynchronous updating mechanisms.

Throughout these simulation studies, it is found that the robustness of the asynchronous updating mechanism brings about a large number of variational patterns which give the appearance of being generated by many ad hoc systems. A suitable choice of the order of updating can explain not only stable patterns in ontogeny and variations in a population but also unpredictable changes of patterns in ontogeny — which looks as if the transitional rule (static structure) for the pigment deposition itself might be ontogenetically transformed in time and space. In addition, this model explains the formation of pigment colour patterns more simply than the existing models (e.g. Meinhardt and Klingler, 1987).

The asynchronous updating model proposed in the present study has the ability to express the transformation of static structure, by a deterministic process without hierarchical dynamics. In some cells time is 'extended' and in other cells time is 'compressed'. This mixture of extension and compression of

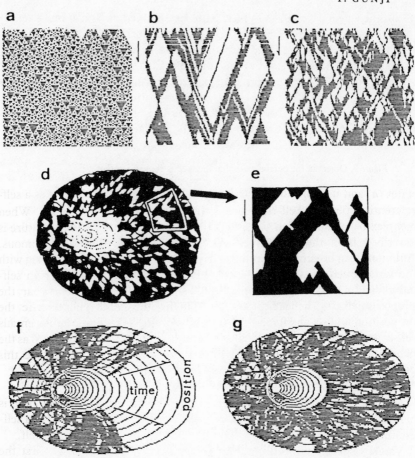

Figure 4. Comparison patterns generated by the simulation of MAA (a-c, f, g) with
natural patterns of species of Acmaeids (d, e). Enlarged sketch of the surrounded area of d.
a) Patterns generated by Rule 182 with asynchronous updating.
b-c) Patterns generated by Rule 182 with asynchronous updating.

time occurs with temporal and spatial variation. Intrinsic time described here
is not explicit, and only from this stance can living systems be described not as
controlled systems but in terms of their autonomy. What is the significance of
the introduction of asynchronous updating? In the following sections, this will
be discussed from the perspective of the subjective stance.

INTRINSIC TIME AUTONOMOUSLY GENERATED

Let us first consider the significance of the introduction of intrinsic time, in
order to grasp the meaning of asynchronous updating. According to Varela
(1979), one of the most important aspects of life, autonomy, can be reduced to
self-reference. A subject observes an object (*a*) as the sequence consisting of its

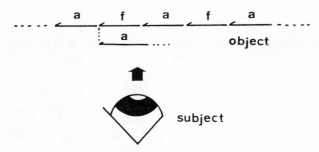

Figure 5. Object in the perspective from the special subjective stance.

states (*a*) and its behaviour (*f*) (Figure 5), i.e. he regards the object as a self-referential operator. Self-reference is written down as $a = foa = f(a)$. When complex behaviour which represents the transformation of static structure is described from the subjective stance, the system is called autonomous. Autonomy can be expressed as the behaviour of self-definition coinciding with the state of selfness. Owing to self-reference, autonomy can result in self-contradiction. Consider the proposition, 'I am a liar'. If the speaker is a liar, the proposition is true, hence he is not a liar. On the other hand, if he tells a lie, the proposition is false, and it means that he is not a liar. So this proposition entails self-contradiction. Similarly, objects (i.e. cells) whose state (*a*) is defined as the behaviour (*f*) of self-definition involve self-contradiction. We resolve this problem by the introduction of time shifting.

$$a(t) = f(a(t-1))$$

Hence the present state has to be determined by the previous state, and *a* is periodic in an autonomous system. In other words, a cell is regarded as a self-exciting oscillator, as far as the observer identifies the object with himself.

Varela's special subjective stance is summarised as follows. At first the object is discriminated as a 'unit' by the observer. The behaviour of the unit is recognised as a self-referential operator owing to the commutability between its operator and operand. The solution of self-contradiction arising from self-reference (time shifting) is interpreted as the model of a finite cellular automaton. Is this model sufficient to explain autonomous behaviour?

The system of a multi-cellular organism is not described as autonomous when it is modelled by a finite cellular automaton in the ordinary sense. Since we aim to describe each cell in a system *A* (system size = *n*) as having an autonomous state, interactions between cells themselves are not regarded as occurring synchronously. As long as the 'present' state of each cell ($a_i(t)$) is regarded as the combination of various *m*-number memory states, each state a_i (*t*) has to be defined by *m* finite cellular automata ($a_{i1}(t), . ., a_{im}(t)$). These are parallel automata (system size $n \times m$, if each system size of a_i is *m*). Since each cell operates with self-reference and oscillates between refractory and active states, interactions occur asynchronously. Therefore, in such a system, time is not considered to exist explicitly.

This concept of asynchronous interaction arises from a generalised subjective stance. It is supposed that the subject does not coincide with the object but identifies with it. The subject as an observer changes with the progress of the transformation of an object, through observation. This stance is investigated more closely in the next section.

SUBJECTIVE STANCE VS. OBJECTIVE STANCE

First, the definition of objective stance and subjective stance is presented. Secondly, it is shown that the concept of autonomy and/or self-organisation results from the attitude of the observer. It is then possible to say that the irregularity of patterns of pigment can be described from the subjective stance.

The objective stance is defined as the viewpoint from which the object is described as what exists independently of the observer. On the other hand, the subjective stance is defined as the viewpoint from which an object is described as a result of the relationship between observer and object. The meaning of the object is given by the observer as subject, and the object cannot exist without the relation to the subject. In this sense, the described object is brought forth by the relationship between the observer and the object, and even if it is recognised by the observer that the object exists, it is thought that the object does not have an actual existence, but is made to exist by the subject.

This concept of the subjective stance is made clear when we think about the description of novelty or emerging properties. First, the recognition of novelty needs to be considered. This arises when observers know both the present object and that in the past. In other words, we recognise novelty when we observe the object accompanied with its past image. In the past the object was recognised (coded), and then the recognised image of the object is reflected (decoded) in the object, then it is recognised again (Figure 6). What is recognised as an emerging property by observers is nothing but the path or sequence which is

object→subject→object reflected by image→subject→. . .
  coding   decoding   coding

The description or model of an emerging property is simply what is recognised. This recursive structure is replaced by the diagram shown in Figure 7. When we see this diagram, we understand that the object itself is described as the same as the relationship between subject and object, from the subjective stance. From this perspective the subject is transformed as well as the object, and it is included in the description of the object. The internal observer is found in the diagram as a reflected image. Therefore, objects described by observers are not actual existences, but the results of both coding and decoding.

Now I evaluate the significance of asynchronous updating introduced in the model for pigmentation. Let us reconsider the diagram of the coding-decoding system (Figure 7). Here the object is represented by both a and f, which are

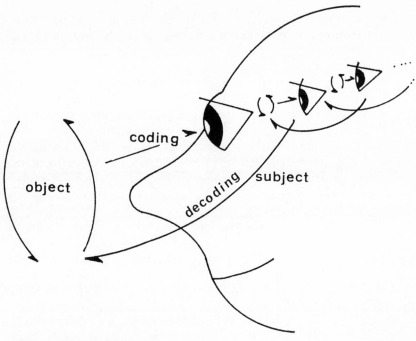

Figure 6. Objects from the subjective stance.

interpreted as state and function in the ordinary sense. The subject is represented by the pair b and b'. This rescursive structure is replaced by the sequence shown in Figure 7. Then object a is expressed according to the formula mentioned before, $a = d \circ b' \circ c \circ f \circ d \circ b \circ c \circ a$. This is also a recursive structure, and if we formulate b as a more complex form, a more complex oscillation is realised. In other words, when b is distinguished from b' (i.e. observers recognise the difference between themselves with a and those with f), refractory and active periods appear reciprocally (Gunji, 1988c). From this subjective stance we describe the behaviour of cells from their own perspective. For example, when we substitute the ordinary cellular automaton rule for f, we describe, in a binary system, the coding-decoding system as

$$\left\{ \begin{array}{l} a_i(t+1) = \overline{\overline{f(a_{i-1}(t), a_i(t), a_{i+1}(t))|} \ \overline{b_i(t)}|} \ \overline{a_i(t)|} \ b_i(t) | \\ b_i(t+1) = g(b_i(t), a_i(t)). \end{array} \right.$$

Here $a_i(t)$ is the state value and $b_i(t)$ the switching value of cell i. This equation implies that the transition of $a_i(t)$ obeys the rule f if $b_i(t)$ is distinct (1) but $a_i(t)$ does not change if $b_i(t)$ is indistinct (0). When the initial configuration of $a_i(0)$ and $b_i(0)$ is taken to be disordered, the transition of $a_i(t)$ appears as if it does not obey the rule f in space and time. In other words, the cell's own behaviour is determined by the switch value of the behaviour $(b_i(t))$, and its own state is determined by the behaviour.

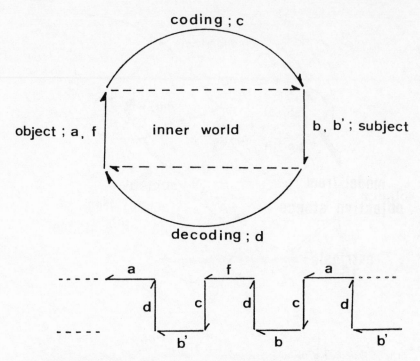

Figure 7. Coding and decoding system in the perspective from the subjective stance. Compared with Figure 6, it is understood that objects described from a subjective stance coincide with the relationship itself between subject and object.

Adopting the subjective stance, in a unit (cell) which interacts with neighbours in a multi-cellular system, self-contradiction can be resolved by the introduction of a time lag between the unit and its neighbours (Gunji, 1988a). This means that observers view a cell from an internal perspective as a self-exciting oscillation or a system with self-reference.

DISCUSSION

Finally, consider the relationship between subjective and objective stance. If we adopt the objective stance, then the object appears as the pair (S, f), where S represents the operand, form or state, and f represents the operator or function. Why is the specific S chosen? The pair (S, f) itself is prescribed by the subjectivity of the observer. When the object is regarded as a stable state, it is sufficient to adopt the objective stance. However, what is the description, when the observer recognises the transformation of the object or novelty in the object? We understand that this character is one of the attributes of living systems connected with self-organisation. Novelty is not recognised if observers do not 'know' both the present object and that in the past. In other words, we recognise novelty when we observe the object accompanied by its

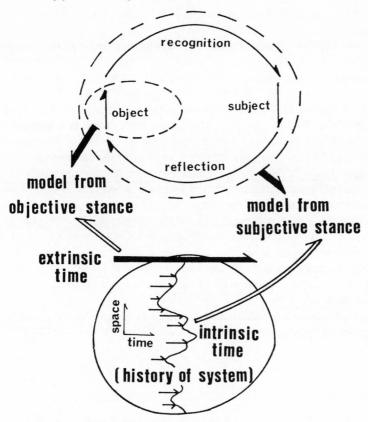

Figure 8. Schematic diagram of the relationship between model from subjective stance and model from objective stance.

past image. The recognised image of the object is reflected in the object (Figure 8). Through finding this re-entrant form of the relationship between observers and objects, we understand that both observers and objects change with the progression of observation. What we recognise as objects arises from this perspective.

Therefore, objects described by observers are not actual existents, but the results of both recognition (coding) and reflection (decoding). On the one hand, the static structure or the model from the objective stance can be regarded as the object recognised as an actual existent; on the other hand, the dynamical structure or the model from the subjective stance can be regarded as what is brought forth from the relationship between object and subject (Figure 8). The coding–decoding algorithm itself is included in the model of living systems from the subjective stance. As discussed in the present chapter, intrinsic time which is heterogeneous in space is described from the subjective stance. Because time is not explicit in such systems, the structural change described from an objective stance can be expressed by a deterministic rule, or a dynamic structure.

When we hold the objective stance, objects have to be perfectly described. If the description is insufficient, we have to introduce an external fluctuation of an external force in order to complete this insufficiency. With improved means of observation, new agents (new components) are discovered and the object is described as a system. Through this process of improvement of observation, the object is understood better as a more complicated system. On the other hand, from the subjective stance, what is regarded as fluctuation or external force from the objective stance is to be described as an expression of the subject itself. In this sense, perturbation arises from the inside of the object. The periodic oscillation caused from the re-entrant form of coding-decoding system can be interpreted as an internal perturbation. Hence, a simultaneous equation composed of object and subject can also be interpreted as that composed of agents a and b. It is concluded that the subjective stance is complementary to the objective stance, and formulations from both stances are not contradictory to one another. It is important to find the mechanism of asynchronous interactions which actualise the non-equilibrium process in living systems.

I would like to give special thanks to Professor K. Ito and Professor B. C. Goodwin for useful discussion and careful reading of the manuscript.

REFERENCES

Goodwin, B. C. (1982) Development and evolution. *J. theor. Biol.* 97. 43-55.
Gunji, Y. (1988a) Pigment color patterns of molluscs as autonomy, generated by asynchronous automata. *J. theor. Biol.* (submitted).
——(1988b) The algebraic properties of finite cellular automata. Physica D (in press).
——(1988c) The significance of subjective stance in biology, compared with Lefevre's hermeneutics (to appear).
Matsuno, K. (1984) In *Individuality and determinism.* (Fox, S. E., ed.) Plenum Publishing Corporation. pp.203-215.
Maturana, U. and Varela, F. (1984) *El Arbol del Conocimiento.* Japanese edt. 1987, Asahi Press, Tokyo.
Meinhardt, H. and Klingler, M. (1987) A model for pattern formation on the shell of molluscs. *J. theor. Biol.* 126. 63-89.
Park, J., Steiglitz, K. and Thurston, W. (1986) Soliton-like behaviour in automata. *Physica.* 19D. 423-32.
Rosen, R. (1985) In *Theoretical Biology and Complexity.* (Rosen, R., ed.). Academic Press. 165.
Rashevsky, N. (1954) Topology and life: In search of general methematical principles in biology and sociology. *Bull. Math. Biophs.* 16. 317-49.
Saunders, P. T. and Ho, M. W. (1984) In *Evolutionary theory: Paths into the Future.* (Pollard, J. W., ed.) John Wiley & Sons Ltd. 121.
Sibatani, A. (1986) An attempt to structuralise biology. *Riv. Biol.-B. Forum.* 80. 178-82.

Spencer-Brown, G. (1969). *Laws of Form*. George Allen and Unwin.

Varela, F. (1979) *Principles of Biological Autonomy*. North Holland.

——(1982) In *L'auto-organisation, de la physique au politique*. (Dumouchel, P. and Dupvy, J. P., eds.) du Seuil.

Waddington, C. H. and Cowe, R. J. (1969) Computer simulation of a molluscan pigmentation pattern. *J. theor. Biol.* 25. 219-25.

Webster, G. and Goodwin, B. C. (1982) The origin of species: a structuralist approach. *J. Soc. Biol. Struc.* 5. 15-47.

Wolfram, S. (1984) Universality and complexity in cellular automata. *Physica*. 10D. 1-35.

19. 'Ethology', 'Ecology' and 'Philosophy'

F. M. Scudo

Most views on human beings tend to polarise into the extreme of a *tabula rasa*, on which society could easily write whatever might fit to its own ends, *versus* regarding them as ant-like social animals, ruled by 'instincts' or 'genes' to perform mostly for the good of their societies. The kind of ethology I shall be considering here is unpopular mainly since, in place of a comfortable middle ground between the two views above, it offers complicated schemes whereby both in turn enter the picture somehow, but only in such ways as to become completely emptied or subverted.

This study celebrates the fiftieth anniversary of ethology as an institutionalised science, with the foundation of both the German and the British societies for the study of behaviour in the spring of 1935. The quotation marks in the title, however, make clear from the outset that I will hardly be directly concerned with the most popular outcomes of this event — e.g. implanting microelectrodes to record the behaviour of neurons or peeping at what animals achieve, or do not, in order to relate these achievements or failures to all sort of physics-like maximisation principles. Much of this does not make much sense since one still lacks set methodologies by which legions of investigators can work out precise mappings of the many complex features of ethology, or these are with us just as embryonic beginnings, or mere possibilities yet to be tested.

What I am celebrating sprang almost exclusively from the idiosyncratic crafts of a few, loosely related men of genius such as Darwin and McDougall, who managed to peep with some accuracy into one or the other corner of ethology's immense domains. It is, then, an ethology whose results beautifully parallel or complement those of a philosophical or psychological tradition that found its modern roots in Descartes — together with some highly misleading suggestions — and had its best expression in the likes of Dugald Stewart or Edward von Hartmann (whence 'philosophy' in my title). Likewise the ecology I am dealing with is the updated and relatively well mathematised version of Darwin's theory of the struggle for existence that I absorbed as a student from D'Ancona. It has hardly anything in common with environmental protection movements — i.e. expensive garbage cleaning

236

operations often associated with 'saving' some outstanding species, or relatively unspoiled pocket of nature originally for symbolic or recreational purposes.

A major purpose of the present chapter was to claim that Darwinian theories, particularly in their developments around the middle of the century, are about the best available embodiments of the most orthodox structuralist prescriptions, Lévi-Strauss' in particular. Much to my regret, lack of space forces me to leave out this aspect (touched upon in Scudo, 1987) as well as discussing theories other than Darwinian ones and their closest kin. I shall start by cramming in my first section some statements on the problem of evolution in modern Darwinian theories, mostly in ecological and developmental terms. The main phenomenological and theoretical aspects of Darwinian theories on behaviour are then presented in subsequent sections. Some final remarks tie up scattered points on evolution, and touch upon some methodological problems ethology shares with other disciplines.

ABOUT DEVELOPMENT, ECOLOGY AND EVOLUTION

Darwinian theories involve all kinds of changes even if they take place in a 'vacuum', such as a cave or a desolated oceanic island. However, much as it is for Lamarckian theories proper and for 'hologenetic' ones, the main concern of Darwinian theories is a sequence of events such as the following:

i) A rich ensemble of specifically compatible or co-adapted plant and animal forms goes on for hundreds of thousands or millions of years while hardly any irreversible morpho-functional change can be noticed.

ii) In a time span several orders of magnitude smaller than the one above this ensemble disappears as such. While some of its component members manage to survive in somewhat modified forms, altogether different forms move in from outside.

iii) In a span of time very few orders of magnitude smaller than in i) few other forms move in from the outside — perhaps a few more of the original ones will disappear — while the morpho-functional variability within all the forms that underwent morpho-physiological changes declines to much the same steady state values as in i).

Modern Lamarckian and Darwinian theories agree in characterising many, if not most, of the morpho-physiological changes that took place above as changes in *norms of reactions* of the genomes of these lineages, corresponding to their changed conditions of life and to more or less marked changes in their genomic compositions. These and 'hologenetic' theories more generally agree on attributing all observed morpho-functional changes in part to the direct effect of changed conditions, in part to the indirect ones connected to behavioural changes in animals, and in part to changes in genomic composition. The same theories also agree in regarding the nature of the morpho-functional changes that took place as being to a degree determined by developmental properties of the lineages, regardless of the nature of the change in conditions (Darwin's 'Law of the Unity of Type') and to a degree being influenced or determined by the latter changes (Darwin's 'Law of the Conditions of Existence'). Darwinian and 'hologenetic' theories also agree on the changes in genomic compositions of the lineages being in part due to effects of the struggle for existence, in part to intrinsic factors of the genomes, and in part having taken place at random (noise). Both within, and even more between these theories there is substantial room for disagreement as to the extent to which the struggle for existence affects genomic changes by interspecific struggle and intraspecific struggle and, particularly in the latter case, as to the extent the selected phenotypic variability is that characteristic of individuals, as such, rather than as pair bonds, families or other units or local demes (cf., for instance, Rosa, 1918; Cuénot and Tetry, 1951; Schmalhausen, 1946a; Croizat, 1962).

Some of the differences above are hardly resolvable at all on the basis of presently available empirical evidence. Consider, for instance, the long-term relationships between the effect of 'unity of type' and of 'conditions of existence' — i.e. to what extent observed morpho-functional similarities are a matter of *bona fide* convergence rather than parallelism. Nearly everybody, of course, appears to agree with Darwin on the obvious — i.e. that the law of Conditions of Existence ultimately takes over that of the Unity of Type, as in *Origin* (Chapter VI) 'Hence, in fact, the law of the Conditions of Existence is the higher law; as it includes, through the inheritance of former variations and adaptations, that of Unity of Type'. Of interest, however, is the range of overall divergence within which conditions of existence take over, i.e. — much depending on the kind of organism, of traits and of classification — whether already within families rather than only within sub-orders etc. On this point hologenetic theorists uniformly tend to assume somewhat higher levels of parallelism than Darwinian ones, while for qualitative behavioural changes it is the other way around (e.g. those at the basis of gametic specialisation such as a 'mother cell' producing eight rather than four gametes or, more commonly, those connected with the working of nervous systems).

Darwinian theorists tend to differ the most from others on the causative roles of the struggle for existence, maintaining that antagonistic and mutualistic interactions would almost always be by far the overwhelming direct causative agents of the distribution and abundance of specific taxa (such as species and races) and, as a consequence, also of their selected changes. While physical factors might have overwhelming direct effects on numbers and distributions over lesser extents of space and time, their long-range effects would be mostly indirect, by influencing the outcome of various forms of intra- and interspecific struggle. The near-universal agreement on such points among Darwinian theorists (e.g. Romanes, 1892; Prenant, 1934; Schmalhausen, 1946; D'Ancona, 1954; Cuénot and Tetry, 1951) sharply contrasts with the most varied and not rarely ambiguous or inconsistent positions within other theoretical bodies (e.g. A. R. Fisher ruled out of consideration all such factors, Lysenko solely ruled out competition at the intra-specific level). Further, a number of Darwinian theorists (e.g. Teissier, 1928) apply much the same theory to individual cells as the main direct justification of phenomena in development, or even in physiological regulation (e.g. Haimovici and Mârza, 1946).

At variance from some Lamarckian theorists the emphasis Darwinian theorists place on *norms* relative to other forms of reactions to specific external circumstances is not at the expense of the latter. This emphasis rather reflects greater interest by Darwinian theorists in higher animals and often mere expediency — i.e. it is extremely laborious to assess the relative causative roles played by external and by different internal factors for most morphogenetic reactions other than norms.

In fact, perhaps the most general statement in modern Darwinian theories concerns the evolution of the modes of regulation in the ontogeny of organs and organ systems that would tend to take place through the four main steps that follow (Schmalhausen, e.g. 1946a):

i) The most primitive form of dependence of any one organ (organ system, possibly tissue) on external conditions would be a direct one, namely the timing and localisation of the corresponding morphogenetic reaction is mainly or solely determined by some external condition. At the extreme, within a certain range of values of the stimulus condition there could be a one to one monotonic correspondence between the value of the stimulus and appropriate values attached to the resulting 'phenotypes'.

ii) A dependence of morphogenesis on some external condition such as one or the other of two morphs (possibly more than two) being manifested according to whether the value of some external stimulus is below or above a given threshold (as characteristic of populations or even individually variable).

iii) Full autonomy of the reaction, namely external conditions just determine whether a normal development is at all possible; if so, the morphogenetic reaction in question does not depend, within narrow limits, upon external conditions. This stage could easily arise from the above through 'speciation', namely each norm becomes sufficiently isolated (segregated) from the other.

iv) Regulatory autonomy, corresponding to a morphogenetic process going on autonomously with respect to external conditions, as above, till its 'maturation', and being after modified in various ways by the activity of the whole organism, usually by differences in behaviour proper.

According to Schmalhausen this sequence ought to be an almost necessary one for all novel organs, or organ systems. This sequence is also generally irreversible in evolution in the sense that it could only be partially reversed during short lasting processes of evolutionary change. The sequence also correlates in parallel ways both with bulk developmental features and ecological ones, though Schmalhausen did not take a firm position on the strength of such correlations. A prevalence of morphogenetic processes of type iv) would be characteristic of the regulatory development of metazoans, while a preeminence of type iii) processes would be characteristic of metazoans with more mosaic modes of development (the other modes prevailing in less stereotyped modes of development). Concerning modes of interspecific association the morphogenetic sequence above would parallel the evolution of tighter associative modalities up to iii), the reversal in iv) corresponding to the behavioural plasticity of higher animals. Equivalently, the relative ubiquity of the very lowest forms would be achieved by passively withstanding all sort of environmental insults, that of the higher animals by actively avoiding many of the same insults — or at least their worst physiological consequences — through the plasticity of their behaviours. Corresponding to both such extremes one also finds an ample phenotypic variability in forms and functions within populations. In the lower forms it is a matter of morphogeny continuing all along with its own laws, under the direct impact of external disturbances on organs or organ system. In the higher animals, instead, ontogeny proper goes on autonomously till it achieves some populational norm, and only then all kinds of variations from this norm are allowed to creep in, under control of active reactions by the whole animal.

I have thus condensed the most basic starting points of Schmalhausen's far more complex theoretical reasoning, each step of which he backs up with a wealth of detailed evidence much in the style of Darwin (e.g. 1946b). Yet, although Schmalhausen's contribution was greatly praised by a few, and put to work on limited topics by some (e.g. Tatarinov, 1988), for the most part it was not even seriously considered in its all-embracing, unifying aspects (but see final note). Besides their complexity, there are many reasons why Schmalhausen's theories fared so poorly and for the most part these are rather obvious — e.g. the long-lasting prevalence of Fisherian or Lysenkoist thinking since it was presented, Schmalhausen's idiosyncratic usage of the Russian language, the admittedly poor editing job done by Dobzhansky on the abridged English version of Schmalhausen (1946a) etc. (e.g. Scudo, 1987).

The major point of this chapter and the only one of some originality is that Schmalhausen's theories are not wholly convincing mostly because they failed to tie up a sound treatment of the consequence of behaviours and their changes with the causal explanations of such changes along Darwin's lines. This failure is hardly surprising since Darwin himself had barely sketched such causal explanations in *Expression*, and a precise characterisation of the 'breakup' of instinct in the vertebrates came mostly later on (cf. the next section). In any case, whichever advances in ethology could have been potentially available to Schmalhausen must have looked alien to a culture still strongly dominated by Pavlovism. Also the classic Darwinian scheme for the evolution of behaviour traces the origin of novelties to intrinsic properties of the nervous systems and the 'useless' motor patterns in which these often result, or to 'habits' perhaps transmitted by 'culture'. This might appear an *ad hoc* contrivance were it not that, as will become more evident in due course, it is just a special version of Schmalhausen's 'organology law' above. In other words, motor patterns 'due to the constitution of the nervous system' or learned ones are altogether equivalent in most respects to Schmalhausen's dependent morphogenesis (i), and the 'breakup' of stereotyped instincts is roughly equivalent to the transition between full (iii) and regulatory autonomy (iv) in Schmalhausen's sense.

THE PHENOMENOLOGY OF BEHAVIOUR

As suggested above, any sufficiently profound analysis of evolution from the standpoint of development and ecology refers to a kind of black box called 'behaviour', which becomes by far the overriding factor for 'intelligent' animals. To get anywhere in analysing this black box in the space allotted, I must abandon any pretense of scholarly discourse, for in the study of behaviour one hardly finds the somewhat rigorous canons of corroboration generally expected in other scientific displines, or substantial cumulative effects of previous knowledge. Rather one is dealing with partial advances in some direction usually achieved at the expense of some loss in some other, or with real facts that keep being forgotten while error can be unusually persistent.

Let me give a few examples. Consider for instance the 'round' and 'waggle' dances of bees and their 'meanings'. These were reasonably well understood by classic Greek zoology and then discovered by Ventris in 1788. However, even von Frisch's more precise analyses became widely known only subsequently (Haldane, 1955). By contrast the now patently false origin of the fear of human beings in birds of oceanic islands — a fear they would have suddenly developed at first contact and which, then, would have rapidly become instinctive — conditioned in different degrees most major nineteenth-century analyses of behaviour (notably Darwin's and Romanes' though not Lamarck's). As another example take the idea that a propensity for any one instinctive action keeps accumulating on its own, and to some degree regardless of external conditions, up to a point to which it might 'need' to be discharged on improper objects or no object whatever. This idea was already relatively clear in Aristotle, Descartes and Dugald Stewart and further perfected by McDougall in the 1910s. And yet in the 1950s the same idea was variously attributed to Haldane, or to Lorenz — who had devised an hydraulic model logically analogous to McDougall's pneumatic one. On this point one might see Haldane (1956), being aware that McDougall had explicitly borrowed his ideas from Stewart (rather than from Descartes), and that it is not at all clear whether Lorenz's original hydraulic model did miss communication among different reservoirs, as Haldane states. In textbooks one generally finds only the 'toilet flush' version attributed to Lorenz. Though perfectly valid, this totally leaves out both McDougall's and Lorenz's main purposes — i.e. to justify 'displacement activities', skipping components in functional circuits and, above all, the very real impredictability of higher behaviours.

After this premise let me start by clarifying what is meant by innate or *umweltstabile* by modern Darwinian theorists, being roughly equivalent to Darwin's usage of the former term. At variance from the most various usages of 'innate', both such terms only apply to any one specific behavioural element, to imply that:

i) it appears in the normal ontogeny of a taxon as a *norm*, namely the structure of this behaviour *in its earliest manifestations* is not noticeably affected by relatively small variations in external conditions, developmental history and genetic endowment, and

ii) the development of the element in question does not require any specific form of learning in the sense, for instance, that most warm blooded vertebrates need to learn features of conspecifics in order to recognise them.

Nothing else is implied by such definitions, while lots of other things are usually implied by *other* definitions of 'innate'. What the above terms mean, in practice, is that the 'more recent in phylogeny' such an element is the lesser disturbancies can prevent its normal maturation in ontogeny or its usage once it has matured, and the more its maturation might depend on the prior development and *usage* of *other* behavioural elements.

It is also clear from the above that 'innate' or *unweltstabile* property of an element — as qualified by properties other than its functions — can either mean that the element persists unchanged after its first performances, or that it might be in any way modified thereafter in the properties by which it is qualified. In other words 'innate' or *unweltstabile* are just conveniently short labels to denote either full or regulatory autonomy in Schmalhausen's sense (iii and iv in section 1). Such a specification is unnecessary in technical consideration of a given element, being usually self-evident from context, and it is usually of scant relevance when not detrimental to general considerations. If needed, the same terms above could be easily specified by a suffix, such as innate$_1$ for full autonomy of the norm and innate$_2$ for regulatory autonomy. As a rule, for instance, reflexes are innate$_1$ as to the structure of the movement, while they might be to any degree learned (conditioned, habituated) concerning the eliciting stimuli.

Instincts might differ from reflexes just by a matter of the degree to which 'appropriate' eliciting stimuli are being actively *sought*, rather than just encountered. By instinct one then means that two distinct innate features mature at about the same time in normal ontogeny, i.e.

i) a specific motor pattern or sequence of patterns as qualified by certain invariant features, whose initial manifestations in ontogeny, if occurring, are remarkably uniform within a taxon, and

ii) some level of propensity to perform the pattern or sequence in question, as generally manifested by actively seeking appropriate eliciting stimuli (appetitive behaviours) and by physiological modifications that are often reflected in postures, in 'higher' animals also facial expressions ('readiness' can be used in lieu of 'propensity' for instinctual traits so as better to agree with common usage).

This definition might appear to have little operative value since it relates a qualitative feature to a quantitative one whose values tends to vary widely, according to circumstances and past history of the individual. Also the motor pattern itself can undergo any amount of modification after its initial manifestations in ontogeny.

In fact instincts are only easy to study when the corresponding appetitive behaviours are sufficiently evident and specific, or so are the postures or facial expressions by which the readiness to perform the instinctual act is manifested. Quite naturally, then, for a long time instincts corresponding to fixed motor patterns and to appetitive behaviours, or expressions, that are both evident and specific have been the favourite objects of study. Also favourite objects of study are instincts whose propensities accumulate to a degree that, lacking an appropriate outlet, the motor pattern ends up to be elicited even by most inappropriate objects, or none whatever, or the individual contrives inappropriate usages of the appropriate object. For instance the functional circuit of predation in cats works in such ways that the propensity for prey catching might often accumulate in excess. Then the cat might well embark on a catching spree of the most useless objects such as flies, or of no object whatever, or it might catch a mouse just to let it free and and catch it again and again (for this and further references on cats see Lorenz and Leyhausen, 1973; Leyhausen, 1979). Yet nothing except the ever increasing amount of work that would be involved prevents a precise study even of the least suitable instincts as that of mother cats 'rescuing lost kitten', which lacks both appetitive behaviours and expressions. Of late these labours might be somewhat reduced through administration of drugs that alter propensity levels or by eliciting instinctive motor patterns regardless of the propensity to perform them through appropriate electrostimulation of the central nervous system.

If instincts are still rather poorly mapped among the most intelligent animals it is not because they are less developed, but mainly because they are more numerous, and mostly difficult to study with any precision. This difficulty is exacerbated for humans, on whom no ethologist in his right mind would use 'invasive' practices for purely cognitive purposes, even if more invasive practices might be routinely used for purported therapeutic purposes. If so, Darwin might have got close to exhausting the range of innate behaviours that could be studied in humans without recourse to any invasive practice. The remarkable knowledge Darwin had accumulated was neglected for all sorts of reasons, possibly the only serious one being that there was hardly any counterpart for animals sufficiently close to us. That a human could get close enough to other higher, wild vertebrates to study them in great detail — while avoiding getting so close as to alter perhaps in profound ways their behaviours — was Lorenz's serendipitous discovery in birds. Only much later was Lorenz's discovery put to use for mammals, with results that occasionally differ from birds and are invariably more laborious to obtain and more difficult to 'digest'. What I am presenting here as phenomenology then summarises many detailed results some of which are recent, not widely known and still contested by many as illegitimate interpretations of the data.

The difference between the behaviours typical of cold-blooded animals and the 'higher' behaviours of warm-blooded vertebrates consists in what Whitman had qualified in the 1910s as the 'breakup of instinct', here alluded to in its more precise characterisation by Leyhausen. In cold-blooded animals an instinct typically consists in a sequence of motor patterns whose performance is controlled by a single propensity, each step having a higher stimulus threshold than the previous one. As a result the sequence runs on until the level of propensity remains sufficiently high relative to the eliciting stimuli, possibly until the last motor pattern or *consummatory action* by which the sequence is shut off. As far as is known, alternative learned behaviours are, then, alternative to the whole instinctive sequence. Much the same function as a typical 'cold-blooded' instinct is often achieved in warm-blooded vertebrates by a functional circuit that comprises a number of instincts or propensities, each generally corresponding to a single motor pattern or action. As a result — depending on the relative levels of the propensities for the different components of the circuit and the intensities of their releasing stimuli — the performance of a component may be reduced or skipped, or perhaps replaced by a learned component. Also, the circuit might be shut off at any step other than the last one, which thus becomes the (generally useless) consummatory action of the whole sequence (as above for cats stopping the predatory sequence at catching). In the same sequence the instinctive killing bite at the nape of the neck is usually replaced in experienced hunters by other techniques, though the same experienced killer will invariably use the 'innate killing bite' on a previously unknown, or dangerous looking prey.

The really novel phenomenological features of behaviours that emerged in the last half century are all of primary relevance for understanding their evolution. In the first place precise phylogenies of considerable length and width are now available for behaviours of warm-blooded vertebrates, as for the courtship behaviours of the *Antinae* by Lorenz and the killing behaviours of carnivore mammals by Leyhausen. By contrast, the most impressive phylogeny of behaviour available half a century ago was still Darwin's analysis of rattling by snakes in *Expression*, or of the movements by climbing plants.

Such phylogenies can now be causally interpreted also in the basis of two classes of related phenomena or, perhaps two ways of looking at the same one — i.e. the effects of perturbations on the operation of the nervous system, including the structure of its instinctual outputs. A common denominator of many specific findings by von Holst since the 1930s is that, by gradually increasing a perturbation such as electrostimulation applied to the neural circuitry, often no change at all is observed till the motor output suddenly switches to a very different one. Much the same was obvious from the outset by perturbing, in a variety of ways, the conditions of growth, or of operation of behaviour. Only since Haas' (1962) classic experiments on bumblebees has it become clear, however, that many discrete changes thus induced are far from haphazard. Rather many such changes are hardly distinguishable from the normal behaviours of different species and, interestingly enough, not only of more primitive ones, but also of clearly more advanced ones. Relapses to primitive behaviours have also been found by Leyhausen in cats, thus indicating that species generally possess greater behavioural possibilities than those displayed in normal conditions. Then, in neurophysiological terms such as evidenced by von Holst, many individual or even evolutionary changes in behaviour appear to correspond just to a 'tuning' of pre-existing 'wired in' machinery.

ETHOLOGICAL THEORY

As anticipated, the theories here considered arise by somehow integrating two sets of data that are more often considered in isolation — i.e. those concerning animal motor outputs and those that mostly derive by introspection in humans, as traditionally analysed by philosophers or psychologists. Aristotle — or whomever else he wrote about, or wrote in his name — was particularly successful in this direction. Only in the seventeenth century can one register marked progress relative to him and only in certain directions, such as by Acquapendente and Descartes. Lamarck's achievements in part III of *Philosophie Zoologique* look all the more remarkable since he apparently did not profit from the above-mentioned theorisations, nor from those of the Scottish psychological school, though he did from Locke. Though influenced by Lamarck and Stewart to a degree not evident in print, Darwin had chosen to stay clear of the level of synthesis here considered, and strong objections can be legitimately raised against his pupil Romanes' efforts at this level (cf. below). The next and still perhaps the most outstanding success in this direction was only achieved by McDougall in the 1920s, particularly with his *Outline of Psychology*. Apparently unaware of Lamarck, McDougall borrowed all he could from the Darwinian tradition, from the Scottish psychological school and from von Hartmann's analyses stressing the roles of unconscious processes. McDougall's *Outline* has thus remained as a standard of reference for all later theorisations, none of which even remotely approaches his breadth and historical perspective. To start from McDougall, then, is not an historical frill or a pedagogical device but rather a necessity. After briefly covering his main points, I shall consider how some of them have been radically changed by later knowledge.

To this end let me start by mentioning the counterparts, as assessed by introspection, to the objective phenomenology related earlier. On the one hand one had ideas or categories that might be interpreted as deriving from manipulation of sensations, or from further manipulations on categories that were so derived. In all theories worth being considered here no such category can be qualified as 'innate', a property only enjoyed by some general features of the machinery by which sensations are processed. In this view intellectual achievement would mostly correlate to this machinery being freed from the basic necessities of survival that, otherwise, would keep it busy most of the time. Much recent work on animals safely kept in the boredom of the laboratory shows that, in such conditions, they can easily learn to master all sorts of esoteric categories.

Emotions, as quite consistently named by all sufficiently developed human languages, are the other counterpart. Only rarely does one encounter them as a legitimate object of scientific enquiry, though this inquiry has been pursued for centuries and it is now also carried on at the neurochemical level. Human languages give a misleading impression of the real nature of emotions through phrasings such as 'I strike because I am angry'. In most treatises of psychology emotions are only encountered through the Lange-James theory which, to the near universal perplexity of readers, consists in little else but reversing the causation ordinary language implies. Even the major analysis by Darwin is misleading in its title — *The Expression of Emotions in Man and Animals* — as it might suggest to a naive reader that emotions are as definite things as, say, reflexes are, and what is perceived in terms of facial expressions etc. are really the expressions of such things. In terms of the phenomenology of the previous section, emotions are just the inner perception, as a rule a somewhat delayed and much oversimplified one, of the physiological changes that accompany the activation of an instinctual propensity — i.e. the internal signal counterpart of the outward manifestations, if any, Darwin had called expression.

An ethological theory in contemporary terms consists of stating the causal relationships among all the objects introduced above and those considered in the previous section. One can easily achieve some ordering of all this phenomenology through the utilitarian theory that dominated European thinking, and pleasure and pain as ultimate causative agents of behaviours. Darwin's *Expression* best exemplifies how far this theory can go in achieving the goals stated above. The main basic theoretical alternative is often called 'hormic' from ὁρμή, vital impulse or urge to action. While already found in naive forms in Aristotle, it was first well developed by Dugald Stewart, a contemporary of Lamarck, and later well polished by Edward von Hartmann at the turn of the century. It holds that conation (attention, desire, effort, volition, any kind of activity) is *directly* determined by knowledge, in the sense of global, individual and perhaps also social experience. According to this theory pleasure and pain are, so to speak, mostly byproducts of relating knowledge to conation — i.e. pleasure derives by realising, or believing, that efforts are bringing closer the achievement of their ultimate goal (and the contrary for pain).

Let me leave aside rather obvious objections to the present procedure that are fully taken care of by subsequent developments, and simply call emotion 'feeling of an emotional quality' — i.e. the internal signal component of a set of physiological changes that might also have an 'expression' and, if so, might elicit a corresponding 'impression' on a sufficiently close and attentive observer. According to the hormic theory the major functions of emotions are those of gauging the progress of a cognitive process and of allowing prior knowledge to influence a choice of avenues to fulfil an instinctual need. On the other hand, expression and the concomitant impression are capable of mediating interactions of a very different nature from those mediated by other means, in particular social interactions whether with the same or a different species that radically differ qualitatively from those mediated by mechanical means or other kinds of signals, as in the 'social insects'. The general validity of the above interpretation ought to be sufficiently self-evident not only by introspection — perhaps aided by some assessment of observer's impressions — which originally led to formulate them, but also by appropriate observations of animals sufficiently close to us.

According to McDougall, humans have a skimpy repertoire of a dozen or so very basic instincts. Emotions would make up a rich repertoire of internal and, for the most part, also external signals relating to the meagre instinctual repertoire in the following ways:

i) primary emotions, corresponding to a single instinctual propensity being sufficiently activated;

ii) blended or secondary emotions, corresponding to a sufficiently high activation of two distinct instinctual propensities;

iii) emotions not attached to the working of any one instinct, but rather to kinds of situations connected to the working of different instincts;

iv) perceiving as qualitatively different what are just grades, or intervals in the intensity of the same underlying physiological process.

Such a procedure is usually criticised for lack of 'objectivity', or found worthless outside humans since it would be 'anthropomorphic'. The former objection is tantamount to dismissing a priori any consideration of internal processes, whether ascertained by introspection or other means, that are at times self-evident also outside humans — e.g. in the behaviour of other anthropoid apes correcting their images at the mirror, in animals with certain brain lesions that 'act' their dreams etc. The latter objection is obviously one of principle against any comparative method involving human behaviours, no more worthy of attention than the argument that such comparisons necessarily imply illegitimate 'zoomorphic' operations on man (as are many of Aesop's fables, much sociobiology etc.).

Rather Mc Dougall's main inferences on the relationships between instincts and emotions appears to be drastically reversed, in a way, by the phenomenology exposed in the previous section, particularly as interpreted by Leyhausen (Lorenz and Leyhausen, 1973). McDougall would have underestimated, by an order of magnitude or thereabout, the number of distinct instincts in the higher mammals. Grossly speaking he would have mistaken as single instincts what in current terminology could be regarded as vaguely defined functional circuits. As far as possible (this being rarely easy), the new phenomenology attempts to work directly in terms of quantitative and *qualitative* distinctions among the physiological states connected with a sufficient activation of one or more instinctual propensities, called *motivational states* or *moods*. Though very poorly mapped as yet, enough of them is known to show that moods are connected to instincts either directly (as for i) in McDougall's scheme) or by blending, superposition or conflict as postulated by Descartes and Darwin (analogous to ii) in McDougall's scheme). For instance, the well-known postures corresponding to different levels of readiness for attack and for defence in domestic cats, and their superposition, turn into a qualitatively distinct 'arch posture' above given threshold levels for the two, from which neither of the corresponding instinctual acts can be performed. While different levels of the same motivational state might be perceived and expressed as distinct emotions (much as for iv) in McDougall's scheme) '"emotion" would only represent the motivational state rather summarily and, in part at least, would not run parallel to it' (Lorenz and Leyhausen, 1973; 282). As a result (ibid. 281) 'it seems that the number of individual propensities vastly exceeds that of qualitatively distinguishable emotions'.

FINAL REMARKS

The reader ought to collate the few suggestions on evolution in general and of behaviours in particular at the end of the first two sections to see for himself that they all make better sense in light of the theory sketched in the third. The whole makes still more sense to the extent that evolution does not consist of producing something really new, but rather in 'better' tuning developmental or operational possibilities that we already present in latent forms, and became consistently expressed as a result of systematic changes in conditions. It is all the more so, of course, to the extent that genetic-selectionist mechanisms are readily available at the outset to 'tune' any such novel reaction into a norm, relatively insensitive to small variations in the new conditions of life. Schmalhausen's theory of stabilising selection claims that this tuning can be easily achieved by relatively small changes in the frequencies at very many loci that are already polymorphic, and here I shall not defend this theory further. Darwin's original scheme for the evolution of radically novel behaviours out of useless motor patterns — mere byproducts of the design of the nervous system — does not seem to require further justification. Nor does Darwin's basic idea on the evolution of behaviour — that much of it consists of, or is strongly connected to pre-existing 'expressions' becoming properly 'read' by observers — require any further corroborations than those provided by Leyhausen (Lorenz and Leyhausen, 1973, chapter 11).

Here I would rather point to three basic methodological problems ethology shares with other behavioural disciplines, and for all of which a solution is already in sight or, to a degree, already operative. Ethology's most distinctive feature on the side of *qualification* — studying first the structure of instinctive motor outputs regardless of functions — has the drawback that, till not long ago, it could only be readily put in practice either on structurally very simple motor patterns, or by observers gifted with exceptional 'gestalt' powers. The Eshkol-Wachmann system of movement notation permits one to 'objectively' assess the invariant features of complex, somewhat variable motor patterns that previously eluded all but the most gifted observers. Its systematic application mainly by Golani has already allowed one to infer features in the ontogeny of movements, or their recovery from injury (e.g. Golani *et al.*, 1981) that had previously passed unnoticed. On the quantitative side it had been claimed for a long time that the variables of most interest also in ethology are not extensive or intensive, so that for them strong forms of measurement akin to those of physics ought to be impossible. Solid proofs to the contrary are relatively recent, and they open the way for the 'ostensive' variables of behavioural sciences to be related to extensive or intensive ones, or among themselves so as to be described, up to a point, by qualitative axioms such as those of physics (e.g. Luce and Narens, 1987). Finally, recent advances in understanding chaotic dynamical behaviours and their relationships with pseudoperiodic ones lend support to the inferences McDougall, Lorenz and others had drawn heuristically from pneumatic or hydraulic models of instinctual behaviour. Nowadays such models could easily materialise through the existing technologies in control and analogue computing, both hydraulic and pneumatic. Alas, ethology is already on its way to become about as precise, cumbersome and boring as most other sciences have been for decades.

NOTE ADDED IN PRESS

An upturn towards wider acceptance of Schmalhausen's theories is strongly suggested by recent publications such as the reissue of the English edition of *Faktorii*, O. I. Schmalhausen's scientific biography of her father (*Ivan Ivanovich Schmalhausen*, Nauka, Moscow, 1988) and A. S. Severtsov's textbook (*Osnovy teorii evoluzii*, Izdavatel'stvo Moskovkaia Universiteta, 1987).

ACKNOWLEDGEMENTS

I am deeply indebted to Dr M. T. Ghiselin, to my wife Katherina and to Ms Ornella Fiorani for their help with this manuscript.

REFERENCES

Croizat, L. (1962) *Space, Time, Form: The Biological Synthesis.* Wheldon and Wesley, Hitchin, distributors.
Cuénot, L. and Tetry, A. (1951) *L'évolution biologique.* Masson, Paris.
D'Ancona, U. (1954) *The struggle for existence.* Brill, Leiden.
Haas, A. (1962) Phylogenetisch bedeutungsvolle Verhaltensänderungen bei Hummeln. *Zeit. für Tierps.* 19. 356-70.
Haimovici, A. and Mârza, D. V. (1946) Dynamique Ovarienne. II. Expression mathématique du développement de l'épithélium folliculaire. *Bull. Sec. Scient. Acad. Roum.* 29. 1-6.
Haldane, J. B. S. (1955) Aristotle's account of bees' dance. *J. Hell. Studies.* 75. 24-5.
——(1956) The sources of some ethological notions. *Br. J. Anim. Behav.* 4. 162-4.
Golani, I., Bronchti, G., Moualem, D. and Teitelblaum, P. (1981) 'Warm-up' along dimensions of movement in the ontogeny of exploration in rats and other infant mammals. *Proc. Natl. Acad. Sci.* 78. 7226-9.
Lorenz, K. Z. and Leyhausen, P. (1973) *Motivation of human and animal behaviour. An ethological view.* D. Van Nostrand Company, New York.
Leyhausen, P. (1979) *Cat behaviour.* Garland, New York.
Luce, R. D. and Narens, L. (1987) Measurement scales on the continuum. *Science.* 236. 1527-32.
Prenant, M. (1934) *Adaptation, écologie et biocoentique.* Hermann, Paris.
Romanes, G. J. (1882) *Darwin and after Darwin. (An exposition of the Darwinian theory and a discussion of post-Darwinian questions). I. The Darwinian Theory* Open Court, Chicago.
Rosa, D. (1918) *Ologenesis.* Bemporad, Firenze.
Scudo, F. M. (1987) Conrad Hall Waddington and his legacy. In *Biological Evolution.* (International symposium, V. Pesce Delfino, ed.) Adriatica, Bari.
Schmalhausen, I. I. (1946a) *Faktory evoliutsii; teoria stabiliziruiushego otbora.* Akademiya Nauk SSSR, Moscow (also in English: 1949. *The theory of stabilising selection.* Blackiston, Philadelphia).
——(1946b) *Problemy darwinizma (Problems of Darwinism).* Academiya Nausk SSSR, Moscow.
Teissier, G. (1928) Croissance des populations et Croissance des organismes. Examen historique et critique de quelques théories. *Ann. Phys. et Phys.-Chim. Biol.* 4. 342-85.
Tatarinov, L. P. (1987) *Ocerki po Teorii Evoluzii. (Sketches on Evolutionary Theory).* Nauka, Moscow.

AUTHOR INDEX

Abdullah, N.F., 206
Abelson, J., with Guthrie, C., 159
Acquapendente, 245
Ahlqvist, J.E., with Sibley, C.G., 45
Ainsworth, R., with Grehan, J.R., 215
Akam, M., 26
Alberch, P. 42; with Shubin, N.H., 58
Alberts, B., 25
Alvarez, F., 28
Ananiev, E.V., 161
Anderson, E., 80
Anderson, J.F., with Horsfall, W.R., 82
Aoki, Kiyoshi, 28
Arendash, G.W., 147
Aristotle, 96, 99, 103, 105, 112, 113, 219, 241, 246
Arnold, A.P., 146
Ayoub, D.M., 147

Bachman, B.J., 159
Baer, K.E. von, 36, 132, 139
Baker, B.S., with Belote, J.M., 144
Baker, W.K., 161
Barbieri, M., 17
Bard, J.B., 20
Bardin, C.W., 147
Barrell, B.G., 158
Barrow, E., 74
Bateson, Gregory, 67–8
Bateson, W., 3, 4, 5, 6, 7, 8, 11, 13, 36
Baum, M.J., 147
Bazin, M.J., 111
Beachy, P.A., 188
Beck, W.S., with Simpson, C.G., 39
Belintsev, B.N., 128
Bell, A.P., 151
Bell, G.I., 186, 187, 188, 198
Belote, J.M., 144
Beloussov, L.V., 126, 128
Benyajati, C., 190
Benzer, S. 145; with Hotta, Y., 144–5
Bernard, C., 151

Bertalanffy, L. von, 69
Bhaskar, R., 8, 12, 73
Birke, L.I.A., 150, 151
Blake, C.C.F., 194, 197
Blumstein, P.W., 151
Bock, W.J., 213
Bogusz, D., 26
Bohm, D., 62, 71, 144
Bostock, C.J., 176
Brady, R.H., 36, 46
Brenner, Sydney, 91
Breuer, H., 147
Briere, C., 58
Broca, 93–4
Brooks, D.R. 140; with Funk, V.A., 213
Brundin, L., 39, 211, 213
Buckle, D.W., 199
Bull, J.J., 144, 145
Burian, R.M., 67
Bush, G.L., 208

Cain, S.A., 212
Callan, H.G., 165
Capra, F., 65, 69
Carbon, J., 163
Carere, A., with Sermonti, G., 179
Cassirer, E., 4, 36, 37
Catterall, J.F., with Bardin, C.W., 147
Cavalier-Smith, T., 164, 196, 197
Chamberlin, M., with Rodriguez, R., 159
Chambon, P., 160
Charlesworth, B., with Abdullah, N.F., 206
Chernavenskii, D., 126; see also Romanovskii, Ju. M.
Chiba, H. 212, 216; with Tsukiyama, H., 216
Chomsky, N., 17, 19, 20, 23, 24, 93
Cifelli, R., 40
Clarke, C.A., 66
Clemens, L.G., 147
Cline, T.W., 144

Commoner, B., 65
Cooke, J., 118
Coope, G.R., 82
Cowe, R.J., with Waddington, C.H., 220
Cracraft, J.M. 45; with Eldredge, N., 211
Craigie, R., 160
Craik, C.S., 198
Craw, R.C., 44, 211, 212, 213, 214; with
    Heads, M., 214
Creaser, E.H., 199
Crick, F.H.C., 65, 90, 93
Croizat, L., 28, 211, 212, 213, 214, 215,
    216, 238
Crosby, J.L., 84
Crovello, T.J., 213
Cuénot, L., 238
Curnow, R.N., 199
Cuvier, G., 35, 36, 97, 105

D'Ancona, U., 236, 238
Darlington, C.D., 85
Darlington, P.J., 211
Darnell, J.E., 194, 197
Darwin, C., 3–4, 5, 6, 6–7, 12, 13, 60, 66,
    70, 78, 79, 83, 112, 139, 212, 214, 215,
    236, 237–9, 240, 241, 242, 243, 245, 246,
    248
Davies, N.B., 28
Davis, C.A., 198
Dawid, I.B., with Long, E.O., 164
Dawkins, R., 119
de Beer, G., 7
de Reyna, A., with Alvarez, F., 28
Deacon, N.J., with Naora, H., 186, 187,
    194, 197
Deevey, E.S., 185
Descartes, R., 65, 236, 241, 245, 248
Descombes, V., 10, 12
Devreotes, P.N., 25
Dhouailly, D., 42
Dickson, R.C., 159
Dobzhansky, T., 49, 50–1, 78, 83, 84, 127,
    240
Döhler, K.D., 147
Dolan, M., 189
Doolittle, W.F., 177, 198; with Darnell,
    J.E., 194, 197
Dörner, G., 146, 147, 150–1
Dose, K., 194
Dover, G., 205
Driesch, H., 3, 4, 5, 12, 89, 94
Driever, W., 54
Dwyer, P., 71

Eckert, E.D., 151
Edelman, G.M., 58
Edgar, B.E., 56
Ehrhardt, A.A., 146; with Mayer-Bahlburg,
    H.F.L., 147; with Money, J., 149

Elder, D., 19, 28, 89, 92, 205
Eldredge, N., 83–4, 204, 211
Emerman, M., 186, 187
Engels, W., with Remin, H.M., 206
English, P.W., 185
Evans, B.A., 198

Feder, H.H., 145, 147
Finnegan, D.J., 160
Fiorani, Ornella, 249
Fisher, A.R., 238
Fisher, C., with Kollar, E.J., 26, 42
Fliers, E., with Swaab, D.F., 146
Ford, J.J., 147
Forey, Peter, 46
Foster, D.W., with Wilson, J.D., 146, 148
Foucault, M., 36
Fratello, B., 179
French, V., 5, 13; with Bard, J.B., 20
Fujita, T., 195
Funk, V.A., 213; with Platnick, N., 213

Gale, E.A., with Alberch, P., 42
Galton, F., 5
Garcia-Bellido, A., 92, 115
Gardiner, B., 39–40, 46
Gellert, 181
Geschwind, N., 93
Ghiselin, M.T., 249
Gibson, Q.H., with Nagel, R.L., 198
Gierer, A., 114
Gilbert, W. 197; with Lonberg, N. 197;
    with Marchionni M., 197
Gladue, B.A., with Clemens, L.G., 147
Goethe, J.W., von, 35, 36, 105
Golani, I., 249
Goldschmidt, R.B., 5, 9, 51, 58, 126, 208
Goodwin, B.C., 11, 36, 38, 53, 56, 121,
    151, 220, 234; with Briere, C., 58; with
    Matheson, A.D., 57; with Webster,
    G.C., 3, 5, 7, 9, 10, 11, 16, 16–17, 35,
    49, 68, 69, 151, 183, 185, 205, 213, 214,
    219
Gorman, G.C., 164
Gorski, R.A.: with Arendash, G.W., 147;
    with Arnold, A.P., 146
Gould, S.J., 18, 20, 22, 28, 45, 68, 69, 70,
    139, 204; with Eldredge, N., 83–4, 204
Goy, R.W., 146
Grant, V., 85
Green, P.B., 58
Greer, J., 198
Grehan, J.R., 212, 215
Grene, M., 73
Gruss, P., with Khoury, G., 161
Gunji, Y., 222, 223, 224, 227, 231, 232
Gursky, G.V., 165
Guthrie, C., 159
Gvozdev, V.A., with Ananiev, E.V., 161

Haas, A., 244
Hailman, Jack, 151
Haimovici, A., 239
Haldane, J.B.S., 241
Hall, J.C., 144; with Tompkins, L., 145
Hall, R., 145
Halliday, T.R., 79
Hammen, L., van der, 131, 132, 133, 136, 138, 139, 140
Harrison, J.W.H., 69
Harrison, R.G., 5
Hartmann, Edward von, 236, 245, 246
Heads, M., 214
Hennig, W., 207, 211, 214, 215
Hennigan, 213
Hentschel, C.C., 192
Herskowitz, I.H., with Muller, H.J., 163
Hess, G.P., 198
Hesse, H., 31
Hirst, with Woolley, 151
Ho, M.-W., 31, 32, 33, 35, 36, 40, 41, 45, 46, 58, 67, 68, 114–16, 144; with Saunders, P.T., 39, 113, 117, 118, 220
Hokkyo, Noboru, 28
Holder, N., 22
Holliday, R., with Maynard-Smith, J., 33
Holmgren, R., 191
Horsfall, W.R., 82
Hotta, Y., 144–5
Htun, H., 192
Hughes, A.J., 49, 68, 70, 71, 72–3, 143, 151; with Lambert, D.M., 4, 65, 143
Hull, D.L., 12
Hulley, P.E., 83
Hunt, G.W., with Thompson, J.M.T., 111
Huxley, J., 177, 212
Hwa, G.-F., with Jin, G.-T., 41

Ikeda, K., 17, 19, 20, 21, 24, 26, 27, 205, 206
Illich, Ivan, 64–5, 74, 143
Imperato-McGinley, 148–50
Irwin, D.M., 197, 198
Ito, K., 234

Jäckle, H., 54
Jacob, F., 175
Jaenish, R., 187
Jagersten, G., 37, 38, 43–4
Jantsch, E., 69, 144
Jaworska, H., with Lima-de-Faria, A., 164
Jeffreys, A.J., 185, 187
Jin, G.-T., 41
Jukes, T.H.: with King, J.L. 86; with Osawa, S., 17, 18

Karathanasis, S., 188

Kauffman, S.A., 50, 92; with Goodwin, B.C., 56
Kauffman, T.C., with Raff, R.A., 92
Kawakami, M., with Dörner, G., 147
Kedes, L.H., 188
Keil, B., 198
Kelvin, Lord (William Thomson), 113
Kepler, J., 108
Kettlewell, H.B.D., 66
Khoury, G., 161
Kimura, M., 86
King, J.L., 86
Kleckner, N., 160
Klingler, M., with Meinhardt, H., 220, 221, 227
Koestler, A., 204
Kollar, E.J., 26, 42
Konishi, M., 23
Kortmulder, K., 25
Koulischer, L., 164
Kühn, A., 26
Kuroiwa, A., 187, 188
Kurosky, A., 198

Lamarck, J.B., 237, 239, 241, 245
Lambert, D.M., 4, 51, 65, 66, 67, 69, 73, 143, 145; with Hughes, A.J., 49, 68, 70, 71, 72–3, 143, 151; with Millar, C.D., 66
Landes, G.M., 189
Lankester, E.R., 112, 132
Larsen, A., 191, 192
Larson, A., with Wake, D.B., 28, 73
Larter, R., 127
Lawn, R.M., 187
Lee, P.A., 146
Lefebvre, Vladimir, 25
Leinfelder, W., 17, 18
Levi-Strauss, C., 1–2, 10, 16–17, 19, 237
Levin, R., 66
Levin, S., with Kauffman, S.A., 50
Lewin, B., 156
Lewis, E.B., 161
Lewis, J., 117
Lewis, M., with Pabo, C., 159
Lewontin, R.C., 65; with Levins, R., 66
Leyhausen, P. 243, 244, 245; with Lorenz, K.Z., 243, 247, 248
Lima-de-Faria, A., 27, 161, 162, 163, 164, 165, 166, 167, 168, 169, 171, 172, 176
Linnaeus, C., 60, 214
Liszczynsky, H.R., 199
Little, J.W., 180
Locke, J., 245
Lompré, A.M., 189
Lonberg, N., 197
Long, E.O., 164
Lorenz, K.Z., 80, 241, 243, 244, 247, 248, 249

Løvtrup, Søren, 38, 40, 46, 151
Luce, R.D., 249
Lyons, J., 107
Lysenko, T.D., 238–9

McDougall, W., 235, 241, 245, 247, 248, 249
McEwan, B.S., with Goy, R.W., 146
MacLusky, N.J., 147
Madden, J.D., 146
Maeda, N., 198
Mahdavi, V., 189
Marchionni, M., 197
Margulis, L., 86
Maruyama, K., 17, 18, 20, 23, 24
Mârza, D.V., with Haimovici, A., 239
Mason, A.J., 198
Matheson, A.D., 57
Matsuno, K., 221
Maturana, H.R., 68, 69–70
Maturana, U., 221
Mayer-Bahlburg, H.F.L., 147
Mayfield, R.C., with English, P.W., 185
Maynard Smith, J., 33, 86, 204, 208
Mayr, E., 82–3, 84, 85, 86, 211, 212
Meinhardt, H., 53, 54, 220, 221, 227
Mendel, G.J., 90–1, 93
Meyer-Bahlburg, H.F.L., with Ehrhardt, A.A., 146
Michaux, B., 74
Millar, C.D., 66, 74
Mitelman, F., with Lima-de-Faria, A., 162, 163
Mittenthal, J.E., 58
Miyahara, K., 191, 192, 199
Mizuno, T., 206
Mizuuchi, K., with Craigie, R., 160
Money, J., 149
Monod, J., 3
Montalenti, G., with Callan, H.G., 165
Morton, 80, 81
Mount, D.W., with Little, J.W., 180
Müller, G., 22
Muller, H.J., 163
Murachi, K., 199
Murray, J.D., 36, 53

Naftolin, F., with MacLusky, N.J., 147
Nagamine, Y., 198
Nagel, R.L., 198
Naora, H., 182, 185, 186, 187, 189, 190, 191, 192, 193, 194, 195, 196, 197; with Miyahara, K., 191
Narens, L., with Luce, R.D., 249
Needham, J., 139
Nelson, G., 44, 46, 211, 213
Newcomb, R.D., 74
Newton, I., 108, 109, 112

Nielsen, P., 127
Nijhout, H.F., 20, 21
Nüsslein-Volhard, C. 54; with Driever, W. 54
Ny, T., 198

Odell, G., 53, 58
Odermatt, E., 199
Ogawa, Fusato, 28
Ogushi, Ryuichi, 28
Ohno, S., 185
Olson, M.O., 194, 198
Ortoleva, P., with Larter, R., 127
Osawa, S., 17, 18
Osborn, H.F., 7
Oster, G.F. 53; with Murray, J.D., 53
Oudemans, J.T., 21
Owen, Richard, 4, 22, 35, 70
Oyama, S., 58

Pabo, C., 159
Page, R. 215; with Craw, R.C., 44, 211
Pankow, W., 72
Park, J., 224
Paterson, Hugh E.H., 25, 78, 83, 84, 85, 92
Patient, R.K., 188
Pattee, Howard H., 65, 74
Payne, A.P., 147
Petersen, T.E., 199
Peterson, R.E., with Imperato-McGinley, 148
Piaget, J., 17, 19, 20, 31, 49, 68, 70, 77, 107, 215
Piattelli-Palmarini, M., 19
Pillard, R.C., 151
Planck, Max, 118
Platnick, N. 213; with Nelson, G., 44, 211, 213
Pohlmann, R.F., 161
Polanyi, M., 16, 19, 71, 72, 73, 143
Pollard, J.W., 33
Pontecorvo, G., 178
Popper, K., 213
Pörsken, U., 65
Portmann, A., 21
Postlethwaite, J.H., 5
Postman, N., 62–3
Pouillon, J., 13
Prenant, M., 238
Prigogine, I., 40
Ptashne, M., 182

Raff, R.A., 92
Rashevsky, N., 220
Remin, H.M., 206
Rhoades, M.M., 164
Richards, R.I., with Evans, B.A., 198
Richardson, J.S., 194

Roberts, L., 164
Robertson, E., 199
Rodriguez, R., 159
Rogers, J., 197, 198, 199
Rohde, W., 151
Romanes, G.J., 212, 238, 241, 245
Romanovskii, Ju. M., 126, 127
Romer, A.S., 12
Rosa, D., 238
Rose, S., 147
Rosen, D.E., with Nelson, G., 211
Rosen, R., 220
Rosenberg, A., 86
Russell, E., 13

Saenger, P., 148
Sagan, D., with Margulis, L., 85
St Hilaire, E. Geoffroy 10, 35, 97, 105
Saphira, Miriam, 151
Sauer, R., with Pabo, C., 159
Saunders, P.T., 39, 46, 92, 113, 117, 118,
   215, 220; with Bazin, M.J. 111; with Ho,
   M.-W., 45, 46
Saussure, Ferdinand de, 17, 18, 19–20, 23,
   92, 93, 107, 119
Savageau, M.A., 94
Schaffner, W., 161
Scherthan, H., 170, 172
Schmalhausen, I.I., 238, 239–41, 242, 249
Schneiderman, H.A., with Postlethwaite,
   J.H., 5
Schoofs, M., 62, 73
Schrodinger, E., 69
Schwanwitsch, B.N., 20–1
Schwartz, P., with Blumstein, P.W., 151
Scoble, M.J., 84
Scudo, F.M., 237, 240
Segura, H., with Alvarez, F., 28
Seif, F.J., 111
Selleck, S.B., 192
Sengel, P., with Dhouailly, D., 42
Sermonti, G., 46, 179
Severtsov, A.S., 249
Shapiro, A.M., 40, 42
Sheldrake, R., 114
Shubin, N.H., 58
Sibatani, A., 16, 17, 19, 20, 21, 25, 93–4,
   151, 199, 205, 213, 215, 219
Sibley, C.G., 45
Siiteri, P.K., 145
Simpson, G.G., 39, 211
Smith, H.O., 158
Smith, M.W., 197
Smithies, O., with Maeda, N., 198
Sneath, P.H.A., with Sokal, R.R., 211–12
Soddy, Frederic, 72
Sokal, R.R., 211–12
Soriano, P., with Jaenish, R., 187

Spencer-Brown, G., 222
Sperber, D., 2
Spirin, A.S., 160
Spofford, J.B., 161
Spritz, R.A., 187
Stanley, S.M., 204, 208
Steele, E.J., 204
Steitz, T.A., 156
Stenseth, N.C., 204
Stepanova, N.V., 126
Stephenson, E.C., 188
Stern, Curt, 178
Stevens, P.M., 74
Stewart, Dugald, 236, 241, 245, 246
Stölzle, R., 132, 139
Strogatz, S.H., with Winfree, A.T., 36
Sturtevant, A.H., 144
Summer, A.T., with Bostock, C.J., 176
Sutton, W.D., 161
Swaab, D.F., 146
Swift, G.H., 198

Tatarinov, L.P., 240
Tautz, D., 54
Taylor, J.H., 159
Teichmüller, G., 132
Teissier, G., 239
Temin, H., with Emerman, M., 186, 187
Templeton, A.R., 84
Tetry, A., with Cuénot, L., 238
Thom, R., 25, 35, 38–9, 68, 103, 111, 121
Thompson, D'Arcy W., 3, 10–11, 13, 36,
   53, 92, 110, 139
Thompson, J.M.T., 111
Thomson, William (Lord Kelvin), 113
Thurillazzi, S., 25
Tompkins, L., 145
Tort, Patrick, 105
Totafurno, J., 53
Trainor, L.E.H.: with Goodwin, B.C., 11,
   38, 53; with Totafurno, J., 53
Traut, T.W., 197
Tsukiyama, H. 216; with Chiba, H., 216
Turing, A.M., 52–3, 112

Udvardy, A., 191, 192
Ullrich, A., 193
Urey, 72

Van der Hammen, L. see Hammen, L. van
   der
van Tets, G.F., 80
Van Valen, L., 209
Vane-Wright, Dick, 46
Varela, F., 219, 220, 228–9; with
   Maturana, U., 221
Ventris, 240
Villeponteau, B., 181, 182, 189, 191

Vom Saal, F.S., 147
Von Baer, K.E. *see* Baer, K.E. von
von Frisch, K., 240
von Hartmann, Edward, 236, 245, 246
von Holst, 244, 245
Vrba, E.S., 44, 92

Waddington, C.H., 5, 35, 43, 51, 53, 126,
   183, 220
Wahli, W., 160
Wake, D.B., 28, 73
Wallace, A.R., 212
Walmsley, W., 164
Walter, G.H., 83, 84
Wang, J.C., 181
Watson, J.D., 90, 156
Webster, G.C., 3, 5, 7, 9, 10, 11, 16–17,
   35, 49, 60, 68, 69, 73, 151, 183, 185, 205,
   213, 214, 219
Wedgwood, J., 6
Weingartner, C., with Postman, N., 62–3
Weinrich, J.D., with Pillard, R.C., 151
Weintraub, H. 191; with Larsen, A., 191,
   192
Weismann, A., 8–9, 33, 91
Weiss, P., 73, 121
Wernicke, 93–4
Wheeler, H., 25

Whitam, F.L., 151
White, C.S., 74
White, M.J.D., 82, 208
Whitehead, A.N., 31
Whitman, 244
Whyte, L.L., 205
Wicken, J.S., 17
Wieschaus, E., with Nüsslein-Volhard, C.,
   54
Wiley, E.O. 211, 212; with Brooks, D.R.,
   140
Williams, George C., 78, 79, 83
Williams, R., 63–4
Wills, P., 65
Wilson, J.D. 146, 148; with Siiteri, P.K.,
   145
Winfree, A.T., with Strogatz, S.M., 36
Wolfram, S., 224
Woodger, J.H., 7–8, 10–11, 12
Woolley, with Hirst, 151

Zaki, L., with Dose, K., 194
Zaraisky, A.G., 129
Zeeman, E.C. 117, 118, 124; with Cooke,
   J., 118
Zent, M., with Whitam, F.L., 151
Zuckerlandl, E., 194

SUBJECT INDEX

adaptation, 66–8, 132
adultation, 44
animal organisation, 97, 99–106
anthropology, 1–2
appendices, 50
arbitrariness, 17–18, 19, 20, 24, 41, 219
 see also randomness
archetypes, 35, 36–8, 139, 140
atavism, 42
autonomy, 220, 229, 239, 242

bacteria, 177, 178
Bauplans, 104–6
bees, 241, 244–5
behaviour, 28, 119, 241, 242–9
 see also ethology
biogeography, 211–16
birds, 28, 70
body plans, 59
 see also animal organisation
brain, 93–4
 and sexual differentiation 150–1
butterflies, 20–1, 40, 41, 42, 214–15
 recognition in 25–6

canalisation, 43
cancers, 105
catastrophe theory, 35, 98–9, 105, 111–12,
 117
catastrophes, 44, 82
cats, 243, 244, 245, 248
causes final and formal, 112–14
Cervidae, 166–72
Chelicerata, 131–41
chromosomes
 crossing-over and 175, 178, 179–80, 183
 domains *see under* DNA
 gene arrangement on, 185–99
cladistics 212–13, 216
classifications, 140–1
 relationships between, 38, 40
coloration, 214–15
 see also melanism

colour patterns *see* patterns
communication, 23–4, 92
 see also language
competition, 79, 238–9
complexity, 175, 220
constraints, 2, 3–5, 22, 92
 social, 18, 20, 150
continuity, 7–9
cross-fertilisation, 180
cusps, 99, 111
cytoplasmic structures, 96

Darwinism, 3, 4, 13, 68, 109, 212, 236–9
 and ecology, 236–7
 laws, 237–8, 240
 neo-Darwinism, 109, 204, 208, 212, 214
 structuralism and, 3, 237
deer, 166–72
descent, theory of, 3, 6, 12
development, 8, 33, 37, 43–4, 117, 239–40
 and classification, 36, 38
 self-organisation and, 122, 125–6
 stages of, 7–8
 see also morphogenesis
digits, 22, 92
discrimination, sensory, 22–3
diverticuli, 50
DNA, 26, 32, 33, 90, 91
 complexity, 176, 177
 crossing-over, 177–81, 183, 206
 domains, 156–72, 181, 182–3, 190
 enhancers, 181–2
 evolution and, 176–83, 196–9, 205–7
 evolution of, 45
 gene arrangement on, 185–99
 reproduction of, 175
domains, 156–72, 181, 182–3, 190
Drosophila 26, 36, 54–7, 114–18, 160–1,
 187, 188, 190–1
 sexual differentiation, 144–5
 see also larval forms
dynamic regulation, 122–4
dynamical levels, 121, 122–9

ecology, 236–7, 239–41
  see also environment
eigenforms, 38–41, 42
emotions, 246–8
environment, 34–5, 66–8, 69, 70
  and reproduction, 185
  and speciation, 81–2, 83
  see also ecology
enzymes, 175, 180
ethology, 236–7, 242–9, 248–9
eukaryotes, 84–5, 175, 176, 177, 178, 181,
    183, 196–7
  recognition in, 25
evolution, 13, 26, 27–8, 33–5, 41–2, 49–51
  and complexity, 175, 176
  and creation, 70–1
  and distribution, 212, 214
  archetypes and, 37
  deep structure, 131–41
  DNA and, 176, 196–9
  environment and, 44, 240, 248
  in Chelicerata, 131–41
  iterative, 40
  macroevolution, 204–9
  microevolution, 204, 209
  of behaviour, 248
  panbiogeography and, 211–16
  parallel, 39–40
  possibilities, 40–1, 44–6, 131, 132, 133,
    140
  species theory, 77–8, 85–6
  structuralism and, 131, 132–41, 204–5,
    237
extinction, 209

facial expressions, 23–4, 242, 243
feeding, 96–7
fertilisation systems, 78–81, 84–6
force, 109–10
form, variation of, 3–5
forms, pure, 35–6
freedom, 41
function, form and, 3–4
functionalism, 3–4, 4, 65–8
  structuralism and, 68–74, 86

game theory, 119
gender identity, 149–50
  see also sexual differentiation
genes, 26–7, 56–7
  arrangement on chromosomes, 185–99
  cryptic, 26
  expression, 185, 186, 189–90, 191, 199
  number necessary, 176–7
  primordial, 194–6, 197–9
  pseudogenes, 189, 193
  size, 186, 189, 194–5, 196
  stabilising, 206–9
  territories, 185–99

see also DNA
genetic codes, 17, 18
gentics, 90, 91
  population, 50
gradualism, 204
gravity, 108, 109

heredity, 31–2, 33
hermaphrodites, 145–6, 148–50
hierarchy, 213, 219
homeomorphs, 40, 41
homology, 6–7, 10
humans, 145–6, 148–51, 176, 236, 243, 245
  emotions, 246–7
  insulin–like growth factor gene, 186, 188

inheritance, 2–3, 5–9, 10, 13
  and feedback, 65
insects, behaviour, 28
instincts, 241, 242–4, 247–8, 249
invasive practices, 243
irrationality *see* arbitrariness
isolation concept, 82–3, 84

kangaroos, 70
keywords, 63–6, 68, 72, 73, 143

language, 17, 19–20, 23, 24, 27, 72, 93–4,
    119
  and emotions, 246
  and perception, 62–6, 70–4, 143
  animals and, 24
larval forms, 38, 41, 43–4
  see also Drosophila
learning, 19, 23–4
lepidopteran wing patterns, 20–1, 40, 42,
    214–15
levels, dynamical, 121, 122–9
life-cycles, chelicerate, 134–6
life-histories, 33–4, 41, 43–4
  see also development
limbs, 22

maize, 160–1
mate recognition, 25, 80–1, 92, 143–4, 147
  see also recognition
mathematics, 108, 110–12, 113, 114, 118,
    119, 129
melanism, 66–8, 69
metabolic pathways, 50
mice, 177
mimicry, 40
molecular biology, 89–90, 91–2, 93
molecular drive, 205, 207, 209
molluscs, 220–34
morphogenesis, 50–9, 96, 99, 239–41
  dynamical variables, 126–9
moths, 66–7, 69
moulds, 178–9

moulting, 131, 134
myths, 1–2

natural selection, 3, 49, 50, 83, 110, 112–
   14, 197, 204, 214–15
   gene pairs and 189
   mimicry and 40
necks, 21–2
nervous system, 93–4
normality, concepts of, 143, 151
novelty, 219, 230, 232–3
numerical phenetics, 211–13

objectivity, 232–4, 247, 249
ontogenesis, 19, 21–2, 43, 50, 69, 105–6,
   220, 239–43

pain, 246
panbiogeography, 211–16
parallelism, 40
parthenogenesis, 122, 131
patterns, 36, 59, 92, 112
   generation of, 52–3, 219–34
   parallels in, 110, 111
   wing, 20–1, 40, 42
phalanges, 22
philosophy, 236, 245
physics, 62, 65, 68, 72, 74, 108, 109–10,
   113
pleasure, 246
pollution, 66, 69
population size, 81, 207–8
prey, 96–7, 99–103, 104, 243, 244
prokaryotes, 175, 176, 177, 178, 181, 183,
   196
   recognition in, 25
proteins, 156, 180
psychology, 245, 246

randomness, 2, 4, 49, 114, 205, 238
   see also arbitrariness
recognition, 23, 25, 25–6, 92
   see also mate recognition
recognition concept, 83–4, 85, 92
recombinagens, 179
reductionism, 16, 89, 90, 93, 94, 96, 108,
   110, 119
reflexes, 242
refraction, 118
reproduction, 9, 32–3, 177
   and inheritance, 2–3, 5, 7–9
   environment and, 185
   sexual, 78, 86, 90–1, 177
revolutions, scientific, 16

segmentation, 131, 132, 133
selection, natural see natural selection
self-definition, 229

self-expression, 132
self-organisation, 121–6
self-reference, 220, 229, 232
senses, 22–3
sex, 78, 86, 143
sexual differentiation, 143–51
sexual orientation, 144, 145, 147, 149, 150,
   151
sexual reproduction, 78, 86, 90–1, 177
sexual selection, 79
signals, chemical, 23
social constraints/conventions, 18, 20, 150
social interactions, 247
speciation, 26–7, 81–3, 207–9
species theory, 77–8, 85–6, 212, 214
specific mate recognition see mate recognition
spirals, 92
stability, 5, 81, 84
structuralism, 1–2, 16–17, 18–20, 31, 49–
   51, 68–70, 107–19
   and change, 219
   and classificaion, 140–1
   and Darwinism, 3, 237
   and evolution, 131, 132–41, 204–5, 237
   and functionalism, 68–74, 86
   and research, 59–60
   levels and, 121
   reductionism and, 94
   two classes, 19–20, 93–4
structures, properties of, 31
subjectivity, 232–4, 247
symbiosis, 85–6
symmetry–breaking, 97–8, 121–6
systematics, 211–16

taxonomy, hierarchical, 59
time 68–9, 69, 219, 220–2, 227–30, 233
   evolutionary spans, 237
transformations, 1–3, 9–13, 33–4, 36, 41–2,
   44, 115–18, 219
   and archetypes, 37–8
   evolutionary, 38–41
   experimental, 42
   in Bauplans, 105
   laws of, 132, 139
   levels, 131
   of myths, 1–2
   possible, 40–1, 44–5, 44–6

variation, 2–5
viruses, 176, 177, 182
vitalism, 89

wing patterns, 20–1, 40, 42, 214–15

yeast, 163, 164